CW00822464

Hyundai Pony
Service and Repair Manual

K Legg *LAE MIMI* and Mark Coombs

Models covered
Hyundai Pony including X2 and special/limited editions;
Saloon and Hatchback models
1298 cc & 1468 cc petrol engines

(3398 - 232)

© Haynes Publishing 1997

A book in the **Haynes Service and Repair Manual Series**

ISBN **1 85960 398 X**

British Library Cataloguing in Publication Data
A catalogue record for this book is available from the British Library

ABCDE
FGHIJ
KI

Printed in the USA

Haynes Publishing
Sparkford, Nr Yeovil, Somerset BA22 7JJ, England

Haynes North America, Inc.
861 Lawrence Drive, Newbury Park, California 91320, USA

Editions Haynes S.A.
147/149, rue Saint Honoré, 75001 PARIS, France

Haynes Publishing Nordiska AB
Fyrisborgsgatan5, 754 50 Uppsala, Sverige

Contents

LIVING WITH YOUR HYUNDAI

Introduction	Page	0•4
Safety First!	Page	0•5

Roadside Repairs

Introduction	Page	0•6
If your car won't start	Page	0•6
Jump starting	Page	0•7
Wheel changing	Page	0•8
Identifying leaks	Page	0•9
Towing	Page	0•9

Weekly Checks

Introduction	Page	0•10
Underbonnet check points	Page	0•10
Engine oil level	Page	0•11
Coolant level	Page	0•11
Brake (and clutch) fluid level	Page	0•12
Screen washer fluid level	Page	0•12
Power steering fluid level	Page	0•13
Wiper blades	Page	0•13
Tyre condition and pressure	Page	0•14
Battery	Page	0•15
Bulbs and fuses	Page	0•15

Lubricants, fluids and tyre pressures

Lubricants, fluids and tyre pressures	Page	0•16

MAINTENANCE

Routine Maintenance and Servicing

Maintenance schedule	Page	1•1
Maintenance procedures	Page	1•6

Contents

REPAIRS & OVERHAUL

Engine and Associated Systems

Engine in-car repair procedures	Page **2A•1**
Engine removal and overhaul procedures	Page **2B•1**
Cooling, heating and ventilation systems	Page **3•1**
Fuel and exhaust systems- carburettor engines	Page **4A•1**
Fuel and exhaust systems - multi-point fuel injection models	Page **4B•1**
Emissions control systems	Page **4C•1**
Engine electrical systems	Page **5•1**

Transmission

Clutch	Page **6•1**
Manual transmission	Page **7A•1**
Automatic transmission	Page **7B•1**
Driveshafts	Page **8•1**

Brakes and Suspension

Braking system	Page **9•1**
Suspension and steering	Page **10•1**

Body equipment

Bodywork and fittings	Page **11•1**
Body electrical systems	Page **12•1**

Wiring Diagrams

	Page **12•1**

REFERENCE

Dimensions and Weights	Page **REF•1**
Conversion Factors	Page **REF•2**
Buying Spare Parts and Vehicle Identification	Page **REF•3**
General Repair Procedures	Page **REF•4**
Jacking and Vehicle Support	Page **REF•5**
Tools and Working Facilities	Page **REF•6**
MOT Test Checks	Page **REF•8**
Fault Finding	Page **REF•12**
Glossary of Technical Terms	Page **REF•19**

Index

	Page **REF•24**

The Hyundai Pony was introduced into the UK in early 1985. Both Saloon and Aeroback models were available from launch, with a choice of 1.3 litre (1298 cc) or 1.5 litre (1468 cc) engines. The Pony was based heavily on the Mitsubishi Lancer, Hyundai having purchased many of the major components and the tooling needed to produce the components from the Mitsubishi.

The engine is a well-proven unit which has appeared in many Mitsubishi vehicles. The engine is of four-cylinder overhead camshaft design, mounted transversely at the front of vehicle with the transmission mounted on its right-hand end. The 1.3 litre model was available with only a manual transmission, but the 1.5 litre model was offered with an automatic transmission option

All models have fully-independent front suspension, incorporating MacPherson struts, and trailing arm rear suspension.

A wide range of standard and optional equipment is available within the range to suit most tastes, including central locking and electric windows.

In late 1990 (1991 model year), the Pony was given a major facelift and rebadged the Pony X2. The new vehicle was bigger and more refined, but was available with the same engine/bodyshell combinations as the earlier version. The only major mechanical change was that the front suspension was redesigned to improve ride quality and roadholding.

Provided that regular servicing is carried out in accordance with the manufacturer's recommendations, the vehicle should prove reliable and very economical. The engine compartment is well-designed, and most of the items requiring frequent attention are easily accessible.

1986 Hyundai Pony 4-door Saloon

1991 Hyundai Pony X2 1.5 GSi 5-door Hatchback

The Hyundai Pony Team

Haynes manuals are produced by dedicated and enthusiastic people working in close co-operation. The team responsible for the creation of this book included:

Authors	Andy Legg
	Mark Coombs
Editor & Page Make-up	Steve Churchill
Workshop manager	Paul Buckland
Photo Scans	John Martin
	Steve Tanswell
Cover illustration & Line Art	Roger Healing
Wiring diagrams	Matthew Marke

We hope the book will help you to get the maximum enjoyment from your car. By carrying out routine maintenance as described you will ensure your car's reliability and preserve its resale value.

Your Hyundai manual

The aim of this manual is to help you get the best value from your vehicle. It can do so in several ways. It can help you decide what work must be done (even should you choose to get it done by a garage). It will also provide information on routine maintenance and servicing, and give a logical course of action and diagnosis when random faults occur. However, it is hoped that you will use the manual by tackling the work yourself. On simpler jobs it may even be quicker than booking the car into a garage and going there twice, to leave and collect it. Perhaps most important, a lot of money can be saved by avoiding the costs a garage must charge to cover its labour and overheads.

The manual has drawings and descriptions to show the function of the various components so that their layout can be understood. Tasks are described and photographed in a clear step-by-step sequence.

Acknowledgements

Thanks are due to Champion Spark Plug, who supplied the illustrations showing spark plug conditions, and to Mr Alan Toms of Bruton who kindly loaned us his Pony X2 GSi which appears in many of the photographs in this manual. Thanks are also due to Sykes-Pickavant Limited, who provided some of the workshop tools, and to all those people at Sparkford and Newbury Park who helped in the production of this manual.

We take great pride in the accuracy of information given in this manual, but vehicle manufacturers make alterations and design changes during the production run of a particular vehicle of which they do not inform us. No liability can be accepted by the authors or publishers for loss, damage or injury caused by any errors in, or omissions from, the information given.

Working on your car can be dangerous. This page shows just some of the potential risks and hazards, with the aim of creating a safety-conscious attitude.

General hazards

Scalding

• Don't remove the radiator or expansion tank cap while the engine is hot.
• Engine oil, automatic transmission fluid or power steering fluid may also be dangerously hot if the engine has recently been running.

Burning

• Beware of burns from the exhaust system and from any part of the engine. Brake discs and drums can also be extremely hot immediately after use.

Crushing

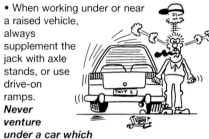

• When working under or near a raised vehicle, always supplement the jack with axle stands, or use drive-on ramps. *Never venture under a car which is only supported by a jack.*
• Take care if loosening or tightening high-torque nuts when the vehicle is on stands. Initial loosening and final tightening should be done with the wheels on the ground.

Fire

• Fuel is highly flammable; fuel vapour is explosive.
• Don't let fuel spill onto a hot engine.
• Do not smoke or allow naked lights (including pilot lights) anywhere near a vehicle being worked on. Also beware of creating sparks
(electrically or by use of tools).
• Fuel vapour is heavier than air, so don't work on the fuel system with the vehicle over an inspection pit.
• Another cause of fire is an electrical overload or short-circuit. Take care when repairing or modifying the vehicle wiring.
• Keep a fire extinguisher handy, of a type suitable for use on fuel and electrical fires.

Electric shock

• Ignition HT voltage can be dangerous, especially to people with heart problems or a pacemaker. Don't work on or near the ignition system with the engine running or the ignition switched on.

• Mains voltage is also dangerous. Make sure that any mains-operated equipment is correctly earthed. Mains power points should be protected by a residual current device (RCD) circuit breaker.

Fume or gas intoxication

• Exhaust fumes are poisonous; they often contain carbon monoxide, which is rapidly fatal if inhaled. Never run the engine in a confined space such as a garage with the doors shut.
• Fuel vapour is also poisonous, as are the vapours from some cleaning solvents and paint thinners.

Poisonous or irritant substances

• Avoid skin contact with battery acid and with any fuel, fluid or lubricant, especially antifreeze, brake hydraulic fluid and Diesel fuel. Don't syphon them by mouth. If such a substance is swallowed or gets into the eyes, seek medical advice.
• Prolonged contact with used engine oil can cause skin cancer. Wear gloves or use a barrier cream if necessary. Change out of oil-soaked clothes and do not keep oily rags in your pocket.
• Air conditioning refrigerant forms a poisonous gas if exposed to a naked flame (including a cigarette). It can also cause skin burns on contact.

Asbestos

• Asbestos dust can cause cancer if inhaled or swallowed. Asbestos may be found in gaskets and in brake and clutch linings. When dealing with such components it is safest to assume that they contain asbestos.

Special hazards

Hydrofluoric acid

• This extremely corrosive acid is formed when certain types of synthetic rubber, found in some O-rings, oil seals, fuel hoses etc, are exposed to temperatures above 400°C. The rubber changes into a charred or sticky substance containing the acid. *Once formed, the acid remains dangerous for years. If it gets onto the skin, it may be necessary to amputate the limb concerned.*
• When dealing with a vehicle which has suffered a fire, or with components salvaged from such a vehicle, wear protective gloves and discard them after use.

The battery

• Batteries contain sulphuric acid, which attacks clothing, eyes and skin. Take care when topping-up or carrying the battery.
• The hydrogen gas given off by the battery is highly explosive. Never cause a spark or allow a naked light nearby. Be careful when connecting and disconnecting battery chargers or jump leads.

Air bags

• Air bags can cause injury if they go off accidentally. Take care when removing the steering wheel and/or facia. Special storage instructions may apply.

Diesel injection equipment

• Diesel injection pumps supply fuel at very high pressure. Take care when working on the fuel injectors and fuel pipes.

⚠️ *Warning: Never expose the hands, face or any other part of the body to injector spray; the fuel can penetrate the skin with potentially fatal results.*

Remember...

DO

• Do use eye protection when using power tools, and when working under the vehicle.

• Do wear gloves or use barrier cream to protect your hands when necessary.

• Do get someone to check periodically that all is well when working alone on the vehicle.

• Do keep loose clothing and long hair well out of the way of moving mechanical parts.

• Do remove rings, wristwatch etc, before working on the vehicle – especially the electrical system.

• Do ensure that any lifting or jacking equipment has a safe working load rating adequate for the job.

DON'T

• Don't attempt to lift a heavy component which may be beyond your capability – get assistance.

• Don't rush to finish a job, or take unverified short cuts.

• Don't use ill-fitting tools which may slip and cause injury.

• Don't leave tools or parts lying around where someone can trip over them. Mop up oil and fuel spills at once.

• Don't allow children or pets to play in or near a vehicle being worked on.

The following pages are intended to help in dealing with common roadside emergencies and breakdowns. You will find more detailed fault finding information at the back of the manual, and repair information in the main chapters.

If your car won't start and the starter motor doesn't turn

☐ If it's a model with automatic transmission, make sure the selector is in 'P' or 'N'.
☐ Open the bonnet and make sure that the battery terminals are clean and tight.
☐ Switch on the headlights and try to start the engine. If the headlights go very dim when you're trying to start, the battery is probably flat. Get out of trouble by jump starting (see next page) using a friend's car.

If your car won't start even though the starter motor turns as normal

☐ Is there fuel in the tank?
☐ Is there moisture on electrical components under the bonnet? Switch off the ignition, then wipe off any obvious dampness with a dry cloth. Spray a water-repellent aerosol product (WD-40 or equivalent) on ignition and fuel system electrical connectors like those shown in the photos. Pay special attention to the ignition coil wiring connector and HT leads.

A Check the condition and security of the battery connections

B Check that the spark plug HT leads are securely connected by pushing them onto the plugs

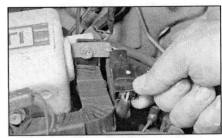

C Check that the HT leads and wiring connectors are securely connected to the distributor (fuel injection model shown).

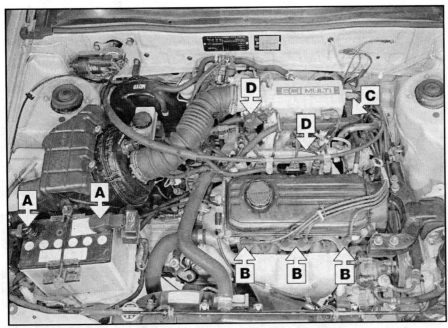

Check that electrical connections are secure (with the ignition switched off) and spray them with a water dispersant spray like WD40 if you suspect a problem due to damp (fuel injection model shown)

D On fuel injection models check that the wiring connectors are securely connected to the various sensors and switches (throttle position sensor shown).

Jump starting

Jump starting will get you out of trouble, but you must correct whatever made the battery go flat in the first place. There are three possibilities:

1) The battery has been drained by repeated attempts to start, or by leaving the lights on.
2) The charging system is not working properly (alternator drivebelt slack or broken, alternator wiring fault or alternator itself faulty).
3) The battery itself is at fault (electrolyte low, or battery worn out).

When jump-starting a car using a booster battery, observe the following precautions:

☐ Before connecting the booster battery, make sure that the ignition is switched off.

☐ Ensure that all electrical equipment (lights, heater, wipers, etc) is switched off.

☐ Take note of any special precautions printed on the battery case.

☐ Make sure that the booster battery is the same voltage as the discharged one in the vehicle.

☐ If the battery is being jump-started from the battery in another vehicle, the two vehicles MUST NOT TOUCH each other.

☐ Make sure that the transmission is in neutral (or PARK, in the case of automatic transmission).

1 Connect one end of the red jump lead to the positive (+) terminal of the flat battery

2 Connect the other end of the red lead to the positive (+) terminal of the booster battery

3 Connect one end of the black jump lead to the negative (-) terminal of the booster battery

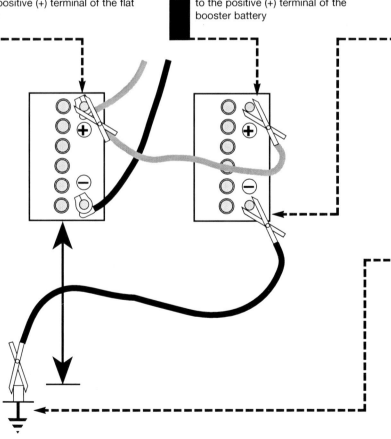

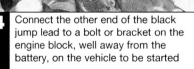

4 Connect the other end of the black jump lead to a bolt or bracket on the engine block, well away from the battery, on the vehicle to be started

5 Make sure that the jump leads will not come into contact with the fan, drivebelts or other moving parts of the engine

6 Start the engine using the booster battery, then with the engine running at idle speed, disconnect the jump leads in the reverse order of connection

Wheel changing

Some of the details shown here will vary according to model. For instance, the location of the spare wheel and jack is not the same on all cars. However, the basic principles apply to all vehicles.

Warning: Do not change a wheel in a situation where you risk being hit by another vehicle. On busy roads, try to stop in a lay-by or a gateway. Be wary of passing traffic while changing the wheel - it is easy to become distracted by the job in hand.

Preparation

☐ When a puncture occurs, stop as soon as it is safe to do so.
☐ Park on firm level ground, if possible, and well out of the way of other traffic.
☐ Use hazard warning lights if necessary.

☐ If you have one, use a warning triangle to alert other drivers of your presence.
☐ Apply the handbrake and engage first or reverse gear (or Park on models with automatic transmission).

☐ Chock the wheel diagonally opposite the one being removed – a couple of large stones will do for this.
☐ If the ground is soft, use a flat piece of wood to spread the load under the jack.

Changing the wheel

1 The spare wheel and tools are stored in the luggage compartment. Lift up the carpet and remove the tool kit and jack.

2 Unscrew the retainer and remove the spare wheel from the luggage compartment.

3 Remove the wheel trim/hub cap (as applicable) and, with the vehicle on the ground, slacken each wheel nut by half a turn.

4 Make sure the jack is located on firm ground and engage the jack head correctly with the sill.

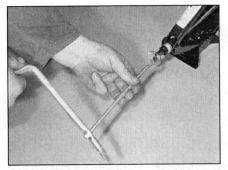

5 Raise the jack using the wheelbrace until the wheel is raised clear of the ground. Unscrew the wheel nuts and remove the wheel. Fit the spare wheel and screw on the nuts. Lightly tighten the nuts with the wheelbrace then lower the vehicle to the ground.

6 Securely tighten the wheel nuts in a diagonal sequence then refit the wheel trim/hub cap (as applicable). Stow the punctured wheel back in the luggage compartment and secure them in position. Note that the wheel nuts should be slackened and retightened to the specified torque at the earliest possible opportunity.

Finally...

☐ Remove the wheel chocks.

☐ Stow the jack and tools in the correct locations in the car.

☐ Check the tyre pressure on the wheel just fitted. If it is low, or if you don't have a pressure gauge with you, drive slowly to the nearest garage and inflate the tyre to the right pressure.

☐ Have the damaged tyre or wheel repaired as soon as possible.

Identifying leaks

Puddles on the garage floor or drive, or obvious wetness under the bonnet or underneath the car, suggest a leak that needs investigating. It can sometimes be difficult to decide where the leak is coming from, especially if the engine bay is very dirty already. Leaking oil or fluid can also be blown rearwards by the passage of air under the car, giving a false impression of where the problem lies.

 Warning: Most automotive oils and fluids are poisonous. Wash them off skin, and change out of contaminated clothing, without delay.

 HAYNES HiNT *The smell of a fluid leaking from the car may provide a clue to what's leaking. Some fluids are distinctively coloured. It may help to clean the car carefully and to park it over some clean paper overnight as an aid to locating the source of the leak.*
Remember that some leaks may only occur while the engine is running.

Sump oil

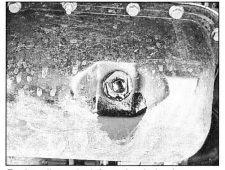

Engine oil may leak from the drain plug...

Oil from filter

...or from the base of the oil filter.

Gearbox oil

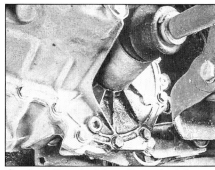

Gearbox oil can leak from the seals at the inboard ends of the driveshafts.

Antifreeze

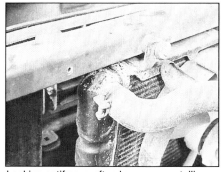

Leaking antifreeze often leaves a crystalline deposit like this.

Brake fluid

A leak occurring at a wheel is almost certainly brake fluid.

Power steering fluid

Power steering fluid may leak from the pipe connectors on the steering rack.

Towing

When all else fails, you may find yourself having to get a tow home – or of course you may be helping somebody else. Long-distance recovery should only be done by a garage or breakdown service. For shorter distances, DIY towing using another car is easy enough, but observe the following points:
☐ Use a proper tow-rope – they are not expensive. The vehicle being towed must display an 'ON TOW' sign in its rear window.
☐ Always turn the ignition key to the 'on' position when the vehicle is being towed, so

that the steering lock is released, and that the direction indicator and brake lights will work.
☐ Only attach the tow-rope to the towing eyes provided.
☐ Before being towed, release the handbrake and select neutral on the transmission.
☐ Note that greater-than-usual pedal pressure will be required to operate the brakes, since the vacuum servo unit is only operational with the engine running.
☐ On models with power steering, greater-than-usual steering effort will also be required.

☐ The driver of the car being towed must keep the tow-rope taut at all times to avoid snatching.
☐ Make sure that both drivers know the route before setting off.
☐ Only drive at moderate speeds and keep the distance towed to a minimum. Drive smoothly and allow plenty of time for slowing down at junctions.
☐ On models with automatic transmission, special precautions apply. If in doubt, do not tow, or transmission damage may result.

Introduction

There are some very simple checks which need only take a few minutes to carry out, but which could save you a lot of inconvenience and expense.

These "Weekly checks" require no great skill or special tools, and the small amount of time they take to perform could prove to be very well spent, for example;

☐ Keeping an eye on tyre condition and pressures, will not only help to stop them wearing out prematurely, but could also save your life.

☐ Many breakdowns are caused by electrical problems. Battery-related faults are particularly common, and a quick check on a regular basis will often prevent the majority of these.

☐ If your car develops a brake fluid leak, the first time you might know about it is when your brakes don't work properly. Checking the level regularly will give advance warning of this kind of problem.

☐ If the oil or coolant levels run low, the cost of repairing any engine damage will be far greater than fixing the leak, for example.

Underbonnet check points

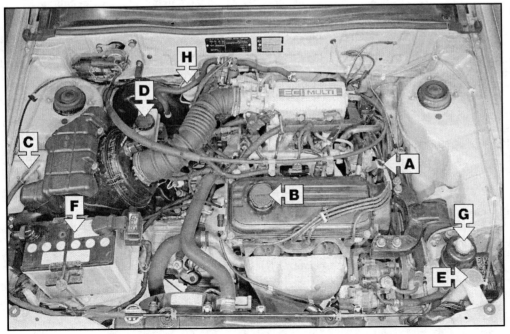

◀ **Fuel injection model**

(carburettor model similar)

A *Engine oil level dipstick*

B *Engine oil filler cap*

C *Coolant expansion tank*

D *Brake fluid reservoir*

E *Screen washer fluid reservoir*

F *Battery*

G *Power steering fluid reservoir*

H *Clutch fluid reservoir (fuel injection models only)*

Engine oil level

Before you start

☐ Make sure that your car is on level ground.
☐ Check the oil level before the car is driven, or at least 5 minutes after the engine has been switched off.

 HAYNES HiNT *If the oil is checked immediately after driving the vehicle, some of the oil will remain in the upper engine components, resulting in an inaccurate reading on the dipstick!*

The correct oil

Modern engines place great demands on their oil. It is very important that the correct oil for your car is used (See "Lubricants, fluids and tyre pressures").

Car Care

☐ If you have to add oil frequently, you should check whether you have any oil leaks. Place some clean paper under the car overnight, and check for stains in the morning. If there are no leaks, the engine may be burning oil *(see "Fault Finding")*.

☐ Always maintain the level between the upper and lower dipstick marks (see photo 3). If the level is too low severe engine damage may occur. Oil seal failure may result if the engine is overfilled by adding too much oil.

1 The dipstick top is often brightly coloured for easy identification (see *"Underbonnet check points"* on page 0•10 for exact location). Withdraw the dipstick.

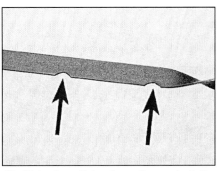

3 Note the oil level on the end of the dipstick, which should be between the upper ("MAX") mark and lower ("MIN") mark. Approximately 1.0 litre of oil will raise the level from the lower mark to the upper mark.

2 Using a clean rag or paper towel remove all oil from the dipstick. Insert the clean dipstick into the tube as far as it will go, then withdraw it again.

4 Oil is added through the filler cap. Unscrew the cap and top-up the level; a funnel may help to reduce spillage. Add the oil slowly, checking the level on the dipstick often. Don't overfill (see *"Car Care" left*).

Coolant level

 Warning: DO NOT attempt to remove the expansion tank pressure cap when the engine is hot, as there is a very great risk of scalding. Do not leave open containers of coolant about, as it is poisonous.

Car Care

☐ With a sealed-type cooling system, adding coolant should not be necessary on a regular basis. If frequent topping-up is required, it is likely there is a leak. Check the radiator, all hoses and joint faces for signs of staining or wetness, and rectify as necessary.

☐ It is important that antifreeze is used in the cooling system all year round, not just during the winter months. Don't top-up with water alone, as the antifreeze will become too diluted.

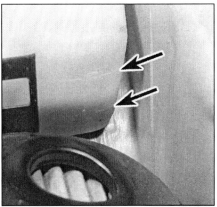

1 The coolant level varies with engine temperature. When cold, the coolant level should be between the "MAX" and "MIN" marks. When the engine is hot, the level may rise slightly above the "MAX" mark.

2 If topping up is necessary, remove the cap and add a mixture of water and antifreeze to the expansion tank until the coolant level is between the level marks. Once the level is correct, securely refit the cap.

Brake (and clutch*) fluid level

*On fuel injection models the clutch fluid level should also be checked at the same time as the brake fluid. The reservoir is located just to the left of the brake reservoir and is checked in the same manner.

Warning:

☐ **Brake fluid can harm your eyes and damage painted surfaces, so use extreme caution when handling and pouring it.**

☐ **Do not use fluid that has been standing open for some time, as it absorbs moisture from the air, which can cause a dangerous loss of braking effectiveness.**

HAYNES HiNT

• **Make sure that your car is on level ground.**
• **The fluid level in the reservoir will drop slightly as the brake pads wear down, but the fluid level must never be allowed to drop below the "MIN" mark.**

Safety First!

☐ If the reservoir requires repeated topping-up this is an indication of a fluid leak somewhere in the system, which should be investigated immediately.

☐ If a leak is suspected, the car should not be driven until the braking system has been checked. Never take any risks where brakes are concerned.

1 The upper (MAX) and lower (MIN) fluid level markings are on the side of the reservoir, which is located in the right-hand rear corner of the engine compartment. The fluid level must always be kept in-between these two marks.

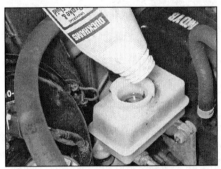

3 Unscrew the reservoir cap and carefully lift it out of position, taking care not to damage the level switch float. Inspect the reservoir, if the fluid is dirty the hydraulic system should be drained and refilled (see Chapter 1).

2 If topping-up is necessary, first wipe clean the area around the filler cap to prevent dirt entering the hydraulic system.

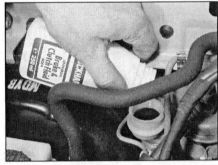

4 Carefully add fluid, taking care not to spill it onto the surrounding components. Use only the specified fluid; mixing different types can cause damage to the system. After topping-up to the correct level, securely refit the cap and wipe off any spilt fluid.

Screen washer fluid level

Screenwash additives not only keep the winscreen clean during foul weather, they also prevent the washer system freezing in cold weather - which is when you are likely to need it most. Don't top up using plain water as the screenwash will become too diluted, and will freeze during cold weather.

☐ **On no account use coolant antifreeze in the washer system - this could discolour or damage paintwork.**

1 The washer fluid reservoir is located in the engine compartment; on carburettor models the reservoir is on the right-hand side of the engine compartment and on fuel injection models it is in the left-hand front corner of the engine compartment. The level is visible through the reservoir body and is topped up via the cap (fuel injection model shown).

2 If topping up is necessary, add water and a screenwash additive in the quantities recommended by the manufacturer. When topping-up the reservoir, add a screenwash additive in the quantities recommended on the bottle.

Power steering fluid level

Before you start:

☐ Park the vehicle on level ground.
☐ Set the steering wheel straight-ahead.
☐ The engine should be turned off.

HAYNES HiNT *For the check to be accurate, the steering must not be turned once the engine has been stopped.*

Safety First!

☐ The need for frequent topping-up indicates a leak, which should be investigated immediately.

1 The reservoir is located in the front left-hand corner of the engine compartment, next to the battery. Wipe clean the area around the reservoir filler neck and unscrew the filler cap/dipstick from the reservoir.

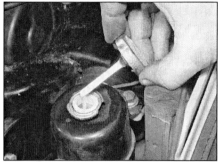

2 Ensure that the front wheels are positioned in the straight-ahead position, then wipe clean the cap dipstick then insert it fully into the reservoir and withdraw it.

3 When topping-up, use the specified type of fluid and do not overfill the reservoir. When the level is correct, securely refit the cap.

Wiper blades

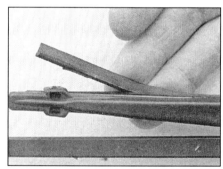

1 Check the condition of the wiper blades; if they are cracked or show any signs of deterioration, or if the glass swept area is smeared, renew them. Wiper blades should be renewed annually.

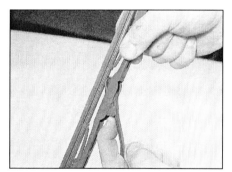

2 To remove a windscreen wiper blade, pull the arm fully away from the screen until it locks. Swivel the blade through 90°, press the locking tab with your fingers and slide the blade out of the arm's hooked end.

Tyre condition and pressure

It is very important that tyres are in good condition, and at the correct pressure - having a tyre failure at any speed is highly dangerous. Tyre wear is influenced by driving style - harsh braking and acceleration, or fast cornering, will all produce more rapid tyre wear. As a general rule, the front tyres wear out faster than the rears. Interchanging the tyres from front to rear ("rotating" the tyres) may result in more even wear. However, if this is completely effective, you may have the expense of replacing all four tyres at once!

Remove any nails or stones embedded in the tread before they penetrate the tyre to cause deflation. If removal of a nail does reveal that the tyre has been punctured, refit the nail so that its point of penetration is marked. Then immediately change the wheel, and have the tyre repaired by a tyre dealer.

Regularly check the tyres for damage in the form of cuts or bulges, especially in the sidewalls. Periodically remove the wheels, and clean any dirt or mud from the inside and outside surfaces. Examine the wheel rims for signs of rusting, corrosion or other damage. Light alloy wheels are easily damaged by "kerbing" whilst parking; steel wheels may also become dented or buckled. A new wheel is very often the only way to overcome severe damage.

New tyres should be balanced when they are fitted, but it may become necessary to re-balance them as they wear, or if the balance weights fitted to the wheel rim should fall off. Unbalanced tyres will wear more quickly, as will the steering and suspension components. Wheel imbalance is normally signified by vibration, particularly at a certain speed (typically around 50 mph). If this vibration is felt only through the steering, then it is likely that just the front wheels need balancing. If, however, the vibration is felt through the whole car, the rear wheels could be out of balance. Wheel balancing should be carried out by a tyre dealer or garage.

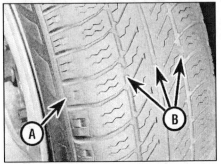

1 *Tread Depth - visual check*
The original tyres have tread wear safety bands (B), which will appear when the tread depth reaches approximately 1.6 mm. The band positions are indicated by a triangular mark on the tyre sidewall (A).

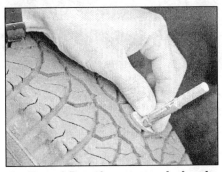

2 *Tread Depth - manual check*
Alternatively, tread wear can be monitored with a simple, inexpensive device known as a tread depth indicator gauge.

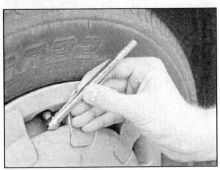

3 *Tyre Pressure Check*
Check the tyre pressures regularly with the tyres cold. Do not adjust the tyre pressures immediately after the vehicle has been used, or an inaccurate setting will result.

Tyre tread wear patterns

Shoulder Wear

Underinflation (wear on both sides)
Under-inflation will cause overheating of the tyre, because the tyre will flex too much, and the tread will not sit correctly on the road surface. This will cause a loss of grip and excessive wear, not to mention the danger of sudden tyre failure due to heat build-up.
Check and adjust pressures
Incorrect wheel camber (wear on one side)
Repair or renew suspension parts
Hard cornering
Reduce speed!

Centre Wear

Overinflation
Over-inflation will cause rapid wear of the centre part of the tyre tread, coupled with reduced grip, harsher ride, and the danger of shock damage occurring in the tyre casing.
Check and adjust pressures

If you sometimes have to inflate your car's tyres to the higher pressures specified for maximum load or sustained high speed, don't forget to reduce the pressures to normal afterwards.

Uneven Wear

Front tyres may wear unevenly as a result of wheel misalignment. Most tyre dealers and garages can check and adjust the wheel alignment (or "tracking") for a modest charge.
Incorrect camber or castor
Repair or renew suspension parts
Malfunctioning suspension
Repair or renew suspension parts
Unbalanced wheel
Balance tyres
Incorrect toe setting
Adjust front wheel alignment
Note: *The feathered edge of the tread which typifies toe wear is best checked by feel.*

Battery

Caution: Before carrying out any work on the vehicle battery, read the precautions given in "Safety first" at the start of this manual.

☐ Make sure that the battery tray is in good condition, and that the clamp is tight. Corrosion on the tray, retaining clamp and the battery itself can be removed with a solution of water and baking soda. Thoroughly rinse all cleaned areas with water. Any metal parts damaged by corrosion should be covered with a zinc-based primer, then painted.

☐ Periodically (approximately every three months), check the charge condition of the battery as described in Chapter 5A.

☐ If the battery is flat, and you need to jump start your vehicle, see *Roadside Repairs*.

HAYNES HINT

Battery corrosion can be kept to a minimum by applying a layer of petroleum jelly to the clamps and terminals after they are reconnected.

1 Check the battery lead clamps for tightness to ensure good electrical connections and check the leads for signs of damage.

3 . . . as well as the battery cable clamps

2 If corrosion (white, fluffy deposits) is evident, remove the cables from the battery terminals, clean them with a small wire brush, then refit them. Automotive stores sell a tool for cleaning the battery post . . .

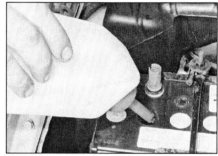

4 Ensure that the electrolyte level is kept between the upper (MAX) and lower (MIN) level markings on the side of the battery. If topping-up is necessary, remove the caps and top-up to the upper level using distilled water only. **Do not** use tap water as this will damage the battery. Once the electrolyte level is correct, securely refit the cell caps and wipe off any spilt water.

Bulbs and fuses

☐ Check all external lights and the horn. Refer to the appropriate Sections of Chap-ter 12 for details if any of the circuits are found to be inoperative.

☐ Visually check all accessible wiring connectors, harnesses and retaining clips for security, and for signs of chafing or damage.

HAYNES HINT *If you need to check your brake lights and indicators unaided, back up to a wall or garage door and operate the lights. The reflected light should show if they are working properly.*

1 If a single indicator light, stop light or headlight has failed, it is likely that a bulb has blown and will need to be replaced. Refer to Chapter 12 for details. If both stop lights have failed, it is possible that the switch has failed (see Chapter 9).

2 If more than one indicator light or tail light has failed it is likely that either a fuse has blown or that there is a fault in the circuit (see Chapter 12). On early models (shown) t he fuses are located behind the driver's side lower facia panel and on later models they are located behind the driver's side footwell side panel.

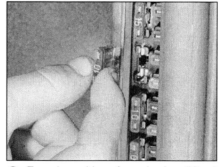

3 To replace a blown fuse, simply pull it out and fit a new fuse of the correct rating (see Chapter 12). If the fuse blows again, it is important that you find out why - a complete checking procedure is given in Chapter 12.

Lubricants and fluids

Engine . . . . Multigrade engine oil, viscosity SAE 10W/30 to 10W/40*
(Duckhams QS, QXR, Hypergrade Plus, Hypergrade or 10W/40 Motor Oil)

Cooling system . . . . Ethylene glycol based antifreeze*
(Duckhams Antifreeze and Summer Coolant)

Manual transmission . . . . Hypoid gear oil SAE 75/85W to API GL-4*
(Duckhams Hypoid 75 Gear Oil)

Automatic transmission . . . . Hyundai Automatic Transmission Fluid (ATF)*
(Duckhams Uni-Matic)

Braking system . . . . Hydraulic fluid to DOT 3*
(Duckhams Universal Brake and Clutch Fluid)

Power steering . . . . Dexron type II automatic transmission fluid (ATF)*
(Duckhams Uni-Matic)

Refer to your Hyundai dealer for brand name and type recommendations

Choosing your engine oil

Oils perform vital tasks in all engines. The higher the engine's performance, the greater the demand on lubricants to minimise wear as well as optimise power and economy. Duckhams tailors lubricants to the highest technical standards, meeting and exceeding the demands of all modern engines.

HOW ENGINE OIL WORKS

• Beating friction

Without oil, the surfaces inside your engine which rub together will heat, fuse and quickly cause engine seizure. Oil, and its special additives, forms a molecular barrier between moving parts, to stop wear and minimise heat build-up.

• Cooling hot spots

Oil cools parts that the engine's water-based coolant cannot reach, bathing the combustion chamber and pistons, where temperatures may exceed 1000°C. The oil assists in transferring the heat to the engine cooling system. Heat in the oil is also lost by air flow over the sump, and via any auxiliary oil cooler.

• Cleaning the inner engine

Oil washes away combustion by-products (mainly carbon) on pistons and cylinders, transporting them to the oil filter, and holding the smallest particles in suspension until they are flushed out by an oil change. Duckhams oils undergo extensive tests in the laboratory, and on the road.

OIL CARE
FOLLOW THE CODE
OIL BANK LINE
0800 66 33 66

Note: It is antisocial and illegal to dump oil down the drain. To find the location of your local oil recycling bank, call this number free.

Engine oil types

Mineral oils are the "traditional" oils, generally suited to older engines and cars not used in harsh conditions. *Duckhams Hypergrade Plus* and *Hypergrade* are well suited for use in most popular family cars.
Diesel oils such as *Duckhams Diesel* are specially formulated for Diesel engines, including turbocharged models and 4x4s.
Synthetic oils are the state-of-the-art in lubricants, offering ultimate protection, but at a fairly high price. One such is *Duckhams QS*, for use in ultra-high performance engines.
Semi-synthetic oils offer high performance engine protection, but at less cost than full synthetic oils. *Duckhams QXR* is an ideal choice for hot hatches and hard-driven cars.

For help with technical queries on lubricants, call Duckhams Oils on 0181 290 8207

Tyre pressures (cold)

Note: *Pressures apply to original-equipment tyres only and may vary if any other make or type of tyre is fitted; check with the tyre manufacturer or supplier for correct pressures if necessary.*
Note: *Tyre pressures must always be checked with the tyres cold to ensure accuracy.*

	Front	Rear
155 R 13 tyres:	27 psi (1.9 bar)	27 psi (1.9 bar)
175/70 R 13 tyres	26 psi (1.8 bar)	26 psi (1.8 bar)

Chapter 1
Routine maintenance and servicing

Contents

Air cleaner element check and clean 5
Air cleaner element renewal 26
Air conditioning refrigerant level check 8
Automatic transmission fluid level check 16
Automatic transmission fluid renewal 30
Auxiliary drivebelt check and renewal 4
Auxiliary drivebelt renewal 34
Brake fluid renewal 38
Clutch and brake pedal free play check 24
Crankcase ventilation hose check 32
Diagnostic test 6
Driveshaft and rubber gaiter check 23
EGR system check 36
Engine coolant renewal 37
Engine oil and filter renewal 3
Evaporative emission control system check 13
Exhaust system check 21
Front brake pads, calipers and discs check 17
Fuel and evaporative emission hose check 33

Fuel filter check (carburettor models only) 11
Fuel filter renewal 25
General information 1
Handbrake operation check 19
Hose and fluid leak check 7
Idle speed and mixture check 14
Ignition timing check and adjustment 10
Intensive maintenance 2
Manual transmission oil level check 15
Manual transmission oil renewal 29
PCV valve check 28
Rear brake shoes and drums check 18
Rear wheel bearings check and grease 22
Spark plug check and clean 12
Spark plug renewal and ignition system check 27
Steering and suspension check 20
Timing belt check 31
Timing belt renewal 35
Valve clearances check and adjustment 9

Degrees of difficulty

Easy, suitable for novice with little experience | **Fairly easy,** suitable for beginner with some experience | **Fairly difficult,** suitable for competent DIY mechanic | **Difficult,** suitable for experienced DIY mechanic | **Very difficult,** suitable for expert DIY or professional

Lubricants and fluids

Refer to "Weekly checks"

Capacities (approximate)

	Including oil filter	**Less oil filter**
Engine oil	3.5 litres	3.0 litres
Cooling system all models	5.3 litres	
Manual transmission	**Early models** 2.1 litres	**Later models** 1.8 litres
Automatic transmission	**From dry** 5.7 litres	**At fluid change** 4.5 litres
Power-assisted steering all models	0.9 litre	

Engine

Oil filter	Champion F110
Valve clearances (hot engine):	
Inlet	0.15 mm
Exhaust	0.25 mm
Jet valve	0.25 mm
Drivebelt deflection (under 10 kg load):	
Alternator drivebelt	7.0 to 8.2 mm
Power steering pump drivebelt	7.0 to 10.0 mm
Air conditioning compressor drivebelt	8.0 to 10.0 mm

Cooling system

Antifreeze mixture (50% antifreeze) .... Protection down to -37°C (5°F)

Note: *Refer to antifreeze manufacturer for latest recommendations.*

Fuel system

Air filter element:		
Carburettor models	Champion W170	
Fuel injection models:		
MFI types 1 and 2	Champion W140	
MFI type 3	Champion type not available	
Fuel filter:		
Carburettor models	Champion L119	
Fuel injection models	Champion type not available	
Idle speed and mixture:	**Idle speed**	**Idle mixture CO content**
Changwon carburettor models:		
Manual transmission models	750 ± 30 rpm	1.5%
Automatic transmission models	850 ± 30 rpm	1.5%
Aisan FBC carburettor models	700 ± 50 rpm	1.0 ± 0.5%
Aisan CONV carburettor models:		
1.3 and 1.5 with manual transmission	800 ± 30 rpm	1.0 ± 0.25%
1.5 with automatic transmission	850 ± 30 rpm	1.0 ± 0.25%
Fuel injection types 1 and 2 models	700 ± 100 rpm	Less than 1.0 % (not adjustable)
Fuel injection type 3 models	825 ± 100 rpm	Less than 1.0 % (not adjustable)

Ignition system

Ignition timing	Refer to Chapter 5
Spark plugs type and electrode gap	Champion RN9YCC, 0.8 mm

The spark plug gap quoted is that recommended by Champion for their specified plug listed above. If spark plugs of any other type are to be fitted, refer to their manufacturer's recommendations.

Brakes

Brake pad friction material/shoe lining thickness, minimum .... 1.0 mm

Torque wrench settings

	Nm	lbf ft
Alternator mounting bolts:		
Lower bolt	23	17
Upper (adjustment) bolt	14	10
Automatic transmission:		
Drain plug	33	24
Sump bolts	11	8
Oil filter bolts	7	5
Engine sump plug	40	30
Fuel filter union bolts	30	22
Manual transmission filler and drain plugs	33	24
Power steering pump mounting bolts	25	19
Roadwheel nuts	100	74
Spark plugs	25	19

The maintenance intervals in this manual are provided with the assumption that you, not the dealer, will be carrying out the work. These are the minimum maintenance intervals recommended by us for vehicles driven daily. If you wish to keep your vehicle in peak condition at all times, you may wish to perform some of these procedures more often. We encourage frequent maintenance, because it enhances the efficiency, performance and resale value of your vehicle.

When the vehicle is new, it should be serviced by a factory-authorised dealer service department, in order to preserve the factory warranty.

Every 6000 miles or 6 months, whichever comes first

Renew the engine oil and filter (Section 3)
Note: *If the vehicle is used under severe conditions, change the engine oil and filter more frequently (ie every 3000 miles or 3 months)*
☐ Check and adjust the tension of the auxiliary drivebelt(s) (Section 4)
☐ Check and clean the air cleaner element (Section 5)
☐ Carry out a diagnostic test (Section 6)
☐ Check hoses for fluid leaks (Section 7)
☐ Check the air conditioning refrigerant level (Section 8)

Every 12 000 miles or 12 months, whichever comes first

☐ Check and adjust the valve clearances (Section 9)
☐ Check and adjust the ignition timing (Section 10)
☐ Check the fuel filter on carburettor models only (Section 11)
☐ Check and clean the spark plugs (Section 12)
☐ Check the evaporative emission control system (Section 13)
☐ Check and adjust the idle speed and mixture (Section 14)
☐ Check the manual transmission oil level (Section 15)
☐ Check the automatic transmission fluid level (Section 16)
☐ Check the front brake pads, calipers and discs for wear (Section 17)
☐ Check the rear brake shoes and drums for wear (Section 18)
☐ Check the operation of the handbrake (Section 19)
☐ Check the steering and suspension components for condition and security (Section 20)
☐ Check the condition of the exhaust system and its mountings (Section 21)
☐ Check and grease the rear wheel bearings (Section 22)
☐ Check the driveshafts and rubber gaiters (Section 23)
☐ Check the clutch and brake pedal free play (Section 24)

Every 18 000 miles or 18 months, whichever comes first

☐ Check the crankcase ventilation hoses at first 30 000 miles, then every 18 000 miles (Section 32)
☐ Check the fuel and evaporative emission hoses, and the fuel filler cap at first 30 000 miles, then every 18 000 miles (Section 33)

Every 24 000 miles or 24 months, whichever comes first

☐ Renew the fuel filter on carburettor and fuel injection models (Section 25)
☐ Renew the air cleaner element (Section 26)
Note: *If the vehicle is used under severe or dusty conditions, change the air cleaner element more frequently (ie every 6000 miles or 6 months)*
☐ Renew the spark plugs and check the ignition system components (Section 27)
Note: *If the vehicle is used under severe conditions (extensive idling or towing), change the spark plugs more frequently (ie every 12 000 miles or 12 months)*
☐ Check the PCV valve (Section 28)
☐ Renew the manual transmission oil (Section 29)
☐ Renew the automatic transmission fluid (Section 30)

Every 30 000 miles or 30 months

☐ Check the timing belt (Section 31)
☐ Check the crankcase ventilation hoses at first 30 000 miles, then every 18 000 miles (Section 32)
☐ Check the fuel and evaporative emission hoses, and the fuel filler cap at first 30 000 miles, then every 18000 miles (Section 33)

Every 48 000 miles or 48 months, whichever comes first

☐ Renew the auxiliary drivebelts (Section 34)
☐ Renew the timing belt (Section 35)
☐ Check the EGR system (Section 36)

Every 2 years regardless of mileage

☐ Renew the engine coolant (Section 37)
☐ Renew the brake fluid (Section 38)

Underbonnet view of an early automatic model (left-hand drive)

1   Automatic transmission fluid level dipstick (below battery)
2   Battery
3   Coolant expansion tank
4   Washer fluid reservoir
5   Brake fluid reservoir
6   Evaporative emission carbon canister
7   Air cleaner
8   Distributor
9   Engine oil level dipstick
10 Auxiliary drivebelt
11 Power steering fluid reservoir
12 Oxygen sensor
13 Engine oil filler cap
14 Radiator filler cap

Underbonnet view of an X2 GSi

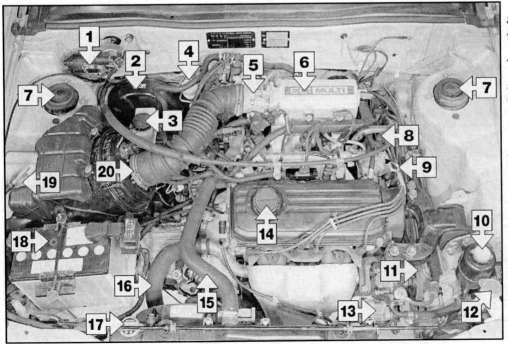

1   Windscreen wiper motor
2   Brake vacuum servo unit
3   Brake hydraulic fluid reservoir
4   Clutch hydraulic fluid reservoir
5   Throttle housing
6   Inlet manifold surge chamber
7   Suspension strut upper mounting
8   Distributor
9   Engine oil level dipstick
10 Power steering fluid reservoir
11 Power steering pump and auxiliary drivebelt
12 Washer fluid reservoir
13 Alternator
14 Engine oil filler cap
15 Radiator top hose
16 Radiator bottom hose
17 Radiator filler cap
18 Battery
19 Coolant expansion tank
20 Airflow meter/air cleaner cover

Front underbody view of an early automatic model (left-hand drive)

1 Front suspension radius arm
2 Front suspension anti-roll bar
3 Engine sump
4 Exhaust front downpipe
5 Engine oil drain plug
6 Brake caliper
7 Driveshaft rubber gaiter
8 Driveshaft
9 Steering track rod end
10 Steering gear rubber boot
11 Exhaust intermediate pipe
12 Steering gear
13 Automatic transmission drain plug
14 Automatic transmission sump

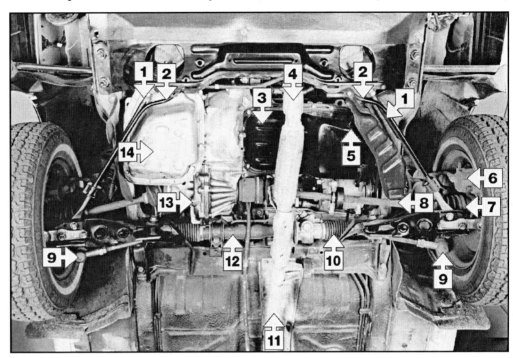

Front underbody view of an X2 GSi

1 Radiator
2 Longitudinal crossmember
3 Exhaust front downpipe
4 Oil filter
5 Auxiliary drivebelt
6 Engine oil drain plug
7 Brake caliper
8 Driveshaft
9 Front suspension lower arm
10 Engine stabilising rod
11 Transmission oil drain plug

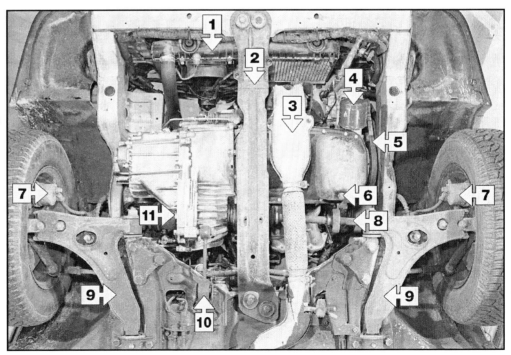

Rear underbody view of an X2 GSi

1 Rear suspension trailing arm
2 Handbrake cable
3 Fuel tank drain plug
4 Fuel tank support straps
5 Exhaust mounting
6 Exhaust tail pipe and silencer

Maintenance procedures

1 General information

This Chapter is designed to help the home mechanic maintain his/her vehicle for safety, economy, long life and peak performance.

The Chapter contains a master maintenance schedule, followed by Sections dealing specifically with each task in the schedule. Visual checks, adjustments, component renewal and other helpful items are included. Refer to the accompanying illustrations of the engine compartment and the underside of the vehicle for the locations of the various components.

Servicing your vehicle in accordance with the mileage/time maintenance schedule and the following Sections will provide a planned maintenance programme, which should result in a long and reliable service life. This is a comprehensive plan, so maintaining some items but not others at the specified service intervals, will not produce the same results.

As you service your vehicle, you will discover that many of the procedures can - and should - be grouped together, because of the particular procedure being performed, or because of the proximity of two otherwise-unrelated components to one another. For example, if the vehicle is raised for any reason, the exhaust can be inspected at the same time as the suspension and steering components.

The first step in this maintenance programme is to prepare yourself before the actual work begins. Read through all the

Sections relevant to the work to be carried out, then make a list and gather all the parts and tools required. If a problem is encountered, seek advice from a parts specialist, or a dealer service department.

2 Intensive maintenance

1 If, from the time the vehicle is new, the routine maintenance schedule is followed closely, and frequent checks are made of fluid levels and high-wear items, as suggested throughout this manual, the engine will be kept in relatively good running condition, and the need for additional work will be minimised.
2 It is possible that there will be times when the engine is running poorly due to the lack of regular maintenance. This is even more likely if a used vehicle, which has not received regular and frequent maintenance checks, is purchased. In such cases, additional work may need to be carried out, outside of the regular maintenance intervals.
3 If engine wear is suspected, a compression test (refer to Chapter 2A) will provide valuable information regarding the overall performance of the main internal components. Such a test can be used as a basis to decide on the extent of the work to be carried out. If, for example, a compression test indicates serious internal engine wear, conventional maintenance as described in this Chapter will not greatly improve the performance of the engine, and may prove a waste of time and money, unless

extensive overhaul work is carried out first.
4 The following series of operations are those most often required to improve the performance of a generally poor-running engine:

Primary operations

a) Clean, inspect and test the battery (refer to "Weekly checks").
b) Check all the engine-related fluids (refer to "Weekly checks").
c) Check the condition and tension of the auxiliary drivebelt (Section 4).
d) Renew the spark plugs (Section 27).
e) Inspect the distributor cap and rotor arm (Section 27).
f) Check the condition of the air cleaner, and renew if necessary (Section 26).
g) Renew the fuel filter (Section 25).
h) Check the condition of all hoses, and check for fluid leaks (Section 7).
i) Check the exhaust gas emissions (Section 21 and Chapter 4C).

5 If the above operations do not prove fully effective, carry out the following secondary operations:

Secondary operations

All items listed under "Primary operations", plus the following:

a) Check the charging system (refer to Chapter 5).
b) Check the ignition system (refer to Chapter 5).
c) Check the fuel system (refer to Chapter 4).
d) Renew the distributor cap and rotor arm (Section 27).
e) Renew the ignition HT leads (Section 27).

Every 6000 miles or 6 months, whichever comes first

3 Engine oil and filter renewal

1 Frequent oil and filter changes are the most important preventative maintenance procedures which can be undertaken by the DIY owner. As engine oil ages, it becomes diluted and contaminated, which leads to premature engine wear.

2 Before starting this procedure, gather together all the necessary tools and materials. Also make sure that you have plenty of clean rags and newspapers handy, to mop up any spills. Ideally, the engine oil should be warm, as it will drain more easily, and more built-up sludge will be removed with it. Take care not to touch the exhaust or any other hot parts of the engine when working under the vehicle. To avoid any possibility of scalding, and to protect yourself from possible skin irritants and other harmful contaminants in used engine oils, it is advisable to wear gloves when carrying out this work.

3 Firmly apply the handbrake then jack up the front of the vehicle and support it on axle stands (see "Jacking and Vehicle Support").

4 Remove the oil filler cap.

5 Using a spanner, or preferably a suitable socket and bar, slacken the drain plug about half a turn (see illustration). Position the draining container under the drain plug, then remove the plug completely.

As the drain plug threads release, move it sharply away so the stream of oil issuing from the sump runs into the container, not up your sleeve!

3.5 Slackening the sump drain plug

6 Allow some time for the oil to drain, noting that it may be necessary to reposition the container as the oil flow slows to a trickle.

7 After all the oil has drained, wipe the drain plug and the sealing washer with a clean rag. Examine the condition of the sealing washer, and renew it if it shows signs of scoring or other damage which may prevent an oil-tight seal. Clean the area around the drain plug opening, and refit the plug complete with the washer and tighten it to the specified torque.

8 Move the container into position under the oil filter which is located on the front of the cylinder block.

9 Use an oil filter removal tool to slacken the filter initially, then unscrew it by hand the rest of the way (see illustration). Empty the oil from the old filter into the container.

10 Use a clean rag to remove all oil, dirt and sludge from the filter sealing area on the engine. Check the old filter to make sure that the rubber sealing ring has not stuck to the engine. If it has, carefully remove it.

11 Apply a light coating of clean engine oil to the sealing ring on the new filter, then screw the filter into position on the engine. Tighten the filter firmly by hand only - do not use any tools.

12 Remove the old oil and all tools from under the car then lower it to the ground.

13 Fill the engine through the filler in the cylinder head cover, using the correct grade and type of oil (refer to "Weekly Checks" for details of topping-up). Pour in half the specified quantity of oil first, then wait a few minutes for the oil to drain into the sump. Continue to add oil, a small quantity at a time, until the level is up to the lower mark on the dipstick. Adding approximately a further 1.0 litre will bring the level up to the upper mark on the dipstick.

14 Start the engine and run it for a few minutes, while checking for leaks around the oil filter seal and the sump drain plug. Note that there may be a delay of a few seconds before the low oil pressure warning light goes out when the engine is first started, as the oil circulates through the new oil filter and the engine oil galleries before the pressure builds up.

15 Stop the engine, and wait a few minutes for the oil to settle in the sump once more.

3.9 Using an oil filter removal tool to slacken the oil filter

With the new oil circulated and the filter now completely full, recheck the level on the dipstick, and add more oil as necessary.

4 Auxiliary drivebelt check and renewal

1 Depending on specification, either one, two or three auxiliary drivebelts are fitted.

Checking the auxiliary drivebelt condition

2 Apply the handbrake, then jack up the front of the vehicle and support it on axle stands (see "Jacking and Vehicle Support"). Remove the left-hand front roadwheel. Access to the crankshaft pulley bolt can be gained by removing the rubber plug from underneath the left-hand wheelarch. If greater access is required, undo the retaining bolts and remove the plastic undercover.

3 Using a suitable socket and extension bar fitted to the crankshaft pulley bolt, rotate the crankshaft so that the entire length of the drivebelt(s) can be examined. Examine the drivebelt(s) for cracks, splitting, fraying or damage. Check also for signs of glazing (shiny patches) and for separation of the belt plies. Renew the belt if worn or damaged.

4 If the condition of each belt is satisfactory, check the drivebelt tension as described below.

Alternator drivebelt - removal, refitting and tensioning

Removal

5 Apply the handbrake, then jack up the front of the vehicle and support it on axle stands (see "Jacking and Vehicle Support"). Remove the left-hand front roadwheel and disconnect the battery negative lead.

6 Where necessary remove the power steering pump belt and/or air conditioning compressor belt(s) as described below (as applicable).

7 Slacken both the alternator upper and lower mounting bolts (see illustration).

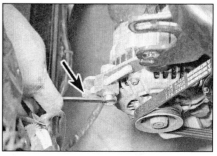

4.7 Slacken the alternator mounting bolts and back off the adjuster bolt (arrowed) to relieve the drivebelt tension

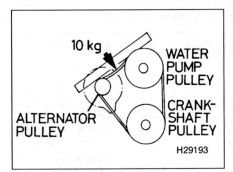

4.12 Checking the tension of the coolant pump/alternator drivebelt

8 Back off the adjuster bolt to relieve the tension in the drivebelt, then slip the drivebelt from the pulleys.

Refitting

9 If the belt is being renewed, ensure that the correct type is used. Fit the belt around the pulleys, ensuring that it is correctly seated, and take up the slack in the belt by tightening the adjuster bolt.
10 Tension the drivebelt as described in the following paragraphs.

Tensioning

11 Correct tensioning of the drivebelt will ensure that it has a long life. A belt which is too slack will slip and perhaps squeal. Beware, however, of overtightening, as this can cause wear in the alternator/coolant pump bearings.
12 The belt tension is checked at the mid-point between the alternator and coolant pump pulleys. Apply a force of approximately 10 kg to the belt at the specified point and check that the belt deflection is within the limits given in the *Specifications* **(see illustration)**.
13 To adjust, with the alternator mounting bolts loosened, turn the adjuster bolt until the correct tension is achieved. Rotate the crankshaft a couple of times, recheck the tension, then tighten both the alternator mounting bolts to their specified torque settings.
14 Refit the roadwheel and reconnect the battery negative lead. Lower the vehicle to the ground and tighten the roadwheel nuts to the specified torque.

4.21 Tension the power steering pump drivebelt by carefully levering the pump away from the engine

4.16a Slacken the power steering pump front mounting bolts (arrowed) . . .

Power steering pump drivebelt - removal, refitting and tensioning

Removal

15 Disconnect the battery negative terminal.
16 Slacken the power steering pump front and rear mounting bolts then slip the belt off its pulleys and remove it from the engine **(see illustrations)**.

Refitting

17 If the belt is being renewed, ensure that the correct type is used. Fit the belt around the pulleys, ensuring that it is correctly seated, and take up the slack in the belt by pivoting the pump away from the engine.
18 Tension the drivebelt as described in the following paragraphs.

Tensioning

19 Correct tensioning of the drivebelt will ensure that it has a long life. A belt which is too slack will slip and perhaps squeal. Beware, however, of overtightening, as this can cause wear in the steering/coolant pump bearings.
20 The belt tension is checked at the mid-point between the pulleys. Apply a force of approximately 10 kg to the belt at the specified point and check that the belt deflection is within the limits given in the *Specifications*.
21 To adjust, with the pump mounting bolts loosened, lever the power steering pump away from the engine until the correct tension is achieved **(see illustration)**. Hold the pump in position and securely tighten its mounting bolts. Rotate the crankshaft a couple of times, recheck the tension, then tighten the pump mounting bolts to the specified torque setting.

Air conditioning compressor drivebelt - removal, refitting and tensioning

Removal

22 Apply the handbrake, then jack up the front of the vehicle and support it on axle stands (see "*Jacking and Vehicle Support*"). Remove the left-hand front roadwheel and disconnect the battery negative lead.
23 Slacken both the idler pulley retaining bolts to relieve the tension in the drivebelt, then slip the drivebelt from the pulleys.

4.16b . . . and the rear mounting bolt (arrowed) and slip the drivebelt off its pulleys

Refitting

24 If the belt is being renewed, ensure that the correct type is used. Fit the belt around the pulleys, ensuring that it is correctly seated, and take up the slack in the belt using the idler pulley.
25 Tension the drivebelt as described in the following paragraphs.

Tensioning

26 Correct tensioning of the drivebelt will ensure that it has a long life. A belt which is too slack will slip and perhaps squeal. Beware, however, of overtightening, as this can cause wear in the compressor bearings.
27 The belt tension is checked at the mid-point of the upper rear run of the belt. Apply a force of approximately 10 kg to the belt at the specified point and check that the belt deflection is as given in the *Specifications*.
28 To adjust, slacken the retaining bolts and reposition the idler pulley until the correct tension is achieved. Rotate the crankshaft a couple of times, recheck the tension, then securely tighten the idler pulley bolts.
29 Refit the roadwheel and reconnect the battery negative lead. Lower the vehicle to the ground and tighten the roadwheel nuts to the specified torque.

---

5   **Air cleaner element check and clean**

Carburettor models

1 Disconnect the breather hose from the air cleaner housing cover on early models.
2 Unscrew the wing nut then release the retaining clips and remove the air cleaner housing cover and filter element **(see illustration)**.
3 Inspect the filter element. If the filter element is excessively dirty or is damaged in anyway, it must be renewed.
4 Wipe clean the filter housing and cover and refit the filter element in position.
5 Refit the housing cover, securing it in position with the wing nut and retaining clips, and reconnect the breather hose on early models.

5.2 Removing the air cleaner element on carburettor models

Fuel injection models

Early models (MFI types 1 and 2)

6 Release the retaining clips and remove the air duct connecting the air cleaner cover to the throttle housing.
7 Disconnect the airflow meter wiring from the air cleaner cover **(see illustrations)**.
8 Release the clips and withdraw the cover **(see illustrations)**.
9 Withdraw the element from the air cleaner body, noting that it has a location tab which engages with a slot in the body **(see illustrations)**.
10 Inspect the filter element. If the filter element is excessively dirty or is damaged in anyway, it must be renewed.
11 Wipe clean the filter housing and cover and refit the filter element in position with the tab engaged with the slot.
12 Refit the cover and reconnect the wiring and air duct.

5.8a ... then release the clips ...

5.8b ... and withdraw the cover
(note the element location tab arrowed)

5.7a On the MFI types 1 and 2 release the wiring ...

Later models (MFI type 3)

13 Unscrew and remove the bolts securing the cover to the air cleaner body.
14 Lift the cover and remove the element, noting which way round it is located.
15 Inspect the filter element. If the filter element is excessively dirty or is damaged in anyway, it must be renewed.
16 Wipe clean the filter housing and cover then refit the filter element in position.
17 Refit the cover and tighten the bolts.

6 Diagnostic test

The diagnostic test requires the use of a special electronic diagnostic tester which is connected to the diagnostic socket in the fusebox. Fault codes stored in the system ECU are accessed and appropriate action taken.

Since it is unlikely that the home mechanic will have access to a tester, this work should be carried out by a Hyundai dealer.

7 Hose and fluid leak check

1 Visually inspect the engine joint faces, gaskets and seals for any signs of water or oil leaks. Pay particular attention to the areas around the cylinder head cover, cylinder head,

5.9a Remove the air cleaner element
(MFI types 1 and 2) ...

5.7b ... and disconnect it from the cover ...

oil filter and sump joint faces. Bear in mind that, over a period of time, some very slight seepage from these areas is to be expected - what you are really looking for is any indication of a serious leak. Should a leak be found, renew the offending gasket or oil seal by referring to the appropriate Chapters in this manual.

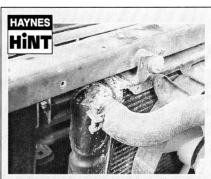

HAYNES HiNT

A leak in the cooling system will usually show up as white- or rust-coloured deposits on the area adjoining the leak

2 Also check the security and condition of all the engine-related pipes and hoses. Ensure that all cable-ties or securing clips are in place and in good condition. Clips which are broken or missing can lead to chafing of the hoses, pipes or wiring, which could cause more serious problems in the future.
3 Carefully check the radiator hoses and heater hoses along their entire length. Renew any hose which is cracked, swollen or

5.9b ... noting the location tab

deteriorated. Cracks will show up better if the hose is squeezed. Pay close attention to the hose clips that secure the hoses to the cooling system components. Hose clips can pinch and puncture hoses, resulting in cooling system leaks.

4 Inspect all the cooling system components (hoses, joint faces etc.) for leaks. A leak in the cooling system will usually show up as white- or rust-coloured deposits on the area adjoining the leak. Where any problems of this nature are found on system components, renew the component or gasket with reference to Chapter 3.

5 From within the engine compartment, check the security of all fuel hose attachments and pipe unions, and inspect the fuel hoses and vacuum hoses for kinks, chafing and deterioration.

6 Where applicable, check the condition of the power steering fluid hoses and pipes.

7 Check all brake hoses and lines for condition and leakage.

8 Air conditioning refrigerant level check

1 Locate the air conditioning system receiver-drier which is situated in the engine bay, on the front left-hand side.

2 Carefully wipe clean the inspection window on the side of the receiver-drier.

3 Start the engine and allow it to idle. Have an assistant turn on the air conditioning at the control panel, whilst observing the inspection window. The refrigerant fluid level should rise into view. Continue watching the fluid level, which should rise beyond the top of the inspection window, until only bubble-free fluid can be seen flowing.

4 If the fluid level appears to be too low, or if there are a lot of bubbles visible, the vehicle should be taken to a Hyundai dealer or air conditioning specialist for diagnosis and/or re-charging.

5 During the winter months it is recommended that the air conditioning system is operated once a week in order to circulate the lubricating oil in the compressor.

Every 12 000 miles or 12 months, whichever comes first

9 Valve clearances check and adjustment

Note: The valve clearances should be checked and adjusted with the engine hot to ensure accuracy. If the clearances are being adjusted with the engine cold, it is recommended that they are rechecked once the engine has been warmed up to normal operating temperature.

1 The importance of having the valve clearances correctly adjusted cannot be overstressed, as they vitally affect the performance of the engine. If the clearances are too big, the engine will be noisy (characteristic rattling or tapping noises) and engine efficiency will be reduced, as the valves open too late and close too early. A more serious problem arises if the clearances are too small, however. If this is the case, the valves may not close fully, resulting in serious damage to the engine (eg. burnt valve seats and/or cylinder head warping/cracking). The clearances are checked and adjusted as follows.

9.3 With No 1 cylinder piston at TDC compression, adjust the valves marked "A" - with No 4 cylinder piston at TDC compression, adjust the valves marked "B"

2 Warm the engine up to normal operating temperature then, working as described in Chapter 2A, remove the cylinder head cover and position No 1 cylinder piston at TDC on its compression stroke.

3 With No 1 cylinder piston at TDC on its compression stroke, check and if necessary adjust the following valve clearances, noting that No 1 cylinder is at the timing belt end of the engine. The valve locations can be determined from the position of the manifolds (see illustration). Note that on engines with jet valves, the jet valves must be adjusted **before** the inlet valves - the inlet valve adjusting screw must be backed off two full turns before adjusting the jet valve.

   Number 1 cylinder inlet valve(s)
   Number 2 cylinder inlet valve(s)
   Number 1 cylinder exhaust valve
   Number 3 cylinder exhaust valve

4 Clearances are checked by inserting a feeler blade of the correct thickness between the valve stem (or jet valve stem) and the rocker arm adjusting screw. The feeler blade should be a light, sliding fit. If adjustment is necessary, slacken the adjusting screw locknut, and turn the screw as necessary. Once the correct clearance is obtained, hold the adjusting screw and tighten the locknut (see illustrations). Recheck the clearance, and adjust again if necessary.

9.4a Checking a jet valve clearance

Warning: Take great care not to burn your hands on the hot engine.

5 Once all the relevant valves have been checked, rotate the crankshaft through one complete turn (360°) in a clockwise direction to bring No 1 cylinder back to TDC (No 4 piston will be at TDC compression). Ensure that the crankshaft pulley mark is correctly aligned with the 0° mark on the timing belt cover scale then check and, if necessary, adjust the following valve clearances.

   Number 3 cylinder inlet valve(s)
   Number 4 cylinder inlet valve(s)
   Number 2 cylinder exhaust valve
   Number 4 cylinder exhaust valve

6 Once all the valve clearances are correctly adjusted, refit the cylinder head cover as described in Chapter 2A.

10 Ignition timing check and adjustment

The ignition timing checking and adjustment procedure is described in Chapter 5. Note that on fuel injection models, the timing is constantly being monitored and adjusted by the engine management ECU, and it is not possible to manually adjust it. It

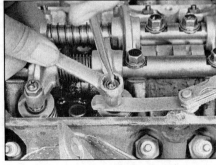

9.4b Adjusting an exhaust valve clearance

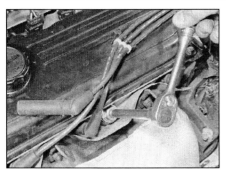

12.4 Removing a spark plug

can therefore be safely assumed that the ignition timing is correct unless the engine management system warning light is illuminated.

11 Fuel filter check (carburettor models only)

1 The fuel filter is located in the engine compartment on the bulkhead, and has a translucent body. Check if there are any deposits or water in the filter.
2 If necessary, clean the filter by disconnecting the inlet and outlet hoses and removing the filter from its retaining spring clip. Using low air pressure (for instance from a footpump), blow through the filter inlet until clean.
3 Refit the filter using a reversal of the removal procedure.

12 Spark plug check and clean

1 The correct functioning of the spark plugs is vital for the correct running and efficiency of the engine. It is essential that the plugs fitted are appropriate for the engine (a suitable type is specified at the beginning of this Chapter). If this type is used and the engine is in good condition, the spark plugs should not need attention between scheduled replacement intervals. Spark plug cleaning is rarely necessary, and should not be attempted unless specialised equipment is available, as damage can easily be caused to the firing ends.
2 If the marks on the original-equipment spark plug (HT) leads cannot be seen, mark the leads to correspond to the cylinder the lead serves. Pull the leads from the plugs by gripping the end fitting, not the lead, otherwise the lead connection may be fractured.
3 It is advisable to remove the dirt from the spark plug recesses using a clean brush, vacuum cleaner or compressed air before removing the plugs, to prevent dirt dropping into the cylinders.
4 Unscrew the plugs using a spark plug spanner, suitable box spanner or a deep socket and extension bar **(see illustration)**.

Keep the socket aligned with the spark plug - if it is forcibly moved to one side, the ceramic insulator may be broken off. As each plug is removed, examine it as follows.
5 Examination of the spark plugs will give a good indication of the condition of the engine. If the insulator nose of the spark plug is clean and white, with no deposits, this is indicative of a weak mixture or too hot a plug (a hot plug transfers heat away from the electrode slowly, a cold plug transfers heat away quickly).
6 If the tip and insulator nose are covered with hard black-looking deposits, then this is indicative that the mixture is too rich. Should the plug be black and oily, then it is likely that the engine is fairly worn, as well as the mixture being too rich.
7 If the insulator nose is covered with light tan to greyish-brown deposits, then the mixture is correct and it is likely that the engine is in good condition.
8 The spark plug electrode gap is of considerable importance as, if it is too large or too small, the size of the spark and its efficiency will be seriously impaired. The gap should be set to the value given in the *Specifications*.
9 To set the gap, measure it with a feeler blade and then bend open, or closed, the outer plug electrode until the correct gap is achieved. The centre electrode should never be bent, as this may crack the insulator and cause plug failure, if nothing worse. If using feeler blades, the gap is correct when the appropriate-size blade is a firm sliding fit **(see illustration)**.
10 Special spark plug electrode gap adjusting tools are available from most motor accessory shops, or from some spark plug manufacturers **(see illustration)**.
11 Before fitting the spark plugs, check that the threaded connector sleeves are tight, and that the plug exterior surfaces and threads are clean.

HAYNES HINT

It is very often difficult to insert spark plugs into their holes without cross-threading them. To avoid this possibility, fit a short length of 5/16 inch internal diameter rubber hose over the end of the spark plug. The flexible hose acts as a universal joint to help align the plug with the plug hole. Should the plug begin to cross-thread, the hose will slip on the spark plug, preventing thread damage to the aluminium cylinder head

12.9 Measuring the spark plug gap with a feeler blade

12 Remove the rubber hose (if used), and tighten the plug to the specified torque using the spark plug socket and a torque wrench. Refit the remaining spark plugs in the same manner.
13 Connect the HT leads in their correct order.

13 Evaporative emission control system check

1 The function of the evaporative emission control system is to draw fuel vapours from the fuel tank and store them in a carbon canister. During normal engine operation, the vapours are drawn into the inlet manifold and then into the combustion chambers.
2 The most common symptom of a fault in the evaporative emissions system is a strong fuel smell in the engine compartment. If this is evident, check that the hoses are correctly attached to the carbon canister located in the engine compartment.
3 Further details of the evaporative emission control system are given in Chapter 4C.

14 Idle speed and mixture check

1 Before checking the idle speed and mixture setting, always check the following first:
  a) *Check the ignition timing (Chapter 5).*
  b) *Check that the spark plugs are in good condition and correctly gapped (Section 12).*

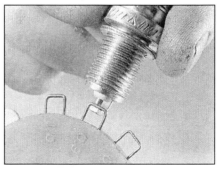

12.10 Measuring the spark plug gap with a wire gauge

c) Check that the accelerator cable is correctly adjusted (see Chapter 4).

d) Check that the crankcase ventilation hoses are secure, with no leaks or kinks (Section 32).

e) Check that the air cleaner filter element is clean (Section 5).

f) Check that the exhaust system is in good condition (Section 21).

g) If the engine is running very roughly, check the compression pressures and valve clearances (see Chapter 2A and Section 9 of this Chapter).

h) On fuel injection models, check that the fuel injection/ignition system warning light is not illuminated (see Chapter 4B).

2 Take the vehicle on a journey of sufficient length to warm it up to normal operating temperature. Proceed as described under the relevant sub-heading.

Note: *Adjustment should be completed within two minutes of return, without stopping the engine. If this cannot be achieved, or if the radiator electric cooling fan operates, first wait for the cooling fan to stop. Clear any excess fuel from the inlet manifold by racing the engine two or three times to between 2000 and 3000 rpm, then allow it to idle again.*

Carburettor models

3 Ensure that all electrical loads are switched off. If the vehicle does not have a tachometer (rev counter), connect one to the engine following its manufacturer's instructions. Note the idle speed, and compare it with that specified.

4 The idle speed adjusting screw is on the throttle linkage on the rear of the carburettor. Turn the idle screw in or out as necessary to obtain the specified speed **(see illustration)**.

5 The idle mixture (exhaust gas CO level) is set at the factory, and should require no further adjustment. If, due to a change in engine characteristics (carbon build-up, bore wear etc) or after a major carburettor overhaul, the mixture setting is lost, it can be

reset. Note, however, that an exhaust gas analyser (CO meter) will be required to check the mixture, in order to set it with the necessary standard of accuracy; if this is not available, the vehicle must be taken to a dealer for the work to be carried out. Also note that a special tool will be required to rotate the mixture adjusting screw. **Note:** *On the FBC carburettor (models with a catalytic converter), idle mixture is controlled by the FBSV (FeedBack Solenoid Valve) and cannot be adjusted manually.*

6 On non-FBC models, if the necessary equipment is available connect the analyser to the vehicle in accordance with the manufacturer's instructions and check the exhaust gas CO level. If adjustment is required, it is made by turning the mixture adjustment screw located at the rear of the carburettor base. The screw is covered with a tamperproof plug to prevent unnecessary adjustment.

7 Remove the tamperproof cap and turn the mixture adjustment screw (in very small increments) until the CO level is correct.

8 When the adjustment is correct, disconnect the test equipment and fit the tamperproof plug to the mixture adjustment screw. Recheck the idle speed and, if necessary, readjust.

Fuel injection models

9 Refer to Chapter 4B, Section 11.

15 Manual transmission oil level check

1 Park the vehicle on a level surface. The oil level must be checked before the vehicle is driven, or at least 5 minutes after the engine has been switched off. If the oil is checked immediately after driving the car, some of the oil will remain distributed around the transmission components, resulting in an inaccurate level reading. For improved access to the transmission filler/level plug, jack up the vehicle and support on axle stands (see *"Jacking and Vehicle Support"*).

2 Wipe clean the area around the filler/level plug, which is situated on the front of the transmission. Unscrew the plug and clean it; discard the sealing washer **(see illustration)**.

3 On models up to 1991 the oil level should reach the lower edge of the filler/level hole, however, from 1992-on the oil level should be between 5.0 and 9.0 mm *below* the lower edge of the filler/level hole. Use a length of bent wire to check the lower level. If necessary, add oil through the filler hole until the level is correct **(see illustration)**.

4 With the level correct, refit and tighten the plug, and lower the vehicle to the ground.

16 Automatic transmission fluid level check

1 Take the vehicle on a short journey, to warm the transmission up to normal operating temperature, then park the vehicle on level ground and firmly apply the handbrake. The fluid level is checked using the dipstick which is situated on the top of the transmission where it is located beside the battery tray.

2 With the engine idling, apply the brakes then move the selector lever from the "P" (Park) position, to the "L" (low) position and then to the "N" (neutral) position. Withdraw the dipstick from the tube (located below the battery position), and wipe all the fluid from its end with a clean rag or paper towel. Insert the clean dipstick back into the tube as far as it will go, then withdraw it once more. Note the fluid level on the end of the dipstick; it should be between the upper and lower marks **(see illustrations)**.

3 If topping-up is necessary, add the required quantity of the specified fluid to the transmission via the dipstick tube. Use a funnel with a fine mesh gauze, to avoid spillage, and to ensure that no foreign matter enters the transmission. **Note:** *Never overfill the transmission so that the fluid level is above the upper mark.*

4 After topping-up, take the vehicle on a short run to distribute the fresh fluid, then recheck the level again, topping-up if necessary.

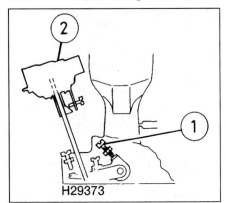

H29373

14.4 When adjusting the engine idle speed, only turn the idle adjustment screw - the other screws are preset

1 Idle adjustment screw
2 Throttle opener

15.2 Loosening the manual transmission filler/level plug

15.3 Topping-up the manual transmission oil level

16.2a The automatic transmission dipstick (arrowed) is located under the battery

5 Always maintain the level between the two dipstick marks. If the level is allowed to fall below the lower mark, fluid starvation may result, which could lead to severe transmission damage.
6 Frequent need for topping-up indicates that there is a leak, which should be found and corrected before it becomes serious.

17 Front brake pads, calipers and discs check

1 Firmly apply the handbrake, then jack up the front of the vehicle and support it securely on axle stands (see *"Jacking and Vehicle Support"*). Remove the front roadwheels.
2 For a quick check, the pad thickness can be carried out via the inspection hole on the front of the caliper **(see illustration)**. Using a steel rule, measure the thickness of the pad linings. This must not be less than that indicated in the *Specifications*.
3 The view through the caliper inspection hole gives a rough indication of the state of the brake pads. For a comprehensive check, the brake pads should be removed and cleaned. The operation of the caliper can then also be checked, and the condition of the brake disc itself can be fully examined on both sides. Chapter 9 contains a detailed description of how the brake disc should be checked for wear and/or damage.
4 If any pad's friction material is worn to the specified thickness or less, *all four pads must be renewed as a set*. See Chapter 9 for details.

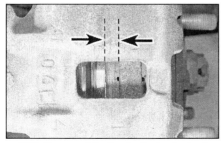

17.2 For a quick check, the brake pad friction material thickness (arrowed) can be checked via the inspection hole on the front of the caliper

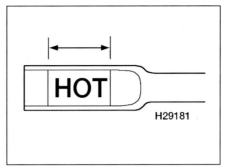

16.2b The fluid level should be between the upper and lower marks on the dipstick

5 On completion, refit the roadwheels and lower the vehicle to the ground.

18 Rear brake shoes and drums check

Refer to the detailed description given in Chapter 9.

19 Handbrake operation check

Checking

1 Apply the handbrake by pulling it through three to four 'clicks' of the ratchet mechanism and check that this locks the rear wheels, holding the vehicle stationary on an incline. In this position, there should be sufficient reserve travel in the handbrake lever to allow for brake shoe wear and cable stretching. If not, the handbrake mechanism is in need of adjustment.

Adjustment

2 Park the vehicle on a level surface, select first gear (or 'Park' on models with automatic transmission) and chock the roadwheels.
3 Remove the rear section of the centre console as described in Chapter 11.
4 If new brake shoes or handbrake cables have been fitted, check that with the handbrake lever in the fully-off position, all tension is removed from the handbrake cables - slacken the two adjustment nuts (early models) or single adjustment nut (later models) if necessary. This ensures that the brake shoe self-adjustment mechanism has enough freeplay to operate correctly (see Chapter 9 for details). The adjustment nut(s) are located on the base of the handbrake lever assembly.
5 Pull the handbrake lever through three 'clicks' of the ratchet mechanism and leave it in this position.
6 Tighten the adjustment nut(s) so that the adjustment mechanism tensions the handbrake cable equaliser bar, until the rear wheels are just locked. On early models make sure that each nut is tightened by the same amount.

7 Release the handbrake lever, then re-apply it and check the operation of the handbrake as described above. Repeat the adjustment procedure if necessary.
8 Chock the front wheels, select reverse gear and raise the rear of the vehicle on axle stands (see *"Jacking and Vehicle Support"*). Release the handbrake lever and check that the rear wheels are free to rotate without binding. Re-adjust the cable if the brakes appear to be binding.
9 On completion, refit the rear section of the centre console.

20 Steering and suspension check

Front suspension and steering check

1 Raise the front of the vehicle, and securely support it on axle stands (see *"Jacking and Vehicle Support"*).
2 Visually inspect the balljoint dust covers and the steering rack-and-pinion gaiters for splits, chafing or deterioration. Any wear of these components will cause loss of lubricant, together with dirt and water entry, resulting in rapid deterioration of the balljoints or steering gear.
3 On vehicles with power steering, check the fluid hoses for chafing or deterioration, and the pipe and hose unions for fluid leaks. Also check for signs of fluid leakage under pressure from the steering gear rubber gaiters, which would indicate failed fluid seals within the steering gear.
4 Grasp the roadwheel at the 12 o'clock and 6 o'clock positions, and try to rock it **(see illustration)**. Very slight free play may be felt, but if the movement is appreciable, further investigation is necessary to determine the source. Continue rocking the wheel while an assistant depresses the footbrake. If the movement is now eliminated or significantly reduced, it is likely that the hub bearings are at fault. If the free play is still evident with the footbrake depressed, then there is wear in the suspension joints or mountings.

20.4 Grasp the roadwheel at the 12 o'clock and 6 o'clock positions, and try to rock it

5 Now grasp the wheel at the 9 o'clock and 3 o'clock positions, and try to rock it as before. Any movement felt now may again be caused by wear in the hub bearings or the steering track-rod balljoints. If the inner or outer track-rod balljoint is worn, the visual movement will be obvious.

6 Using a large screwdriver or flat bar, check for wear in the suspension mounting bushes by levering between the relevant suspension component and its attachment point. Some movement is to be expected as the mountings are made of rubber, but excessive wear should be obvious. Also check the condition of any visible rubber bushes, looking for splits, cracks or contamination of the rubber.

7 With the vehicle standing on its wheels, have an assistant turn the steering wheel back and forth about an eighth of a turn each way. There should be very little, if any, lost movement between the steering wheel and roadwheels. If this is not the case, closely observe the joints and mountings previously described, but in addition, check the steering column universal joints for wear, and the rack-and-pinion steering gear itself.

Suspension strut/shock absorber check

8 Check for any signs of fluid leakage around the suspension strut/shock absorber body, or from the rubber gaiter around the piston rod. Should any fluid be noticed, the suspension strut/shock absorber is defective internally, and should be renewed. **Note:** *Suspension struts/shock absorbers should always be renewed in pairs on the same axle.*

9 The efficiency of the suspension strut/shock absorber may be checked by bouncing the vehicle at each corner. Generally speaking, the body will return to its normal position and stop after being depressed. If it rises and returns on a rebound, the suspension strut/shock absorber is probably suspect. Examine also the suspension strut/shock absorber upper and lower mountings for any signs of wear.

21 Exhaust system check

1 Park the vehicle on a level surface and switch off the engine. Chock the front wheels, then raise the rear of the vehicle and support it securely on axle stands (see *"Jacking and Vehicle Support"*).

2 Check the complete exhaust system from the engine to the end of the tailpipe.

⚠️ **Warning:** *If the engine is not cold, take suitable precautions to prevent burn injuries!*

3 Check the exhaust pipes and connections for evidence of leaks, severe corrosion and damage. Make sure that all brackets and mountings are in good condition, and that all

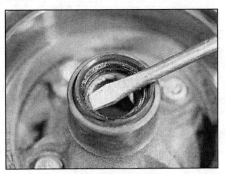

22.3 Prise the grease seal from the inboard side of the hub, using a large flat bladed screwdriver

relevant nuts and bolts are tight. Leakage at any of the joints or in other parts of the system will usually show up as a black sooty stain in the vicinity of the leak.

4 Rattles and other noises can often be traced to the exhaust system, especially the brackets and mountings. Try to move the pipes and silencers; if the components are able to come into contact with the body or suspension parts, secure the system with new mountings. Otherwise, with reference to the relevant part of Chapter 4, loosen the joints between adjacent sections of the exhaust pipe by slackening the joints (where possible) and twist the pipes as necessary to provide additional clearance. Re-tighten the exhaust pipe fasteners on completion.

22 Rear wheel bearings check and grease

1 On a level surface, jack up the rear of the vehicle and support on axle stands (see *"Jacking and Vehicle Support"*).

2 Remove the rear roadwheels, then remove the brake drums and wheel bearings, with reference to Chapters 9 and 10.

3 Prise the grease seal from the inboard side of the hub, using a large flat bladed screwdriver **(see illustration)**.

4 Wipe all traces of the old grease from the bearing races. Take this opportunity to inspect the bearings for signs of wear or damage.

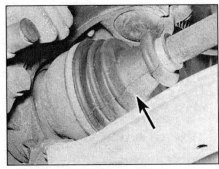

23.1 Check the driveshaft rubber gaiters for signs of cracking or splitting

22.5 If the bearings are in good condition, re-pack them with suitable grease

5 If the bearings are in good condition, re-pack them with suitable grease **(see illustration)**.

6 Press a new grease seal into position over the bearing races, with reference to Chapter 10.

7 Refer to Chapter 9 and refit the brake drum/bearing assembly to the stub axle.

8 Refit the roadwheel and lower the vehicle to the ground.

23 Driveshaft and rubber gaiter check

1 With the vehicle raised and securely supported on stands (see *"Jacking and Vehicle Support"*), turn the steering onto full lock, then slowly rotate the roadwheel. Inspect the condition of the outer constant velocity (CV) joint rubber gaiters, squeezing the gaiters to open out the folds **(see illustration)**. Check for signs of cracking, splits or deterioration of the rubber, which may allow the grease to escape, and lead to water and grit entry into the joint. Also check the security and condition of the retaining clips. Repeat these checks on the inner CV joints. If any damage or deterioration is found, the gaiters should be renewed (see Chapter 8).

2 At the same time, check the general condition of the CV joints themselves by first holding the driveshaft and attempting to rotate the wheel. Repeat this check by holding the inner joint and attempting to rotate the driveshaft. Any appreciable movement indicates wear in the joints, wear in the driveshaft splines, or a loose driveshaft retaining nut.

24 Clutch and brake pedal free play check

Refer to Chapter 6 for details of the clutch pedal check, and to Chapter 9 for details of the brake pedal check.

Every 24 000 miles or 24 months, whichever comes first

25 Fuel filter renewal

 Warning: Before carrying out the following operation, refer to the precautions given in "Safety first!" at the beginning of this manual, and follow them implicitly. Petrol is a highly-dangerous and volatile liquid, and the precautions necessary when handling it cannot be overstressed.

Carburettor models

1 The fuel filter is situated in the engine compartment where it is clipped onto the bulkhead.
2 Unclip the filter from its retaining clip on the bulkhead.
3 Release the retaining clips then detach the inlet and outlet hoses, noting the fitted position of each hose, and remove the filter.

 Warning: Dispose safely of the old filter; it will be highly flammable.

4 Connect the hoses to the new filter making sure that the inlet hose (from the fuel tank) is connected to the lower filter stub, and the outlet hose (to the carburettor) is connected to the upper filter stub. Secure both hoses in position with their retaining clips and clip the filter back into position on the bulkhead.
5 Start the engine, check the filter hose connections for leaks.

Fuel injection models

Note: New union bolt sealing washers will be required.
6 Working as described in Chapter 4B, depressurise the fuel system then remove the air duct from between the air cleaner and throttle housing. The fuel filter is mounted on the engine compartment bulkhead **(see illustration)**.
7 Slacken the inlet and outlet hose union bolts whilst retaining the filter using an open-ended spanner on the flats provided. Remove the union bolts and detach the hoses from the

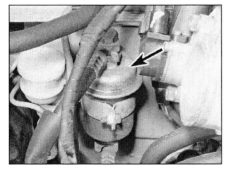

25.6 The fuel filter location on the bulkhead on fuel-injected models

filter **(see illustration)**. Discard the sealing washers; these should be renewed whenever they are disturbed.
8 Unbolt and remove the filter, noting which way around it is fitted.

 Warning: Dispose safely of the old filter; it will be highly flammable.

9 Fit the new filter ensuring it is fitted the correct way around with the "OUT" marking uppermost. Tighten the mounting bolts.
10 Position the outlet hose between the locating lugs on the top of the fuel filter then position a new sealing washer on each side of the hose union. Refit the union bolt and tighten it to the specified torque whilst retaining the filter with an open-ended spanner.
11 Reconnect the inlet hose to the base of the filter in the same manner and tighten the union bolt to the specified torque.
12 Start the engine and check the filter hose connections for leaks, prior to refitting the air duct as described in Chapter 4B.

26 Air cleaner element renewal

Refer to Section 5, but renew the element regardless of its apparent condition.

27 Spark plug renewal and ignition system check

Spark plug renewal

1 Refer to Section 12, renewing the spark plugs regardless of their condition.

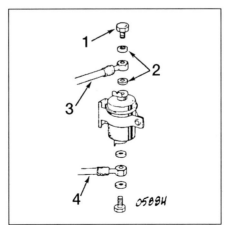

25.7 Fuel filter connections on fuel-injected models

1 *Union bolt*
2 *Sealing washers*
3 *Fuel hose to fuel rail*
4 *Fuel hose from fuel tank*

Ignition system check

2 Pull the HT leads from the spark plugs by gripping the end fitting, not the lead, otherwise the lead connection may be fractured.

HAYNES HiNT *Ensure that the leads are numbered before removing them, to avoid confusion when refitting.*

3 Check inside the end fitting for signs of corrosion, which will look like a white crusty powder. Push the end fitting back onto the spark plug, ensuring that it is a tight fit on the plug. If not, remove the lead again and use pliers to carefully crimp the metal connector inside the end fitting until it fits securely on the end of the spark plug.
4 Using a clean rag, wipe the entire length of the lead to remove any built-up dirt and grease. Once the lead is clean, check for burns, cracks and other damage. Do not bend the lead excessively, nor pull the lead length-ways - the conductor inside might break.
5 Disconnect the other end of the lead from the distributor cap. Again, pull only on the end fitting. Check for corrosion and a tight fit in the same manner as the spark plug end. If an ohmmeter is available, check the resistance of the lead by connecting the meter between the spark plug end of the lead and the segment inside the distributor cap. Refit the lead securely on completion.
6 Check the remaining leads one at a time, in the same way.
7 If new spark plug (HT) leads are required, purchase a set for your specific vehicle and engine.
8 Release the retaining clips and remove the distributor cap. Wipe it clean, and carefully inspect it inside and out for signs of cracks, black carbon tracks (tracking) and worn, burned or loose contacts; check that the cap's carbon brush is unworn, free to move against spring pressure, and making good contact with the rotor arm. Also inspect the cap seal for signs of wear or damage, and renew if necessary. Remove the rotor arm and inspect it. It is common practice to renew the cap and rotor arm whenever new spark plug (HT) leads are fitted. When fitting a new cap, remove the leads from the old cap one at a time, and fit them to the new cap in the exact same location - do not simultaneously remove all the leads from the old cap, or firing order confusion may occur. When refitting, ensure that the rotor arm is securely pressed on, then fit the distributor cap and secure it in position with the retaining clips.
9 Even with the ignition system in first-class condition, some engines may still occasionally experience poor starting attributable to damp ignition components. To disperse moisture, a water-dispersant aerosol can be very effective.

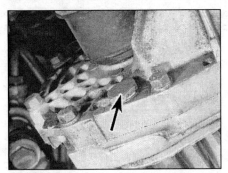

29.4 Manual transmission drain plug

28 PCV valve check

Check the PCV valve and hose as described in Chapter 4C.

29 Manual transmission oil renewal

1 This operation is much quicker and more efficient if the vehicle is first taken on a journey of sufficient length to warm the engine/transmission up to normal operating temperature.

2 Park the vehicle on level ground, switch off the ignition and apply the handbrake firmly. For improved access, jack up the front of the vehicle and support it securely on axle stands (see "*Jacking and Vehicle Support*"). Note that the vehicle must be lowered to the ground and level, to ensure accuracy, when refilling and checking the oil level.

3 Wipe clean the area around the filler/level plug, which is situated on the front of the transmission then unscrew the plug and remove it.

4 Position a suitable container under the drain plug situated on the right-hand side of the transmission housing, directly below the driveshaft **(see illustration)**.

5 Unscrew the drain plug and allow the oil to drain completely into the container. If the oil is hot, take precautions against scalding. Clean both the filler/level and the drain plugs, being especially careful to wipe any metallic particles off the magnetic inserts. Discard the original sealing washers; they should be renewed whenever they are disturbed.

6 When the oil has finished draining, clean the drain plug threads and those of the transmission casing, fit a new sealing washer and refit the drain plug, tightening it to the specified torque setting. It the vehicle was raised for the draining operation, now lower it to the ground.

7 When refilling the transmission, allow plenty of time for the oil level to settle properly before checking it. Note that the vehicle must be parked on flat level ground when checking the oil level.

8 Refill the transmission via the filler/level plug hole with the exact amount of the specified type of oil then check the oil level as described in Section 15. When the level is correct, refit the filler/level plug with a new sealing washer and tighten it to the specified torque. **Note:** *If the correct amount was poured into the transmission and a large amount flows out on checking the level, refit the filler or filler/level plug and take the vehicle on a short journey so that the new oil is distributed fully around the transmission components, then check the level again on your return.*

30 Automatic transmission fluid renewal

1 Take the vehicle on a short run, to warm the transmission up to normal operating temperature.

2 Park the vehicle on level ground, then switch off the ignition and apply the handbrake firmly. For improved access, jack up the front of the vehicle and support it securely on axle stands (see "*Jacking and Vehicle Support*"). Note that, when refilling and checking the fluid level, the vehicle must be lowered to the ground, and level, to ensure accuracy.

3 Remove the dipstick, then position a suitable container under the transmission drain plug which is situated on the right-hand side of the transmission housing, directly below the driveshaft.

4 Unscrew the drain plug, and allow the fluid to drain completely into the container **(see illustration)**. Clean the drain plug, being especially careful to wipe any metallic particles off the magnetic insert. Discard the original sealing washer; it should be renewed whenever disturbed.

⚠️ *Warning: If the fluid is hot, take precautions against scalding.*

5 When the fluid has finished draining, clean the drain plug threads and those of the transmission casing. Fit a new sealing washer to the drain plug, and refit the plug to the transmission, tightening it to the specified torque setting.

6 If the drained fluid appears to be very dirty and is discoloured, it is recommended that the internal filter be cleaned or renewed. To do this, unbolt and remove the sump from the bottom of the transmission, then remove and discard the gasket. Unscrew the four mounting bolts and lower the filter from the transmission - be careful when lowering the filter as it will still have fluid in it.

7 Check the transmission filter gauze for signs of debris or damage. Renew the filter if necessary, otherwise clean it thoroughly. Refit the filter and tighten its mounting bolts to the specified torque. Clean the sump and transmission gasket surfaces, then wash out the sump. Clean off any accumulated metallic particles from the magnet **(see illustration)**.

8 Refit the sump together with a new gasket, and tighten the bolts to the specified torque.

9 On all models, if the vehicle was raised for the draining operation, now lower it to the ground. Make sure that the vehicle is level (front-to-rear and side-to-side).

10 Refill the transmission with fluid, adding the specified type and amount of fluid a little at a time via the dipstick tube. Use a funnel with a fine mesh gauze, to avoid spillage, and to ensure that no foreign matter enters the transmission. Allow plenty of time for the fluid level to settle properly.

11 Check and top-up the fluid level with reference to Section 16.

30.4 Unscrewing the automatic transmission fluid drain plug

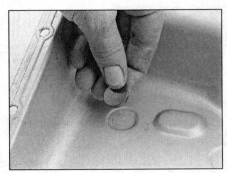

30.7 Clean the magnet then replace it in its recess in the bottom of the sump

Every 30 000 miles or 30 months

31 Timing belt check

Remove the timing belt upper cover and check the timing belt for signs of wear or damage whilst turning the engine over using a socket on the crankshaft pulley bolt (see Chapter 2A). If damage, such as damaged or missing teeth, or signs of oil contamination are found, then the belt must be renewed.

32 Crankcase ventilation hose check

Check on the crankcase emission control (PCV) valve and hose as described in Chapter 4C.

33 Fuel and evaporative emission hose check

Check all fuel lines and hoses with reference to Section 7.
Refer to Chapter 4C and check the evaporative emission hoses for damage, condition and blockage.

Every 48 000 miles or 48 months, whichever comes first

34 Auxiliary drivebelt renewal

Refer to Section 4 for details of removing, refitting and adjusting the drivebelts. The drivebelts should be renewed only if they have completed 48 000 miles or 48 months.

35 Timing belt renewal

Refer to Chapter 2A.

36 EGR system check

Refer to Chapter 4C.

Every 2 years regardless of mileage

37 Engine coolant renewal

Cooling system draining

 Warning: Wait until the engine is cold before starting this procedure. Do not allow antifreeze to come in contact with your skin, or with the painted surfaces of the vehicle. Rinse off spills immediately with plenty of water. Never leave antifreeze lying around in an open container, or in a puddle in the driveway or on the garage floor. Children and pets are attracted by its sweet smell, but antifreeze can be fatal if ingested.

1 With the engine completely cold, cover the radiator cap with a wad of rag, and slowly turn the cap anti-clockwise to relieve the pressure in the cooling system (a hissing sound will normally be heard). Wait until any pressure remaining in the system is released, then continue to turn the cap until it can be removed **(see illustration)**.
2 Position a suitable container beneath the radiator, then unscrew and release the drain plug **(see illustration)**. Allow the coolant to drain into the container.
3 If the coolant has been drained for a reason other than renewal, then it can be re-used, provided it is clean and less than two years old. If the coolant contains corrosion deposits or has been allowed to overheat, it should be renewed.

4 Once all the coolant has drained, tighten the drain plug.

Cooling system flushing

5 If coolant renewal has been neglected, or if the antifreeze mixture has become diluted, then in time, the cooling system may gradually lose efficiency, as the coolant passages become restricted due to rust, scale deposits, and other sediment. The cooling system efficiency can be restored by flushing the system clean.
6 The radiator should be flushed independently of the engine, to avoid unnecessary contamination.

Radiator flushing

7 To flush the radiator disconnect the top and bottom hoses and any other relevant hoses from the radiator, with reference to Chapter 3.

8 Insert a garden hose into the radiator top inlet. Direct a flow of clean water through the radiator, and continue flushing until clean water emerges from the radiator bottom outlet.
9 If after a reasonable period, the water still does not run clear, the radiator can be flushed with a good proprietary cooling system cleaning agent, but note that the manufacturer's instructions must be adhered to. If the contamination is particularly bad, remove the radiator and reverse-flush the radiator by inserting the hose in the bottom outlet.

Engine flushing

10 To flush the engine, remove the thermostat as described in Chapter 3, then temporarily refit the thermostat cover.

37.1 Radiator pressure cap

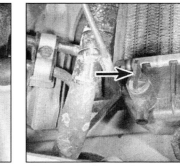

37.2 Drain plug on the bottom left-hand side of the radiator

11 With the top and bottom hoses disconnected from the radiator, insert a garden hose into the radiator top hose. Direct a clean flow of water through the engine, and continue flushing until clean water emerges from the radiator bottom hose.

12 On completion of flushing, refit the thermostat and reconnect the hoses with reference to Chapter 3.

Cooling system filling

13 Before attempting to fill the cooling system, make sure that all hoses and clips are in good condition, and that the clips are tight. Note that an antifreeze mixture must be used all year round, to inhibit the corrosion of the engine components (see following sub-Section).

14 Remove the radiator filler cap and fill the system by slowly pouring the coolant into the filler neck, to prevent airlocks from forming.

15 If the coolant is being renewed, begin by pouring in a couple of litres of water, followed by the correct quantity of antifreeze, then top-up with more water.

16 When the level in the radiator reaches the bottom of the filler neck, squeeze the radiator top and bottom hoses to help expel any trapped air in the system and top-up again to the bottom of the filler neck. Refit the radiator cap.

17 On models fitted with a bleed screw on the top of the inlet manifold, slacken the screw until coolant begins to flow out, then re-tighten the screw.

18 Once all the air is expelled from the hoses, remove the cap and top-up the coolant in the expansion tank to a point midway between the "MAX" and "MIN" marks on the side of the tank.

19 Start the engine and run it until warm coolant can be felt flowing through the radiator top hose (proving that the thermostat has opened). Stop the engine and allow it to cool.

20 Check for leaks, particularly around disturbed components. Check the coolant level in the radiator and expansion tank, and top-up if necessary.

Caution: If the radiator cap is removed while the engine is still warm, cover the cap with a thick cloth, and unscrew the cap slowly to gradually relieve the system pressure (a hissing sound will normally be heard). Wait until any pressure remaining in the system is released, then continue to turn the cap until it can be removed.

Antifreeze mixture

21 The antifreeze should always be renewed at the specified intervals. This is necessary not only to maintain the antifreeze properties, but also to prevent corrosion which would otherwise occur as the corrosion inhibitors become progressively less effective.

22 Always use an ethylene-glycol based antifreeze which is suitable for use in mixed-metal cooling systems. The quantity of antifreeze and levels of protection are indicated in the *Specifications*.

23 Before adding antifreeze, the cooling system should be completely drained, preferably flushed, and all hoses checked for condition and security.

24 After filling with antifreeze, a label should be attached to the expansion tank, stating the type and concentration of antifreeze used, and the date installed. Any subsequent topping-up should be made with the same type and concentration of antifreeze.

25 Do not use engine antifreeze in the windscreen/tailgate washer system, as it will cause damage to the vehicle paintwork. A screenwash additive should be added to the washer system in the quantities stated on the bottle.

 Warning: Brake hydraulic fluid can harm your eyes and damage painted surfaces, so use extreme caution when handling and pouring it. Do not use fluid that has been standing open for some time, as it absorbs moisture from the air. Excess moisture can cause a dangerous loss of brakes.

1 The procedure is similar to that for the bleeding of the hydraulic system as described in Chapter 9, except that the brake fluid reservoir should be emptied by siphoning, using a clean poultry baster or similar before starting, and allowance should be made for the old fluid to be expelled when bleeding a section of the circuit.

2 Working as described in Chapter 9, open the first bleed screw in the sequence, and pump the brake pedal gently until nearly all the old fluid has been emptied from the master cylinder reservoir. Note that old hydraulic fluid is invariably much darker in colour than new fluid, making it easy to distinguish between the two.

3 Top-up to the "MAX" level with new fluid, and continue pumping until only the new fluid remains in the reservoir, and new fluid can be seen emerging from the bleed screw. Tighten the screw, and top the reservoir level up to the "MAX" level line.

4 Work through all the remaining bleed screws in the sequence until new fluid can be seen at all of them. Be careful to keep the master cylinder reservoir topped-up to above the "MIN" level at all times, or air may enter the system and greatly increase the length of the task.

5 When the operation is complete, check that all bleed screws are securely tightened, and that their dust caps are refitted. Wash off all traces of spilt fluid, and recheck the master cylinder reservoir fluid level.

Chapter 2 Part A:
Engine in-car repair procedures

Contents

Camshaft - removal, inspection and refitting 9
Camshaft oil seal - renewal 8
Compression test 2
Crankshaft oil seals - renewal 13
Cylinder head - dismantling and overhaul . . . . .See Chapter 2B
Cylinder head - removal and refitting 10
Cylinder head cover - removal and refitting 4
Engine oil and filter - renewal . . . . .See Chapter 1
Engine oil level - check .See "Weekly Checks"
Engine/transmission mountings - inspection and renewal 15

Flywheel/driveplate - removal, inspection and refitting 14
General information 1
Oil pump and pick-up strainer - removal, inspection and refitting . . 12
Rocker arm assembly - removal, inspection and refitting 5
Sump - removal and refitting 11
Timing belt - removal, inspection and refitting 6
Timing belt sprockets and tensioner pulley - removal, inspection
    and refitting 7
Top dead centre (TDC) for No 1 piston - locating 3
Valve clearance check . . . . .See Chapter 1

Degrees of difficulty

Easy, suitable for novice with little experience	**Fairly easy,** suitable for beginner with some experience	**Fairly difficult,** suitable for competent DIY mechanic	**Difficult,** suitable for experienced DIY mechanic	**Very difficult,** suitable for expert DIY or professional

Specifications

General

Type	Four-cylinder, in-line, single-overhead camshaft, 8-valve
Engine code*	
1.3 litre engine	G4AG
1.5 litre engine	G4AJ

*Note: See "Buying Spare Parts and Vehicle Identification" for the location of code marking on the engine.

Capacity	
1.3 litre engine	1298 cc
1.5 litre engine	1468 cc
Bore:	
1.3 litre engine	71.0 mm
1.5 litre engine	75.5 mm
Stroke:	
1.3 and 1.5 litre engines	82.0 mm
Direction of crankshaft rotation	Clockwise (viewed from left-hand side of vehicle)
Cylinder compression pressures:	
1.3 litre engine	14.5 bars at 250 to 400 rpm
1.5 litre engine	13.5 bars at 250 to 400 rpm
Maximum difference between cylinders	1.0 bar
Firing order	1-3-4-2
No 1 cylinder location	Timing belt (left-hand) end of the engine

Camshaft

Drive	Toothed belt from crankshaft	
Number of bearings	3	
Camshaft endfloat	0.05 to 0.20 mm	
Cam lobe height:	**Inlet**	**Exhaust**
FBC engine	38.909 mm	38.648 mm
MPI (EC) and Conventional Carburettor engines	38.077 mm	38.150 mm
Wear limit	0.5 mm	
Camshaft bearing oil clearance (running clearance)	0.05 to 0.09 mm	

Timing belt

Timing belt deflection	7.0 to 9.0 mm

Lubrication system

Oil pump type	Bi-rotor (toothed type) driven from front of crankshaft
System pressure at idle - at normal operating temperature	At least 0.8 bar
Oil pump clearances:	
Outer rotor -to-housing	0.10 to 0.20 mm
Inner rotor-to-crescent	0.21 to 0.32 mm
Outer rotor-to-crescent	0.22 to 0.34 mm
Rotor endfloat	0.04 to 0.10 mm

Torque wrench settings

	Nm	lbf ft
Camshaft sprocket bolt	70	52
Connecting rod (big-end) cap nuts	35	25
Water pump pulley bolts	10	7
Cylinder head cover bolt	2	1.5
Rocker arm shaft bolt	24	18
Jet valve	20	15
Camshaft thrust plate retaining bolt	24	18
Cylinder head bolts:		
Cold engine	73	54
Hot engine	83	61
Crankshaft pulley bolts	14	10
Crankshaft pulley/sprocket centre bolt	85	63
Oil pressure switch	18	13
Oil pump cover bolts	9	7
Oil pump-to-block bolts	14	10
Oil pump pick-up/strainer bolts	19	14
Sump bolts	7	5
Sump drain plug	40	30
Flywheel/driveplate bolts	135	100
Main bearing cap bolts	52	38
Timing belt cover bolts	11	8
Cylinder head rear cover bolts	9	7
Timing belt tensioner bolt	24	18
Engine rear plate bolt	9	7
Roadwheel nuts	100	74
Engine mountings:		
Front support bracket bolt	60	44
Front mounting bracket bolt	65	48
Rear mounting bracket bolt	120	89
Left engine support bracket bolt	36	27
Left engine mounting insulator nut (large)	100	74
Left engine mounting insulator nut (small)	53	39
Left engine mounting bracket to engine nuts and bolts	58	43
Transmission mounting insulator bolt	100	74
Transmission mounting insulator bracket to side member bolts	35	26
Automatic transmission mounting bracket to transmission nut	70	52
Rear mounting insulator nut	53	39
Rear mounting bracket to centre member bolts	53	39
Front mounting roll rod upper through-bolt (early models)	34	25
Front mounting roll rod lower through-bolt (early models)	62	46
Front mounting insulator nut	53	39
Front mounting bracket to centre member bolts	35	26
Centre member to body	70	52
Roll rod to engine (manual transmission models)	60	44
Roll rod to bracket nut (manual transmission models)	53	39
Roll rod bracket to body bolt (manual transmission models)	83	61

1 General information

Using this Chapter

Chapter 2 is divided into two Parts; A and B. Repair operations that can be carried out with the engine in the vehicle are described in Part A. Part B covers the removal of the engine/transmission as a unit, and describes the engine dismantling and overhaul procedures.

In Part A the assumption is made that the engine is installed in the vehicle, with all ancillaries connected. If the engine has been removed for overhaul, the preliminary dismantling information which precedes each operation may be ignored.

Engine description

Throughout this Chapter, the engines are identified by their capacity and/or their code letters as given in the Specifications.

The engines are water-cooled, single-overhead camshaft, in-line four-cylinder units, with cast-iron cylinder blocks and aluminium-alloy cylinder heads. They are mounted transversely at the front of the vehicle, with the transmission bolted to the right-hand side of the engine.

The cylinder head carries the camshaft which is driven by a toothed timing belt. It also houses the inlet and exhaust valves, which are closed by single coil springs, and which run in guides pressed into the cylinder head. The camshaft actuates the inclined valves by rocker arms mounted on two shafts (inlet and exhaust) bolted to the cylinder head above the camshaft.

The pistons are attached to the connecting rods by gudgeon pins which are an interference fit in the connecting rods. The distributor is gear-driven from the left-hand end of the exhaust camshaft and is mounted on the left-hand rear of the cylinder head, whilst the oil pump is driven from the front of the crankshaft. The cast-iron crankshaft runs in five main bearings; endfloat is controlled by semi-circular thrust surfaces incorporated in the upper and lower central main bearing shells.

The water pump is located on the left-hand end of the cylinder block and is driven from the crankshaft by the auxiliary drivebelt.

Repair operations possible with the engine in the car

The following work can be carried out with the engine in the car:
a) Removal and refitting of the timing belt, sprockets and tensioner.
b) Renewal of the camshaft oil seal.
c) Removal and refitting of the rocker arm and shaft assemblies.
d) Removal and refitting of the camshaft.
e) Removal and refitting of the cylinder head*.
f) Removal and refitting of the sump.
g) Removal and refitting of the oil pump.
h) Removal and refitting of the flywheel/driveplate.
i) Renewal of the crankshaft oil seals.
j) Renewal of the engine mountings.
*Cylinder head dismantling procedures are detailed in Chapter 2B.

Note: It is possible to remove the pistons and connecting rods (after removing the cylinder head and sump) without removing the engine, however, this is not recommended. Work of this nature is more easily and thoroughly completed with the engine on the bench, as described in Chapter 2B.

2 Compression test

1 When engine performance is down, or if misfiring occurs which cannot be attributed to the ignition or fuel systems, a compression test can provide diagnostic clues as to the engine's condition. If the test is performed regularly, it can give warning of trouble before any other symptoms become apparent.

2 The engine must be fully warmed-up to normal operating temperature, the battery must be fully charged, and all the spark plugs must be removed (Chapter 1). The aid of an assistant will also be required.

3 On fuel injection models, depressurise the fuel system (see Chapter 4A), then temporarily remove the fuel injection system relay (see Chapter 12) and remove all the spark plugs.

4 Fit a compression tester to the No 1 cylinder spark plug hole - the type of tester which screws into the plug thread is to be preferred.

5 Have an assistant hold the throttle wide open, and crank the engine on the starter motor; after one or two revolutions, the compression pressure should build up to a maximum figure, and then stabilise. Record the highest reading obtained.

6 Repeat the test on the remaining cylinders, recording the pressure in each.

7 All cylinders should produce very similar pressures; any difference greater than that specified indicates the existence of a fault. Note that the compression should build up quickly in a healthy engine; low compression on the first stroke, followed by gradually increasing pressure on successive strokes, indicates worn piston rings. A low compression reading on the first stroke, which does not build up during successive strokes, indicates leaking valves or a blown head gasket (a cracked head could also be the cause).

8 If the pressure in any cylinder is reduced to the specified minimum or less, carry out the following test to isolate the cause. Introduce 5 ml of clean oil into that cylinder through its spark plug hole and repeat the test.

9 If the addition of oil temporarily improves the compression pressure, this indicates that bore or piston wear is responsible for the pressure loss. No improvement suggests that leaking or burnt valves, or a blown head gasket, may be to blame.

10 A low reading from two adjacent cylinders is almost certainly due to the head gasket having blown between them. Renew the head gasket if this is the case.

11 If one cylinder is about 20 percent lower than the others and the engine has a slightly rough idle, a worn camshaft lobe could be the cause.

12 On completion of the test, refit the spark plugs and the fuel injection relay.

3 Top dead centre (TDC) for No 1 piston - locating

Note: The following procedure is based on the assumption that the spark plug HT leads and distributor are correctly fitted. If you are trying to locate TDC to install the distributor correctly, piston position must be determined by feeling for compression at the number one spark plug hole, then aligning the ignition timing marks as described in paragraph 6.

1 Top Dead Centre (TDC) is the highest point in the cylinder that each piston reaches as it travels up-and-down when the crankshaft turns. Each piston reaches TDC on the compression stroke and again on the exhaust stroke, but unless otherwise stated TDC refers to piston position on the compression stroke.

2 Positioning the piston at TDC is an essential part of many procedures such as rocker arm and shaft removal, camshaft and timing belt/sprocket removal and distributor removal.

3 Before beginning this procedure, be sure to place the transmission in Neutral and apply the handbrake. Also, disable the ignition system by detaching the coil HT lead from the centre terminal of the distributor cap and grounding it on the block with a jumper lead.

HAYNES HiNT Remove all four spark plugs; this will make the engine easier to turn; refer to Chapter 1 for details.

4 In order to bring any piston to TDC, the crankshaft must be turned using one of the methods outlined below. When looking at the timing end of the engine, normal crankshaft rotation is clockwise.
a) The preferred method is to turn the crankshaft on the crankshaft pulley bolt, using a socket and ratchet inserted through the hole in the left-hand wheelarch liner (see illustration).
b) A remote starter switch, which may save some time, can also be used. Follow the instructions included with the switch. Once the piston is close to TDC, use a socket and ratchet as described in the previous sub-paragraph.
c) If an assistant is available to turn the ignition switch to the Start position in short bursts, you can get the piston close to TDC without a remote starter switch.

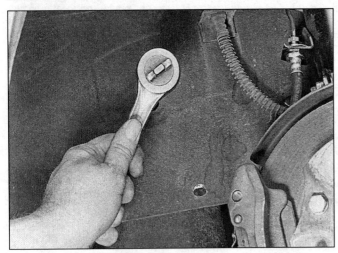

3.4 Turn the crankshaft on the crankshaft pulley bolt, using a socket and ratchet inserted through the hole in the left-hand wheelarch liner

3.6 Align the notch in the pulley (arrowed) with the T on the timing plate (drivebelts and water pump pulley removed)

Then make sure your assistant is out of the vehicle, away from the ignition switch, and use a socket and ratchet as described previously to complete the procedure.

5 Remove the cap from the distributor and place to one side (see Chapter 1).
6 Turn the crankshaft (see paragraph 4) until the notch in the crankshaft pulley is aligned with the T on the timing plate (located at the front of the engine) **(see illustration)**.
7 Look at the distributor rotor arm and check that it is pointing straight downwards.
8 If the rotor arm is pointing straight upwards (ie 180° out), the No 1 piston is at TDC on the exhaust stroke. To get the piston to TDC on the compression stroke, turn the crankshaft one complete turn (360°) clockwise. The rotor arm should now be pointing straight down. When the rotor arm is pointing at the No 1 spark plug HT segment in the distributor cap and the ignition timing marks are aligned, the No 1 piston is at TDC on the compression stroke.
9 After the No 1 piston has been positioned at TDC on the compression stroke, TDC for any of the remaining pistons can be located by turning the crankshaft 180° at a time and following the firing order. With the distributor cap installed, use a felt tip pen or chalk to make a mark on the distributor body directly beneath each of the segments on the distributor cap. Then number the marks to correspond with the cylinder numbers. As you turn the crankshaft, the rotor arm will also turn. When it is pointing directly at one of the marks on the distributor, the piston for that particular cylinder is at TDC on the compression stroke.

4 Cylinder head cover - removal and refitting

Removal

1 Disconnect the battery negative lead.
Caution: If the radio/cassette in your vehicle is equipped with an anti-theft system, make sure you have the correct activation code before disconnecting the battery.
2 On carburettor models, remove the air cleaner assembly as described in Chapter 4A.
3 Identify the HT leads for position, then disconnect them from the spark plugs and from the holder on the top of the timing cover **(see illustration)**.
4 Unbolt the accelerator cable support bracket from the cylinder head cover.
5 As applicable, clearly label and then disconnect the emission hoses which cross over the cylinder head cover.
6 Progressively unscrew the mounting bolts and lift the cover from the top of the cylinder head. If the cover sticks to the head, tap on it with a soft-faced mallet or place a block of

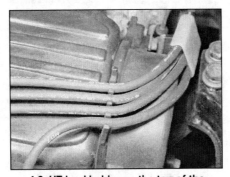

4.3 HT lead holder on the top of the timing cover

wood against the cover and tap on the wood with a hammer. Remove the gasket.
7 Thoroughly clean the mating surfaces of the cylinder head cover and cylinder head, and remove all traces of old gasket material.

Refitting

8 Locate a new gasket on the cylinder head, then refit the cover and insert the mounting bolts. Progressively tighten the bolts to the specified torque.
9 Where applicable, reconnect the emission hoses.
10 Refit the accelerator cable support bracket and tighten the mounting bolt.
11 Reconnect the HT leads to the spark plugs and holder.
12 On carburettor models, refit the air cleaner assembly with reference to Chapter 4A.
13 Reconnect the battery negative lead.

5 Rocker arm assembly - removal, inspection and refitting

Removal

1 Remove the cylinder head cover as described in Section 4.
2 Position the No 1 piston at TDC as described in Section 3.
3 Check the rocker arm assemblies for identification marks. If necessary, mark each assembly for position to ensure correct refitting, noting that the rear assembly is Inlet and the front assembly is Exhaust.
4 Working on each assembly in turn, progressively loosen the mounting bolts until the valve spring pressure is relieved; **do not** withdraw the bolts fully from the shafts as they will retain the rocker arms in position as the shaft assembly is removed **(see illustration)**.

5.4 Rocker arm assembly mounting bolts

5 Lift the rocker arm assemblies away from the top of the cylinder head complete with the retaining bolts and washers.

Inspection

6 Mark the shafts on their timing ends and identify them for Inlet and Exhaust. The timing ends of the shafts have larger chamfered edge than the opposite ends.

7 With the bolts removed from the shafts, slide off the rocker arms and springs one at a time until they are all removed. Keep the components in order so that you can reassemble them in the same positions. Note that the springs on the exhaust rocker shaft are shorter than those on the inlet rocker shaft. The free length of the exhaust shaft springs is 47.0 mm, and of the inlet shaft springs is 77.0 mm **(see illustration)**.

8 Thoroughly clean the components and inspect them for wear and damage. Check the rocker arm faces that contact the camshaft and the adjusting screw tips that contact the valve stems - the screw tips can be renewed separately. On jet valve engines also check the jet valve contact faces **(see illustration)**. Renew any components that are damaged or worn excessively. Also, make sure that the oil holes in the shafts are clear of any debris by blowing through them with air pressure from an air line or footpump.

9 Lubricate the bearing surfaces of all the components with engine oil then reassemble the shafts in reverse order to dismantling. Note that the rocker arms themselves are angled, and are identified with cylinder numbers. For example, a rocker arm with numbers "2-4" on it must be fitted to the valve positions for cylinders 2 and 4. If any of the rocker arms have been renewed, make sure the correct replacement has been obtained. Insert the bolts in their holes to keep the components on the shafts.

Refitting

10 If new components have been fitted make sure that the adjusting screws are fully backed off, otherwise there is the possibility that some valves may be forced onto the tops of the pistons. On engines with air jet valves, back off the jet valve adjusting screws as well. The lower tips of the adjusting screws should

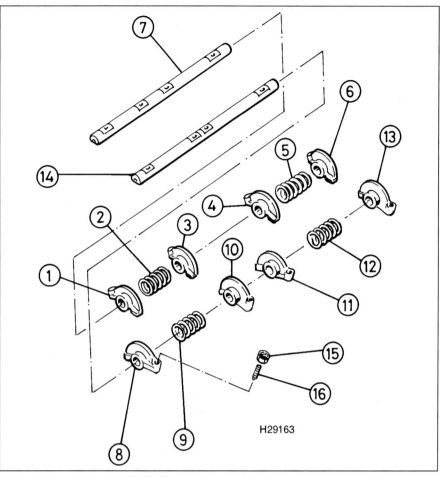

H29163

5.7 Rocker arm assembly components

1 Rocker arm (1-3)	6 Rocker arm (2-4)	11 Rocker arm (1-3)
2 Spring	7 Exhaust valve rocker	12 Spring
3 Rocker arm (2-4)	shaft	13 Rocker arm (2-4)
4 Rocker arm (1-3)	8 Rocker arm (1-3)	14 Inlet valve rocker shaft
5 Spring	9 Spring	15 Locknut
	10 Rocker arm (2-4)	16 Adjusting screw

protrude approximately 1.0 mm from the surface of the rocker arms.

11 Position the rocker arm assemblies on the cylinder head and insert the mounting bolts finger tight.

12 Working on each assembly in turn, progressively tighten the bolts to the specified torque.

Caution: As the rocker shaft bolts are tightened, take great care not to trap any of the rocker arms/spacers (as applicable) between the shaft and the top of the cylinder head. As the shafts are pulled down onto the cylinder head ensure that each rocker arm/spacer is correctly positioned so that it bears against the side of the cylinder head casting.

13 Adjust the valve clearances (cold) as described in Chapter 1.

14 Temporarily refit the cylinder head cover (see Section 4) and run the engine to normal operating temperature.

15 Check and readjust the valve clearances while the engine is still warm as described in Chapter 1.

16 Refit the cylinder head cover as described in Section 4.

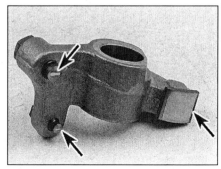

5.8 Check the contact faces and adjusting screw tips (arrowed) (jet valve model shown)

6.9a The upper timing cover is attached with three bolts

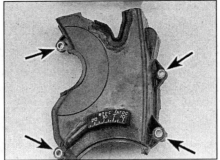

6.9b Lower timing cover showing bolt hole locations

6.11 Using a wide-bladed screwdriver in the starter ring gear to hold the crankshaft stationary

6 Timing belt - removal, inspection and refitting

Removal

1 Disconnect the battery negative lead.
Caution: If the radio/cassette in your vehicle is equipped with an anti-theft system, make sure you have the correct activation code before disconnecting the battery.
2 Apply the handbrake then jack up the front of the vehicle and support on axle stands (see "Jacking and Vehicle Support"). Remove the left-hand roadwheel.
3 Remove the splash guard from beneath the timing end of the engine.
4 For additional working room on carburettor models, remove the air cleaner assembly and air ducting with reference to Chapter 4A.
5 Set the engine at TDC for No 1 cylinder (nearest the timing belt) as described in Section 3.
6 Remove the auxiliary drivebelt(s) with reference to Chapter 1
7 Remove the left-hand engine mounting as described in Section 15.
8 Unbolt and remove the pulley from the water pump.
9 Unbolt and remove the upper timing cover then unbolt and remove the lower timing cover together with their sealing strips (see illustrations).

10 If the timing belt is to be re-used, paint an arrow on it to indicate the direction of rotation so that it can be refitted in the same direction.
11 The crankshaft must be held stationary while the crankshaft sprocket bolts (both the large centre bolt and the smaller outer bolts) are loosened. On manual transmission models, have an assistant engage 4th gear and apply the footbrake. On automatic transmission models (and also if preferred on manual transmission models), unbolt and remove the flywheel/driveplate cover from the bottom of the transmission bellhousing, then have an assistant insert a wide-bladed screwdriver into the teeth of the starter ring gear (see illustration). Access to the large centre bolt is gained by inserting a socket through the hole in the left-hand wheel arch liner. The bolt is very tight and a long breaker bar will be required to loosen it.
12 Unscrew and remove the pulley to sprocket retaining bolts and remove the pulley and retaining plate from the locating pin on the crankshaft sprocket, then refit the pulley bolt to the end of the crankshaft to hold the sprocket in position.
13 Loosen the adjusting bolt and move the timing belt tensioner towards the water pump as far as possible - use a screwdriver to lever the tensioner. Secure the tensioner in this position by tightening the bolt (see illustration).
14 Slide the timing belt from the crankshaft and camshaft sprockets.
15 Do not alter the position of the camshaft

or crankshaft sprockets with the timing belt removed.

Inspection

16 With the timing belt removed, check it thoroughly for damage and deterioration. In particular check for cracking at the base of the teeth.
17 In addition to the regular renewal called for as part of the service schedule at 48 000 miles (Chapter 1), the timing belt should be renewed, regardless of age or mileage if it appears to be defective in any manner or if it has been in contact with water, oil or steam.
18 Check that the tensioner pulley turns smoothly without any signs of roughness. Check the tensioner spring for signs of damage, and renew if necessary.

Refitting

19 Before refitting the timing belt, check that the TDC timing mark on the camshaft sprocket is aligned with the pointer on the cylinder head. Also check that the crankshaft pulley locating dowel on the outside of the crankshaft sprocket is aligned with the pointer on the oil pump housing (see illustration).
20 Engage the timing belt with the crankshaft and camshaft sprockets, making sure that the sprockets remain at their TDC positions and the rear run of the belt is taught between the camshaft and crankshaft sprockets. If the original belt is being refitted, ensure that the arrow marked on the belt during removal faces the correct way.

6.13 Loosen the bolt and use a screwdriver to lever the tensioner against the spring tension

6.19 Line up the dowel on the crankshaft sprocket with the pointer on the oil pump housing

6.21 Loosen the tensioner bolts to tension the timing belt

6.24a Apply firm thumb pressure to the timing belt at the point where it passes the tensioner lockbolt . . .

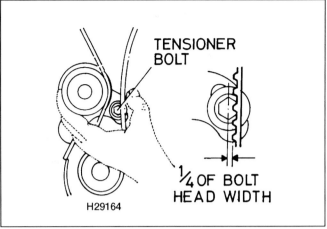

6.24b . . . and check that the inner edge of the belt teeth align with a point approximately 1/4 of the width across the tensioner lockbolt head

21 Loosen the tensioner pivot and lockbolts to allow the tensioner spring to apply tension to the timing belt **(see illustration)**. Tighten the bolts to the specified torque starting with the lockbolt then tighten the pivot bolt which goes through the tension spring..

22 Remove the temporarily fitted pulley bolt then fit the crankshaft pulley and retaining plate, taking care to align the locating pin with the small hole in the pulley and plate. Insert the bolts (both the large centre bolt and the smaller outer bolts) and tighten them to the specified torque. Hold the crankshaft stationary while tightening the bolts using the method described in paragraph 11.

23 Use a spanner or socket on the crankshaft pulley bolt to turn the crankshaft clockwise (viewed from the vehicle's left-hand side) through two full turns, then check that the camshaft and crankshaft sprocket timing marks remain aligned. If the marks are not correctly aligned, re-position the timing belt on the sprockets as previously described, then rotate the crankshaft through two further turns and recheck.

24 Check for correct timing belt tension by pressing the rear run of the belt towards the tensioner pulley at the point where the belt passes in front of the tensioner lockbolt. Apply firm thumb pressure to the belt and check the belt deflection; if the belt is correctly tensioned the inner edge of the belt teeth should align with a point approximately one quarter of the width across the tensioner pulley lockbolt head **(see illustrations)**. If not, repeat the procedure again and check. If any doubt exists, obtain and fit a new tensioner pulley spring.

25 Refit the timing covers and tighten the retaining bolts. Make sure that the sealing strips are correctly located.

26 Refit the water pump pulley and tighten the bolts to the specified torque (see Chapter 3).

27 Refit the left-hand engine mounting with reference to Section 15.

28 Refit and tension the auxiliary drivebelt(s) with reference to Chapter 1.

29 Where removed, refit the air cleaner assembly and air ducting with reference to Chapter 4A.

30 Refit the splash guard beneath the timing end of the engine.

31 Refit the left-hand roadwheel and lower the vehicle to the ground.

32 Reconnect the battery negative lead.

7 Timing belt sprockets and tensioner pulley - removal, inspection and refitting

Removal

1 Remove the timing belt as described in Section 6, noting that there is no need to remove the left-hand engine mounting. When removing the crankshaft pulley, it is not necessary to refit the crankshaft pulley bolt (see Section 6, paragraph 12). It is not necessary to remove the crankshaft pulley when removing the camshaft sprocket or tensioner pulley.

Camshaft sprocket

2 Hold the camshaft sprocket stationary by inserting a large screwdriver through one of the sprocket holes onto the upper edge of the cylinder head cover. To prevent damage to the cover, locate a piece of wood or a suitable cloth pad under the end of the screwdriver. Alternatively, fabricate a suitable tool to hold the sprocket as follows. Use two lengths of steel strip (one long, the other short), and three nuts and bolts; one nut and bolt forms the pivot of a forked tool, with the remaining two nuts and bolts at the tips of the "forks" to engage with the sprocket holes as shown **(see illustrations)**.

3 Unscrew and remove the securing bolt and washer then slide the sprocket from the end of the camshaft. If necessary, remove the locating pin from the end of the camshaft. Examine the oil seal and if necessary renew it as described in Section 8 **(see illustrations)**.

Crankshaft sprocket

4 Slide the sprocket from the flats on the end of the crankshaft, followed by the belt guide flange. Note that the chamfered side of the flange faces out - the side with the tooth marks from the timing belt **(see illustrations)**.

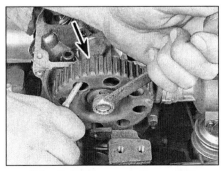

7.2a Hold the camshaft sprocket stationary with a screwdriver inserted through one of the sprocket holes

7.2b Using a home-made tool to hold the camshaft sprocket stationary as the bolt is loosened

7.3a Remove the retaining bolt and washer . . .

7.3b . . . and withdraw the sprocket from the camshaft

7.4a Remove the crankshaft sprocket . . .

5 Examine the oil seal for signs of oil leakage and, if necessary renew as described in Section 13.

Tensioner pulley

6 Using a large screwdriver, carefully unhook the tensioner spring from behind the pulley backplate lug to relieve the spring tension **(see illustration)**.
7 Unscrew the tensioner pulley spring pivot bolt and remove it along with the spacer and spring, noting the correct fitted location of each component **(see illustration)**.
8 Slacken and remove the lockbolt and remove the pulley assembly from the oil pump housing **(see illustration)**.

Inspection

9 Inspect the teeth of the sprockets for signs of nicks and damage. The teeth are not prone to wear, and should normally last the life of the engine.
10 Spin the tensioner pulley by hand, and check for any roughness or tightness. Do not attempt to clean the pulley with solvent, as this may enter the bearings. If wear is evident, renew the tensioner pulley assembly. The tensioner spring should also be renewed if there is any doubt about its condition.

Refitting

Camshaft sprocket

11 Refit the locating pin to the end of the camshaft and refit the sprocket, making sure its locating hole engages correctly with the pin.
12 Refit the sprocket retaining bolt and washer, ensuring that the washer hole is

7.4b . . . and slide off the belt guide flange, noting which way around it is fitted

correctly located with the sprocket pin. Tighten the bolt to the specified torque setting, using the holding tool to prevent rotation.
13 Ensure all timing marks are correctly positioned then refit and tension the timing belt as described in Section 6. Where the crankshaft pulley was not removed, use the TDC marks on the lower timing cover and pulley to position the crankshaft at TDC.

Crankshaft sprocket

14 Slide the spacer onto the crankshaft end ensuring it is fitted with its chamfered face facing outwards (away from the cylinder block).
15 Fit the sprocket to the crankshaft making sure the pulley locating pin is facing outwards. The sprocket has two different size flats which match those on the crankshaft.
16 Ensure all timing marks are correctly positioned then refit and tension the timing belt as described in Section 6.

7.4c The chamfered side of the belt guide flange faces out

Tensioner pulley

17 Locate the tensioner pulley assembly into position on the oil pump housing and refit the tensioner lockbolt loosely.
18 Slide the spacer onto the spring pivot bolt, making sure its collar is against the bolt head, then fit the spring making sure it is fitted the correct way around. Insert the pivot bolt and spring and tighten the bolt lightly. Hook the tensioner spring into position behind the cylinder block and backplate lugs then pivot the tensioner fully away from the belt and tighten its retaining bolts to hold it in position.
19 Ensure all timing marks are correctly positioned then refit and tension the timing belt as described in Section 6. Where the crankshaft pulley was not removed, use the TDC marks on the lower timing cover and pulley to position the crankshaft at TDC.

7.6 Unhook the spring from behind the tensioner . . .

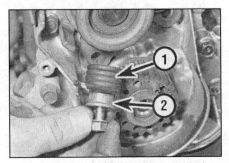

7.7 . . . then unscrew the tensioner bolts, noting the correct fitted position of the spring (1) and spacer (2) . . .

7.8 . . . and remove the tensioner pulley

8.2a Carefully drill two holes in the oil seal and screw in self-tapping screws . . .

8 Camshaft oil seal - renewal

1 Remove the camshaft sprocket as described in Section 7.
2 Make a note of the correct fitted depth of the seal then drill two small holes opposite each other in the oil seal. Screw a self-tapping screw into each hole and pull on the screws with pliers to extract the seal. Alternatively, if care is taken not to damage the surface of the camshaft, a small screwdriver may be used to prise out the oil seal **(see illustrations)**.
3 Clean the seal housing and polish off any burrs or raised edges which may have caused the seal to fail in the first place.
4 Lubricate the lips of the new seal with clean engine oil and ease it into position on the end of the shaft. Press the seal into its housing until it is positioned at the same depth as the original was prior to removal. If necessary, a tubular drift, such as a socket, which bears only on the hard outer edge of the seal can be used to tap the seal into position **(see illustration)**. Take great care not to damage the seal lips during fitting and ensure that the seal lips face inwards. If the surface of the shaft was noticed to be badly scored, press the new seal slightly less into its housing so that its lip is running on an unmarked area of the shaft.
5 Refit the camshaft sprocket as described in Section 7 and refit and tension the timing belt as described in Section 6.

8.2b . . . then pull out the oil seal with a pair of pliers

9 Camshaft - removal, inspection and refitting

Removal

1 Disconnect the battery negative lead.
Caution: If the radio/cassette in your vehicle is equipped with an anti-theft system, make sure you have the correct activation code before disconnecting the battery.
2 Drain the cooling system (see Chapter 1) and disconnect the upper radiator hose from the thermostat housing. Position the hose to one side away from the right-hand end of the cylinder head.
3 Remove the distributor as described in Chapter 5.
4 Remove the camshaft sprocket as described in Section 7 (this procedure includes removal of the timing belt).
5 Remove the rocker arm assemblies as described in Section 5 (this procedure includes removal of the cylinder head cover).
6 On carburettor models, remove the fuel pump as described in Chapter 4A.
7 Undo the retaining screws and remove the cover plate from the right-hand end of the cylinder head. Recover the gasket and discard it, a new one will be needed on refitting.
8 Unscrew and remove the camshaft thrust case retaining bolt from the top of the cylinder head.
9 Slide the camshaft and thrust case out from the right-hand end of the cylinder head. Where

8.2c If a small screwdriver is used to remove the oil seal, take care not to damage the surface of the camshaft

necessary on carburettor models, temporarily unbolt and move the windscreen washer reservoir to one side to provide additional working room.
10 Prise out the old camshaft oil seal from the cylinder head.

Inspection

11 Thoroughly clean the camshaft, the thrust case, the rear cover plate and gasket surfaces.
12 Examine the camshaft bearing surfaces and lobes for wear ridges, pitting or scoring. Renew the camshaft if evident. The camshaft oil seal should be renewed as a matter of course.
13 Examine the camshaft bearing surfaces in the cylinder head. Deep scoring or other damage means that the cylinder head must be renewed.
14 Using a micrometer, measure the camshaft lobe heights and compare them to the *Specifications* **(see illustration)**.
15 Inspect the rocker arms as described in Section 5.
16 Using feeler blades, measure the clearance between the end of the camshaft and the camshaft thrust case on the right-hand end of the camshaft **(see illustration)**. If the measurement is not within the specified endfloat range given in the *Specifications*, the thrust case and its retaining washer must be renewed. To do this, firmly grip the camshaft in a vice between blocks of wood, then slacken and remove the thrust case retaining bolt and washer. Fit the new thrust case and washer and securely tighten the retaining bolt.

8.4 Tap the new seal into position using a hammer and suitable socket

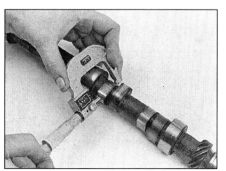

9.14 Checking the camshaft lobe heights with a micrometer

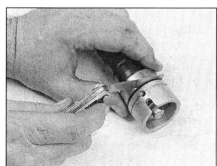

9.16 Checking the camshaft endfloat with a feeler blade

Refitting

17 Lubricate the camshaft bearings with clean engine oil.

18 Slide the camshaft into position in the cylinder head, aligning the thrust case threaded hole with the cylinder head hole. Refit the thrust case retaining bolt and tighten it securely.

19 Ensure the mating surfaces are clean and dry then refit the cylinder head end cover plate using a new gasket, and securely tighten its retaining bolts.

20 Fit a new camshaft oil seal with reference to Section 8.

21 Rotate the camshaft so that the camshaft sprocket locating pin hole is uppermost; this will position the camshaft correctly with the No 1 cylinder at TDC on its compression stroke.

22 On carburettor models refit the fuel pump as described in Chapter 4A.

23 Refit the camshaft sprocket (including the timing belt) with reference to Section 7.

24 Refit the distributor as described in Chapter 5.

25 Reconnect the battery negative lead.

26 Refit the rocker arm assemblies (including the cylinder head cover) with reference to Section 5. Check and adjust the valve clearances (cold) before refitting the cover.

27 Reconnect the upper radiator hose to the thermostat housing and tighten the clip, then refill the cooling system (see Chapter 1).

28 Warm the engine up to its normal operating temperature and recheck the valve clearances with the engine hot.

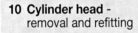

10 Cylinder head -
removal and refitting

Caution: Allow the engine to cool completely before following this procedure.

HAYNES HINT *To aid refitting, note the locations of brackets and the routing of hoses and cables before removal.*

Removal

1 Disconnect the battery negative lead.
Caution: If the radio/cassette in your vehicle is equipped with an anti-theft system, make sure you have the correct activation code before disconnecting the battery.

2 Drain the cooling system with reference to Chapter 1.

3 Remove the timing belt with reference to Section 6 - make sure the engine is adequately supported while the left-hand engine mounting is removed. It is not necessary to remove the crankshaft pulley.

4 On carburettor models, remove the air cleaner assembly and intake duct then remove the fuel pump (refer to Chapter 4A).

10.18 Locate the new cylinder head gasket on the dowels

5 Remove the inlet and exhaust manifolds as described in Chapter 4A or 4B (as applicable).

6 Remove the distributor as described in Chapter 5, and the spark plugs as described in Chapter 1.

7 Remove the cylinder head cover as described in Section 4.

8 Working in the **reverse** of the sequence shown in **illustration 10.22**, progressively slacken the cylinder head bolts by half a turn at a time until all bolts can be unscrewed by hand and removed along with their washers. An 8 mm Allen key socket will be required to unscrew the bolts.

9 Lift the cylinder head upwards and off the cylinder block. If it is stuck, tap it upwards using a hammer and block of wood. *Do not* try to turn it (it is located by two dowels), nor attempt to prise it free using a screwdriver inserted between the block and head faces. If the locating dowels are a loose fit, remove them and store them with the head for safe-keeping.

Inspection

10 The mating faces of the cylinder head and block must be perfectly clean before refitting the head. Use a scraper to remove all traces of gasket and carbon, and also clean the tops of the pistons. Where applicable, clean out the EGR and jet air (FBC) passages in the cylinder head. Take particular care with the aluminium cylinder head, as the soft metal is damaged easily. Also, make sure that debris is not allowed to enter the oil and water channels - this is particularly important for the oil circuit, as carbon could block the oil supply

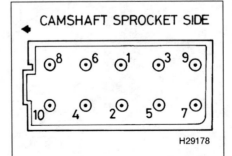

CAMSHAFT SPROCKET SIDE

H29178

10.22 Cylinder head bolt tightening sequence

to the camshaft or crankshaft bearings. Using adhesive tape and paper, seal the water, oil and bolt holes in the cylinder block. To prevent carbon entering the gap between the pistons and bores, smear a little grease in the gap. After cleaning the piston, rotate the crankshaft so that the piston moves down the bore, then wipe out the grease and carbon with a cloth rag. Clean the piston crowns in the same way.

11 Check the block and head for nicks, deep scratches and other damage. If slight, they may be removed carefully with a file. More serious damage may be repaired by machining, but this is a specialist job.

12 If warpage of the cylinder head is suspected, use a straight-edge to check it for distortion. Refer to Chapter 2B if necessary.

13 Ensure that the cylinder head bolt holes in the block are clean and free of oil. Syringe or soak up any oil left in the bolt holes. This is most important in order that the correct bolt tightening torque can be applied and to prevent the possibility of the block being cracked by hydraulic pressure when the bolts are tightened.

14 Examine the cylinder head bolt threads in the cylinder block for damage. If necessary, use the correct-size tap to chase out the threads in the block, and use a die to clean the threads on the bolts.

15 Although Hyundai do not actually specify that the cylinder head bolts must be renewed, it is highly recommended that new bolts are used on refitting.

Refitting

16 Ensure that the mating faces of the cylinder block and head are spotlessly clean, that the retaining bolt threads are also clean and dry, and that they screw easily in and out of their locations.

17 Check that No 1 piston is still at TDC, and that the camshaft sprocket timing mark is correctly aligned with the mark on the cylinder head (see Section 6).
Caution: If the camshaft/crankshaft is positioned wrongly, there is a risk of valves touching pistons as the head is refitted.

18 Ensure the locating dowels are correctly fitted to the block and fit a new cylinder head gasket, making sure it is the right way up **(see illustration)**.

19 Carefully lower the cylinder head onto the block, engaging it over the dowels.

20 Lightly oil the new cylinder head bolts, both on their threads and under their heads and allow excess oil to drain off.

21 Fit the washers to the cylinder head bolts and carefully insert the bolts into the cylinder head tightening them all by hand only.

22 Working progressively and in the sequence shown, tighten the cylinder head bolts to the specified torque setting, using a torque wrench and socket **(see illustration)**. It is recommended that the bolts are tightened in several stages, ie. tighten all bolts in sequence first to approximately a third of the

11.5a Unscrew the retaining bolts (visible ones arrowed) . . .

11.5b . . . then tap the sump with a mallet to break the seal

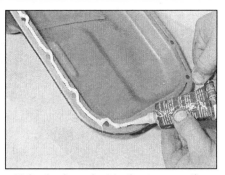

11.9a Apply sealant to the sump mating surface . . .

specified torque, then go around and tighten all bolts to approximately two thirds of the specified torque before finally tightening them to the full specified torque setting.

23 Refit the timing belt as described in Section 6; use the TDC marks on the lower timing cover and pulley to position the crankshaft at TDC.

24 Refit the inlet and exhaust manifolds as described in Chapter 4A or 4B.

25 On carburettor models, refit the fuel pump and reconnect the fuel hoses as described in Chapter 4A.

26 Refit the distributor and its wiring (see Chapter 5). Refit the spark plugs as described in Chapter 1.

27 Refit the cylinder head cover as described in Section 4. If the cylinder head has been overhauled, adjust the valve clearances as described in Chapter 1 prior to refitting the cover.

28 Reconnect the battery, then refill the cooling system as described in Chapter 1.

29 Before starting the engine, check the oil level (see "Weekly checks").

30 On completion, warm the engine up to normal operating temperature, then remove the cylinder head cover and re-torque to cylinder head bolts to the "Hot" torque wrench setting and recheck the valve clearances (see Chapter 1). Refit the cylinder head cover on completion.

11 Sump - removal and refitting

Removal

1 Firmly apply the handbrake, then jack up the front of the vehicle and support it securely on axle stands (see "Jacking and Vehicle Support").

2 Remove the splash guard from under the timing end of the engine. Remove the dipstick from its location on the left-hand rear of the engine.

3 Drain the engine oil as described in Chapter 1, then fit a new sealing washer and refit the drain plug, tightening it to the specified torque.

4 Unbolt the front exhaust pipe from the exhaust manifold (see Chapter 4A or 4B). Lower and support it to provide room to remove the sump.

5 Unscrew and remove the bolts securing the sump to the crankcase. Tap the sump with a hide or plastic mallet to break the seal, then remove the sump. On early engines recover the gasket **(see illustrations)**.

6 While the sump is removed, take the opportunity to check the oil pump pick-up/strainer for signs of clogging or splitting. If necessary, unbolt the pick-up/strainer and remove it from the base of the oil pump housing along with its gasket. The strainer can then be cleaned easily in solvent or renewed.

Refitting

7 Remove all traces of dirt, oil and gasket from the mating surfaces of the sump and cylinder block and (where removed) the pick-up/strainer and oil pump housing.

8 Where necessary, position a new gasket on top of the oil pump pick-up/strainer and fit the strainer, tightening its retaining bolts to the specified torque.

9 On early engines, locate a new gasket on the sump mating surfaces. On later engines, using a good quality sealant apply a bead of sealant approximately 4 mm in diameter to the sump mating surface. Ensure that the bead is located in the sump groove, in between the retaining bolts holes, and around the inside of each hole **(see illustrations)**.

10 Lift the sump into position, then insert the bolts and tighten them progressively to the specified torque.

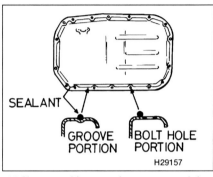

11.9b . . . making sure it goes around the inside of every retaining bolt hole and in the groove between the bolt holes

11 Refit the exhaust pipe to the exhaust manifold with reference to Chapter 4A or 4B.

12 Refit the splash guard under the timing end of the engine, then refit the engine oil level dipstick.

13 Lower the vehicle to the ground and fill the engine with fresh oil (see Chapter 1).

12 Oil pump and pick-up strainer - removal, inspection and refitting

Removal

1 Remove the sump (see Section 11), then unbolt and remove the oil pump pick-up strainer from the bottom of the oil pump housing. Recover the gasket **(see illustrations)**.

12.1a Unscrew the retaining bolts . . .

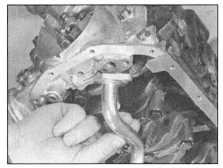

12.1b . . . and remove the oil pump pick-up strainer and gasket

12.4 Oil pump retaining bolt locations

1 Short (20 mm) bolts *2 Medium (30 mm) bolts* *3 Long (60 mm) bolts*

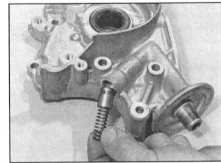

12.6 Oil pump cover retaining screw locations

2 Remove the oil filter as described in Chapter 1. If the filter is damaged on removal, a new one will have to be used on refitting.
3 Remove the timing belt tensioner pulley, the crankshaft sprocket and timing belt guide flange as described in Section 7. This procedure includes removal of the timing belt.
4 Slacken and remove the oil pump housing retaining bolts, noting the location of each bolt since the bolts are of different lengths **(see illustration)**.
5 Slide the oil pump housing assembly off the end of the crankshaft, taking care not to lose the locating dowels. Remove the housing gasket and discard it.

Inspection

6 Undo the retaining screws and lift off the pump cover from the rear of the housing **(see illustration)**.
7 Check if the rotors are marked for position ; they should have indentations on their outer facing surfaces. If not, use a marker pen to mark the surface of both the pump inner and outer rotors **(see illustration)**.
8 Lift out the inner and outer rotors from the pump housing.
9 Unscrew the oil pressure relief valve plug from the top of the housing and recover its sealing washer. Withdraw the spring and

plunger from the housing noting which way around the plunger is fitted **(see illustrations)**.
10 Clean the components, and carefully examine the rotors, pump body and relief valve plunger for any signs of scoring or wear. Individual components are available but it is highly recommended that the complete pump is renewed if excessive wear is evident.
11 If the components appear serviceable, measure the clearances given in the *Specifications* using feeler blades. Also measure the rotor endfloat, and check the flatness of the end cover **(see illustrations)**. If the clearances exceed the specified tolerances, the pump must be renewed.

12.7 The indentations on the inner and outer rotors must face outwards

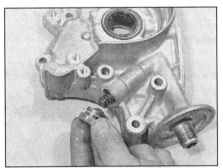

12.9a Unscrew and remove the oil pressure relief valve plug . . .

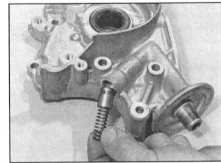

12.9b . . . and withdraw the spring and plunger

12.11a Using a feeler blade to measure the outer rotor-to-housing clearance . . .

12.11b . . . the inner rotor-to-crescent clearance . . .

12.11c . . . the outer rotor-to-crescent clearance . . .

12.11d . . . and the rotor endfloat

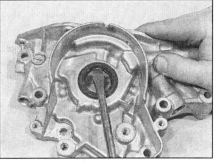

12.13a Prior to refitting, carefully lever out the oil seal . . .

12.13b . . . and fit a new one using a socket as a drift

12 If the pump is satisfactory, reassemble the components in the reverse order of removal, tightening the cover screws and relief valve bolt to the specified torque. Prime the oil pump by filling it with clean engine oil whilst rotating the inner rotor.

Refitting

13 Prior to refitting, note the correct fitted depth of the crankshaft oil seal then carefully lever out the seal using a flat-bladed screwdriver. Fit the new oil seal, ensuring its sealing lip is facing inwards, and press it squarely into the housing using a socket which bears only on the hard outer edge of the seal **(see illustrations)**.

14 Ensure the locating dowels are in position, then wipe clean the mating faces of the oil pump housing and cylinder block and position the new gasket on the cylinder block face **(see illustration)**.

15 Carefully manoeuvre the oil pump housing into position, engaging the inner rotor with the flats on the crankshaft, and taking care not damage the oil seal lip **(see illustration)**.

16 Refit the pump housing retaining bolts in their original locations and tighten them to the specified torque **(see illustration)**.

17 Refit the oil pick-up strainer to the bottom of the oil pump housing together with a new gasket and tighten the mounting bolts to the specified torque **(see illustration)**.

18 Refit the sump together with a new gasket as described in Section 11.

19 Refit the timing belt tensioner pulley, the crankshaft sprocket and timing belt guide flange (together with the timing belt) as described in Section 7.

20 Fit the oil filter and refill the engine with clean oil as described in Chapter 1.

13 Crankshaft oil seals - renewal

Front (timing belt end) oil seal

1 Remove the crankshaft sprocket and belt guide flange as described in Section 7. This procedure includes removal of the timing belt.

2 Note the correct fitted depth of the crankshaft oil seal then carefully lever out the seal using a flat-bladed screwdriver. Alternatively, carefully drill two small holes opposite each other in the oil seal. Screw a self-tapping screw into each and pull on the screws with pliers to extract the seal from the oil pump housing.

Caution: Care must be taken to avoid damage to the oil pump.

3 Clean the seal seating in the oil pump housing and polish off any burrs or raised edges which may have caused the seal to fail in the first place.

4 Lubricate the lips of the new seal with clean engine oil and ease it into position on the end of the crankshaft. Press the seal squarely into position to the previously noted depth. If necessary, a tubular drift, such as a socket, which bears only on the hard outer edge of the seal can be used to tap the seal into position. Take great care not to damage the seal lips during fitting and ensure that the seal lips face inwards **(see illustration)**.

5 Refit the timing belt guide flange and crankshaft sprocket including the timing belt as described in Section 7.

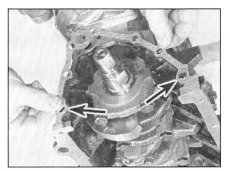

12.14 Fit the new gasket over the locating dowels

12.15 When refitting the oil pump, locate the inner rotor on the flats on the crankshaft

12.16 Tightening the oil pump retaining bolts

12.17 Tightening the oil pump pick-up strainer bolts

13.4 Using a socket and drift to tap the new crankshaft oil seal into the oil pump housing

13.7 Using a hooked instrument to prise out the old crankshaft rear oil seal

13.10 Tapping the new crankshaft rear oil seal into position

13.15 After removing the rear oil seal housing, support it on blocks of wood then use a drift to tap out the old seal

Rear (flywheel/driveplate end) oil seal

Method 1

6 Remove the flywheel/driveplate as described in Section 14.

7 Prise out the old oil seal using a small screwdriver, taking care not to damage the surface of the crankshaft (see illustration). Alternatively, the oil seal can be removed as described in paragraph 2.

8 Clean the seal housing and polish off any burrs or raised edges which may have caused the seal to fail in the first place.

9 Wipe clean the oil seal seating, then dip the new seal in fresh engine oil. Locate it over the crankshaft, making sure its sealing lip is facing inwards. Make sure that the oil seal lip is not damaged as it is located on the rear of the crankshaft.

10 Using metal tube or a drift, drive the oil seal squarely into position until it is in firm contact with the housing (see illustration).

11 Refit the flywheel/driveplate with reference to Section 14.

Method 2 (preferred)

12 Remove the flywheel/driveplate as described in Section 14.

13 Remove the sump as described in Section 11.

14 Unscrew the mounting bolts and remove the rear oil seal housing from the rear of the cylinder block. Recover the gasket.

15 Note the position of the oil seal so that the new one can be located in the same place.

Support the housing on blocks of wood, then use a suitable drift to drive out the oil seal (see illustration).

16 Clean the seal housing and polish off any burrs or raised edges which may have caused the seal to fail in the first place.

17 Wipe clean the oil seal seating, then dip the new seal in fresh engine oil. Drive the new seal into the housing with a mallet and block of wood (see illustration).

18 Locate a new gasket on the rear of the cylinder block, then refit the oil seal housing. Insert the mounting bolts and tighten securely.

19 Refit the sump as described in Section 11.

20 Refit the flywheel/driveplate with reference to Section 14.

14 Flywheel/driveplate - removal, inspection and refitting

Removal

Manual transmission models

1 Remove the transmission as described in Chapter 7A then remove the clutch assembly as described in Chapter 6.

2 Prevent the flywheel from turning by locking the ring gear teeth with a similar arrangement to that shown (see illustration). Alternatively, bolt a strap between the flywheel and the cylinder block/crankcase. Make alignment marks between the flywheel and crankshaft using paint or a marker pen.

13.17 Using a block of wood and mallet to fit the new rear oil seal

3 Slacken and remove the flywheel retaining bolts and remove the flywheel (see illustration). Do not drop it, as it is very heavy. If loose, remove the location dowel from the rear of the crankshaft and store it in a safe place.

Automatic transmission models

4 Remove the transmission as described in Chapter 7B.

5 Prevent the driveplate from turning by bolting it to the cylinder block/crankcase with a metal strap. Make alignment marks between the driveplate and crankshaft using paint or a marker pen.

6 Slacken and remove the retaining bolts and remove the driveplate, noting which way around it is fitted, along with the spacers which are fitted on each side of the plate (see illustration).

14.2 Home-made tool for holding the crankshaft stationary

14.3 Loosening the flywheel retaining bolts with the locking tool (arrowed) in position

14.6 The flywheel/driveplate retaining bolts are unequally spaced so they only align in one position

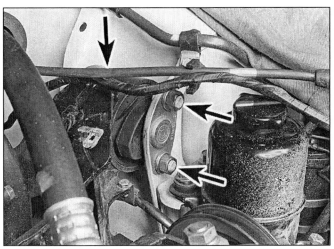

15.7a Left-hand engine mounting through-bolt attachment points

15.7b Left-hand engine mounting bracket-to-cylinder head mounting nuts and bolts

Inspection

7 On models with manual transmission, examine the flywheel for scoring of the clutch face, and for wear or chipping of the ring gear teeth. If the clutch face is scored, the flywheel may be surface-ground, but renewal is preferable. Seek the advice of a Hyundai dealer or engine reconditioning specialist to see if machining is possible. It is possible to renew the ring gear separately, but this task should be entrusted to a suitably equipped workshop as the temperature to which the ring gear needs to be heated is critical; if the gear is overheated the hardness of the teeth will be affected.

8 On models with automatic transmission, check the torque converter driveplate carefully for signs of distortion. Look for any hairline cracks around the bolt holes or radiating outwards from the centre. If any sign of wear or damage is found, the driveplate must be renewed.

Refitting

Manual transmission models

9 Clean the mating surfaces of the flywheel and crankshaft. If removed, refit the location dowel.

10 Apply a little locking fluid to the threads of the retaining bolts, then offer up the flywheel and refit the bolts. If the original flywheel is being refitted align the marks made prior to removal.

11 Lock the flywheel using the method employed on dismantling, and tighten the retaining bolts to the specified torque.

12 Refit the clutch as described in Chapter 6 then remove the locking tool, and refit the transmission as described in Chapter 7A.

Automatic transmission models

13 Clean the mating surfaces of the driveplate, spacers and crankshaft. If removed, refit the location dowel.

14 Apply a little locking fluid to the threads of the retaining bolts, then offer up the driveplate and spacers and refit the bolts. Ensure the driveplate is the correct way around, and align the previously made marks if the original driveplate is being refitted.

15 Lock the driveplate using the method employed on dismantling and tighten the retaining bolts to the specified torque.

16 Refit the transmission (see Chapter 7B).

15 Engine/transmission mountings - inspection and renewal

Inspection

1 If improved access is required, raise the front of the car and support it securely on axle stands (see "Jacking and Vehicle Support").

2 Check each mounting rubber to see if it is cracked, hardened or separated from the metal at any point; renew the mounting if any such damage or deterioration is evident.

3 Check that all the mounting's fasteners are securely tightened; use a torque wrench to check if possible.

4 Using a large screwdriver or a crowbar, check for wear in the mounting by carefully levering against it to check for free play. Where this is not possible, enlist the aid of an assistant to move the engine/transmission unit back and forth, or from side to side, while you watch the mounting. While some free play is to be expected even from new components, excessive wear should be obvious. If excessive free play is found, check first that the fasteners are correctly secured, then renew any worn components as described below.

Renewal

Left-hand mounting

5 Disconnect the battery negative lead.
Caution: If the radio/cassette in your vehicle is equipped with an anti-theft system, make

sure you have the correct activation code before disconnecting the battery.

6 Place a jack beneath the engine, with a block of wood on the jack head (if necessary, remove the splash guard to improve access to the sump). Raise the jack until it is supporting the weight of the engine. Alternately, attach an engine support bar to the lifting brackets and support the weight of the engine with the bar.

7 On early models the through-bolt has a bracket attached to its forward end which is located on two studs and secured with nuts. On later models the through-bolt head has just one stud and securing nut. Unscrew and remove the main nut from the through-bolt, then unscrew the small locking nut(s) and withdraw the through-bolt. Undo the mounting nuts and bolts and remove the left-hand mounting bracket assembly from the engine (see illustrations). Note the position of the spacers and washers.

8 Check carefully for signs of wear or damage on all components, and renew them where necessary.

9 Locate the mounting bracket assembly into position and tighten its retaining nuts and bolts to their specified torque settings. Insert the through-bolt then refit its retaining nut and main nut and tighten them to their specified torque settings.

15.7c Left-hand engine mounting on a later model

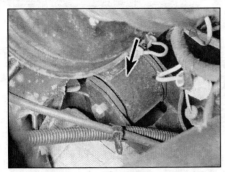

15.13 Right-hand engine mounting

10 Remove the jack from underneath the engine or the engine support bar (as applicable), and reconnect the battery negative lead.

Right-hand mounting

11 Firmly apply the handbrake then jack up the front of the vehicle and support it on axle stands (see *"Jacking and Vehicle Support"*). Remove the right-hand front roadwheel then undo the retaining screws and remove the undercover to improve access to the mounting assembly. On fuel-injected models, to further improve access, remove the air cleaner housing (see Chapter 4B). On 5-speed manual transmission models, remove the gearchange control cable (see Chapter 7A).

12 Place a jack beneath the transmission, with a block of wood on the jack head. Raise the jack until it is supporting the weight of the transmission.

13 Slacken and remove the through-bolt and nut then prise out the trim caps from underneath the right-hand wheelarch to reveal the mounting retaining bolts. Undo the bolts securing the mounting to the body and remove the mounting from the engine compartment. If necessary, undo the retaining nuts/bolts and remove the mounting bracket from the transmission housing **(see illustration)**.

14 Check carefully for signs of wear or damage on all components, and renew them where necessary.

15 Where removed, refit the mounting bracket to the transmission unit and tighten its retaining bolts.

15.21 Front engine mounting (later models)

15.20 Front engine mounting through-bolt (early models)

16 Manoeuvre the mounting into position then tighten its retaining bolts to the specified torque and refit the trim caps. Insert the through-bolt and tighten its nut to the specified torque.

17 Remove the jack from below the transmission then refit the undercover and roadwheel. Lower the vehicle to the ground and tighten the roadwheel nuts to the specified torque. Where necessary, refit the air cleaner housing and gearchange control cable.

Front mounting/roll rod

18 Early models were fitted with a roll rod with two rubbers at the front of the engine. On later models this was replaced by a single mounting with an enlarged mounting bracket.

19 Firmly apply the handbrake then jack up the front of the vehicle and support it on axle stands (see *"Jacking and Vehicle Support"*). If necessary, undo the retaining screws and remove the undercover to improve access to the mounting assembly.

20 On early models, unscrew and remove the through-bolts and remove the roll rod from the brackets. If necessary, unbolt the bracket from the engine **(see illustration)**.

21 On later models, unscrew and remove the mounting through-bolt and nut, then undo the retaining bolts and remove the mounting from the crossmember, noting which way around it is fitted **(see illustration)**. If necessary, the mounting bracket can then be unbolted and removed from the engine.

22 Check carefully for signs of wear or damage on all components, and renew them

15.33 Stabilising rod

where necessary. On early models the rubbers can be renewed separately.

23 Where removed, refit the mounting bracket and tighten the retaining bolts to the specified torque.

24 On early models, make sure that the rubbers are located in the roll rod correctly then position the rod at the front of the engine and insert the through-bolts. Tighten the nuts to the specified torque.

25 On later models, locate the mounting in position and tighten its retaining bolts to the specified torque. Insert the through-bolt and tighten its nut to the specified torque.

26 Refit the undercover (where removed) and lower the vehicle to the ground.

Rear mounting

27 Firmly apply the handbrake then jack up the front of the vehicle and support it on axle stands (see *"Jacking and Vehicle Support"*).

28 Slacken and remove the mounting through-bolt and nut then undo the retaining bolts and remove the mounting from the crossmember, noting which way around it is fitted. If necessary, the mounting bracket can then be unbolted and removed from the engine.

29 Check carefully for signs of wear or damage on all components, and renew them where necessary.

30 Where removed, refit the mounting bracket to the engine and tighten its retaining bolts to the specified torque.

31 Manoeuvre the mounting into position and tighten its retaining bolts to the specified torque. Insert the through-bolt and tighten its nut to the specified torque then lower the vehicle to the ground.

Stabilising rod - manual transmission models only

32 Firmly apply the handbrake then jack up the front of the vehicle and support it on axle stands (see *"Jacking and Vehicle Support"*).

33 Before removing the rod, mark its underside to ensure correct refitting; the rod is not symmetrical and the largest half of the rear mounting hole must be at the bottom **(see illustration)**.

34 Slacken and remove the bolt and washers securing the stabilising rod to the rear of the transmission unit then remove the nut and bolt securing the rod to the body and remove the stabilising rod from underneath the vehicle, noting which way around it is fitted.

35 Check the rod and rubbers for signs of wear or damage and renew if necessary.

36 Offer up the rod, making sure it is fitted the correct way around, and insert the bolt securing it to the body bracket. Position a washer on each side of the transmission end of the rod then screw in the mounting bolt. Tighten both bolts to their specified torque settings then lower the vehicle to the ground.

Chapter 2 Part B:
Engine removal and overhaul procedures

Contents

Crankshaft - inspection 13
Crankshaft - refitting and main bearing running clearance check . . . 16
Crankshaft - removal 10
Cylinder block/crankcase - cleaning and inspection 11
Cylinder head - dismantling 6
Cylinder head - reassembly 8
Cylinder head and valves - cleaning and inspection 7
Engine - initial start-up after overhaul 19
Engine and transmission - removal, separation and refitting 4
Engine overhaul - dismantling sequence 5

Engine overhaul - general information 2
Engine overhaul - reassembly sequence 15
Engine removal - methods and precautions 3
General information 1
Main and big-end bearings - inspection 14
Piston rings - refitting 17
Piston/connecting rod assembly - inspection 12
Piston/connecting rod assembly - refitting and big-end bearing
    running clearance check 18
Piston/connecting rod assembly - removal 9

Degrees of difficulty

Easy, suitable for novice with little experience	Fairly easy, suitable for beginner with some experience	Fairly difficult, suitable for competent DIY mechanic	Difficult, suitable for experienced DIY mechanic	Very difficult, suitable for expert DIY or professional

Specifications

Engine codes
See Chapter 2A.

Cylinder head

Gasket face distortion:	
Standard	0.05 mm
Service limit	0.10 mm
Valve guide bore diameter - for use when renewing the valve guides:	
1st (0.05 mm) oversize	12.050 to 12.068 mm
2nd (0.25 mm) oversize	12.250 to 12.268 mm
3rd (0.50 mm) oversize	12.500 to 12.518 mm
Valve seat bore diameter - for use when renewing the valve seats:	
Inlet:	
1st (0.3 mm) oversize	36.300 to 36.325 mm
2nd (0.6 mm) oversize	36.600 to 36.625 mm
Exhaust:	
1st (0.3 mm) oversize	32.300 to 32.325 mm
2nd (0.6 mm) oversize	32.600 to 32.625 mm

Valves, valve springs and guides

Valve stem diameter:
Inlet . . . . 6.565 to 6.580 mm
Exhaust . . . . 6.530 to 6.550 mm
Valve seat angle . . . . 45°
Valve-to-valve seat contact width . . . . 0.9 to 1.3 mm
Valve guide external diameter:
Standard . . . . 12.00 mm
Oversizes available . . . . 0.05, 0.25 and 0.50 mm
Valve guide length:
Inlet . . . . 44.1 mm
Exhaust . . . . 49.5 mm
Valve stem to guide clearance:
Inlet:
Standard . . . . 0.03 to 0.06 mm
Maximum . . . . 0.10 mm
Exhaust:
Standard . . . . 0.05 to 0.09 mm
Maximum . . . . 0.15 mm
Valve spring free length:
Standard . . . . 44.6 mm
Minimum . . . . 43.6 mm

Cylinder block

Cylinder bore diameter (standard):
1.3 litre engine . . . . 71.00 to 71.03 mm
1.5 litre engine . . . . 75.50 to 75.53 mm
Cylinder bore out-of-round/taper limits . . . . 0.02 mm

Pistons

Piston diameter (standard):
1.3 litre engine . . . . 70.97 to 71.00 mm
1.5 litre engine . . . . 75.47 to 75.50 mm
Oversizes available . . . . 0.25, 0.50, 0.75 and 1.00 mm
Piston-to-bore clearance (all engines) . . . . 0.02 to 0.04 mm

Connecting rod

Big-end side clearance:
Standard . . . . 0.10 to 0.25 mm
Service limit . . . . 0.40 mm

Crankshaft

Endfloat:
Standard . . . . 0.05 to 0.18 mm
Service limit . . . . 0.25 mm
Main bearing journal diameter:
Standard . . . . 48.000 mm
1st (0.25 mm) undersize . . . . 47.735 to 47.750 mm
2nd (0.50 mm) undersize . . . . 47.485 to 47.500 mm
3rd (0.75 mm) undersize . . . . 47.235 to 47.250 mm
Big-end bearing journal diameter:
Standard . . . . 42.000 mm
1st (0.25 mm) undersize . . . . 41.735 to 41.750 mm
2nd (0.50 mm) undersize . . . . 41.485 to 41.500 mm
3rd (0.75 mm) undersize . . . . 41.235 to 41.250 mm
Maximum bearing journal out-of-round . . . . 0.01 mm
Maximum bearing journal taper . . . . 0.01 mm
Main bearing running clearance:
Standard . . . . 0.02 to 0.07 mm
Service limit . . . . 0.15 mm
Big-end bearing running clearance:
Standard . . . . 0.02 to 0.06 mm
Service limit . . . . 0.15 mm

Piston rings

Ring end gap:
  Compression ring:
    Standard . . . . 0.20 to 0.35 mm
    Service limit . . . . 0.80 mm
  Oil control ring:
    Standard . . . . 0.20 to 0.70 mm
    Service limit . . . . 1.00 mm
Ring side clearance:
  No 1 compression ring:
    Standard . . . . 0.03 to 0.07 mm
    Service limit . . . . 0.15 mm
  No 2 compression ring:
    Standard . . . . 0.02 to 0.06 mm
    Service limit . . . . 0.12 mm
  Oil control ring . . . . N/A

Torque wrench settings

Refer to Chapter 2A Specifications

1 General information

Included in this Part of Chapter 2 are details of removing the engine from the vehicle, and general overhaul procedures for the cylinder head, cylinder block/crankcase and all other engine internal components.

The information given ranges from advice concerning preparation for an overhaul and the purchase of replacement parts, to detailed step-by-step procedures covering removal, inspection, renovation and refitting of engine internal components.

After Section 8, all instructions are based on the assumption that the engine has been removed from the vehicle. For information concerning in-car engine repair, as well as the removal and refitting of those external components necessary for full overhaul, refer to Part A of this Chapter. Ignore any preliminary dismantling operations described in Part A that are no longer relevant once the engine has been removed from the vehicle.

Apart from torque wrench settings, which are given at the beginning of Part A, all specifications relating to engine overhaul are at the beginning of this Part of Chapter 2.

2 Engine overhaul - general information

It is not always easy to determine when, or if, an engine should be completely overhauled, as a number of factors must be considered.

High mileage is not necessarily an indication that an overhaul is needed, while low mileage does not preclude the need for an overhaul. Frequency of servicing is probably the most important consideration. An engine which has had regular and frequent oil and filter changes, as well as other required maintenance, should give many thousands of miles of reliable service. Conversely, a neglected engine may require an overhaul very early in its life.

Excessive oil consumption is an indication that piston rings, valve seals and/or valve guides are in need of attention. Make sure that oil leaks are not responsible before deciding that the rings and/or guides are worn. Perform a compression test, as described in Part A of this Chapter, to determine the likely cause of the problem.

Check the oil pressure with a gauge fitted in place of the oil pressure switch, and compare it with that specified (in Chapter 2A). If it is extremely low, the main and big-end bearings, and/or the oil pump, are probably worn out.

Loss of power, rough running, knocking or metallic engine noises, excessive valve gear noise, and high fuel consumption may also point to the need for an overhaul, especially if they are all present at the same time. If a complete service does not remedy the situation, major mechanical work is the only solution.

An engine overhaul involves restoring all internal parts to the specification of a new engine. During an overhaul, the pistons and the piston rings are renewed. New main and big-end bearings are generally fitted; if necessary, the crankshaft may be reground, to restore the journals. The valves are also serviced as well, since they are usually in less-than-perfect condition at this point. While the engine is being overhauled, other components, such as the distributor, starter and alternator, can be overhauled as well. The end result should be an as-new engine that will give many trouble-free miles.

Cooling system components such as the hoses, thermostat and water pump should be renewed when an engine is overhauled. The radiator should be checked carefully, to ensure that it is not clogged or leaking. Also, it is a good idea to renew the oil pump whenever the engine is overhauled.

Before beginning the engine overhaul, read through the entire procedure, to familiarise yourself with the scope and requirements of the job. Overhauling an engine is not difficult if you follow carefully all of the instructions, have the necessary tools and equipment, and pay close attention to all specifications. It can, however, be time-consuming. Plan on the car being off the road for a minimum of two weeks, especially if parts must be taken to an engineering works for repair or reconditioning. Check on the availability of parts, and make sure that any necessary special tools and equipment are obtained in advance. Most work can be done with typical hand tools, although a number of precision measuring tools are required for inspecting parts to determine if they must be renewed. Often, the engineering works will handle the inspection of parts, and can offer advice concerning reconditioning and renewal.

Always wait until the engine has been completely dismantled, and until all components (especially the cylinder block/crankcase and the crankshaft) have been inspected, before deciding what service and repair operations must be performed by an engineering works. The condition of these components will be the major factor to consider when determining whether to overhaul the original engine, or to buy a reconditioned unit. Do not, therefore, purchase parts or have overhaul work done on other components until they have been thoroughly inspected. As a general rule, time is the primary cost of an overhaul, so it does not pay to fit worn or sub-standard parts.

As a final note, to ensure maximum life and minimum trouble from a reconditioned engine, everything must be assembled with care, in a spotlessly-clean environment.

3 Engine removal -
methods and precautions

If you have decided that the engine must be removed for overhaul or major repair work, several preliminary steps should be taken.

Locating a suitable place to work is extremely important. Adequate work space, along with storage space for the vehicle, will be needed. If a workshop or garage is not available, at the very least, a flat, level, clean work surface is required.

Cleaning the engine compartment and engine/transmission before beginning the removal procedure will help keep tools clean and organised.

An engine hoist or A-frame will also be necessary. Make sure that the equipment is rated in excess of the combined weight of the engine and transmission. Safety is of primary importance, considering the potential hazards involved in removing the engine/transmission from the vehicle.

If this is the first time you have removed an engine, an assistant should ideally be available. Advice and aid from someone more experienced would also be helpful. There are many instances when one person cannot simultaneously perform all of the operations required when lifting the engine out of the vehicle.

Plan the operation ahead of time. Before starting work, arrange for the hire of, or obtain, all of the tools and equipment you will need. Some of the equipment necessary to perform engine/transmission removal and installation safely and with relative ease (in addition to an engine hoist) is as follows: a heavy-duty trolley jack, complete sets of spanners and sockets as described in the Reference section of this manual, wooden blocks, and plenty of rags and cleaning solvent for mopping up spilled oil, coolant and fuel. If the hoist must be hired, make sure that you arrange for it in advance, and perform all of the operations possible without it beforehand. This will save you money and time.

Plan for the vehicle to be out of use for quite a while. An engineering works will be required to perform some of the work which the do-it-yourselfer cannot accomplish without special equipment. These places often have a busy schedule, so it would be a good idea to consult them before removing the engine, in order to accurately estimate the amount of time required to rebuild or repair components that may need work.

Always be extremely careful when removing and refitting the engine/transmission. Serious injury can result from careless actions. Plan ahead and take your time, and a job of this nature, although major, can be accomplished successfully.

The engine and transmission is removed as an assembly upwards from the engine compartment.

4 Engine and transmission -
removal, separation and refitting

Note: *The engine is removed from the car only as a complete unit with the transmission; the two are then separated for overhaul.*

Removal

1 Park the vehicle on firm, level ground and apply the handbrake. Jack up the front of the vehicle and support on axle stands (see "*Jacking and Vehicle Support*").
2 Remove both front roadwheels, and remove the splash guards from under the engine compartment.
3 Remove the bonnet as described in Chapter 11.
4 Remove the battery as described in Chapter 5.
Caution: If the radio/cassette in your vehicle is equipped with an anti-theft system, make sure you have the correct activation code before disconnecting the battery.
5 Depressurise the fuel system as described in Chapter 4A.
6 Drain the cooling system (see Chapter 1), saving the coolant if it is fit for re-use. On pre-1992 models, also remove the coolant reservoir from the left-hand side of the engine compartment.
7 Drain the transmission oil/fluid with reference to Chapter 7A or 7B (as applicable). Refit and tighten the drain and filler plugs.
8 If the engine is to be dismantled, working as described in Chapter 1, drain the oil and if required remove the oil filter. Clean and refit the drain plug, tightening it to the specified torque.
9 On models with power steering remove the power steering pump (and reservoir if fitted) with reference to Chapter 10 but leave the hydraulic lines connected. Tie the pump to one side.
10 On models equipped with air conditioning, remove the auxiliary drivebelt (see Chapter 1) then unbolt the compressor, and position it clear of the engine. Support the weight of the compressor by tying it to the vehicle body, to prevent any excess strain being placed on the compressor lines whilst the engine is removed. **Do not** disconnect the refrigerant lines from the compressor (refer to the warnings given in Chapter 3).
11 Remove the air cleaner assembly and air ducting as described in Chapter 4A.
12 Disconnect the wiring from the reversing light switch on the transmission.
13 Disconnect the engine wiring harness at the connector.
14 On manual transmission models, disconnect the selector rods (early models) or cables (later models) from the transmission with reference to Chapter 7A. On early 5-speed models also disconnect the 5th speed vacuum control lines.

4.15 Oil pressure warning switch

15 Disconnect the wiring from the alternator and oil pressure warning switch **(see illustration)**.
16 On automatic transmission models, position a suitable container beneath the transmission then loosen and disconnect the oil cooler lines. Note the location of the lines to ensure correct refitting, and tape over or plug the lines and unions to prevent entry of dust and dirt.
17 Remove the radiator as described in Chapter 3.
18 Disconnect the ignition coil HT cable and the low tension wiring from the distributor with reference to Chapter 5.
19 Unbolt the engine earth cable.
20 Loosen the clip and disconnect the vacuum hose from the brake servo unit.
21 Loosen the clips and disconnect the fuel supply hose from the carburettor or fuel rail (as applicable). Also disconnect the fuel return hose.
22 Disconnect the heater supply and return hoses at the bulkhead. Note their locations for correct refitting.
23 Disconnect the accelerator cable at the carburettor or throttle housing with reference to Chapter 4A. On early carburettor models disconnect the choke cable with reference to Chapter 4A.
24 On pre-1992 models, remove the windscreen washer reservoir from the right-hand side of the engine compartment.
25 On manual transmission models, disconnect the clutch cable or clutch hydraulic lines from the transmission with reference to Chapter 6.
26 On automatic transmission models, disconnect the selector cable with reference to Chapter 7B. Also disconnect the wiring from the inhibitor switch, kick-down switch, pulse generator, solenoid valve and temperature sensor. Disconnect the speedometer cable.
27 Refer to Chapter 4A and disconnect the exhaust front downpipe from the exhaust manifold and from the bracket.. Support the pipe on an axle stand or tie it to one side.
28 Working on each side at a time, unbolt the front suspension lower balljoints and antiroll bar from the lower arms (refer to Chapter 10 if necessary).

29 Using a suitable lever against the transmission casing, carefully force the driveshafts from each side of the transmission (refer to Chapter 8 if necessary). Support them to one side on axle stands or tie them from the body with wire.

30 Manoeuvre the hoist into position, and attach it to the lifting brackets on the engine. Raise the hoist until it is supporting the weight of the engine.

31 Disconnect the front and rear engine mountings with reference to Chapter 2A. On early models, remove the roll rod link.

32 Remove the left-hand engine mounting as described in Chapter 2A.

33 Make sure that the weight of the engine is not resting on the right-hand engine mounting; if necessary raise the assembly slightly. Working under the right-hand wheelarch, prise out the caps and unscrew the bolts securing the engine mounting to the body **(see illustration)**. Refer to Chapter 2A if necessary.

34 Make a final check that any components which would prevent the removal of the engine/transmission from the car have been removed or disconnected. Ensure that components such as the driveshafts are secured so that they cannot be damaged on removal.

35 Lift the engine/transmission out of the car, ensuring that nothing is trapped or damaged. Enlist the help of an assistant during this procedure, as it will be necessary to tilt the assembly slightly to clear the body panels **(see illustration)**.

36 Once the engine is high enough, lift it out over the front of the body, and lower the unit to the ground.

Separation

37 With the engine/transmission assembly removed, support the assembly on suitable blocks of wood, on a workbench or failing that, on a clean area of the workshop floor. If the hoist is still available, it may be an advantage to raise the engine/transmission slightly to allow access to the bolts on the underside of the assembly.

38 Unbolt and remove the bellhousing lower cover.

39 On automatic transmission models unscrew and remove the bolts securing the torque converter to the driveplate. Turn the crankshaft as necessary for access to each of the bolts. Also unbolt and remove the right-hand engine mounting bracket.

40 Unscrew the retaining bolts, and remove the starter motor from the transmission (refer to Chapter 5 if necessary).

41 Ensure that both engine and transmission are adequately supported, then slacken and remove the bolts securing the transmission to the engine. Note the correct fitted positions of each bolt (and, where fitted, the relevant brackets) as they are removed, to use as a reference on refitting.

42 With the help of an assistant, withdraw the transmission from the engine. On manual transmission models, ensure that the weight of the transmission is not allowed to hang on the input shaft while it is engaged with the clutch friction disc. On automatic transmission models ensure that the torque converter remains fully engaged with the transmission.

43 If they are loose, remove the locating dowels from the engine or transmission, and keep them in a safe place.

44 If necessary, remove the clutch components and flywheel (manual transmission models) or driveplate (automatic transmission models) with reference to Chapter 2A.

Refitting

45 If the engine and transmission have been separated, perform the operations described below in paragraphs 46 to 53. If not, proceed as described from paragraph 54 onwards.

46 Where removed refit the clutch components and flywheel (manual transmission models) or driveplate (automatic transmission models) with reference to Chapter 2A.

47 On manual transmission models, apply a smear of high-melting-point grease to the splines of the transmission input shaft. Do not apply too much, otherwise there is a possibility of the grease contaminating the clutch friction plate. Also ensure that the clutch release bearing is correctly engaged with the fork.

48 On automatic transmission models make sure that the torque converter remains fully engaged with the transmission (see Chapter 7B).

49 Ensure that the locating dowels are correctly positioned in the engine or transmission. Carefully offer the transmission to the engine, until the locating dowels are engaged. On manual transmission models, ensure that the weight of the transmission is not allowed to hang on the input shaft.

50 Refit the transmission-to-engine bolts, ensuring that all the necessary brackets are correctly positioned, and tighten them to the specified torque setting.

51 Refit the starter motor and tighten the retaining bolts (refer to Chapter 5 if necessary).

52 On automatic transmission models align the holes in the driveplate and torque converter then insert the bolts and tighten them to the specified torque.

53 Refit the bellhousing lower cover and tighten the bolts to the specified torque.

54 Reconnect the hoist to the engine lifting brackets. With the aid of an assistant, lift the assembly over the front of the body and lower it into the engine compartment, making sure that it clears the surrounding components.

55 Refit the right-hand engine mounting and tighten the bolts to the specified torque (refer to Chapter 2A if necessary).

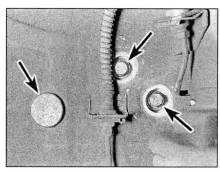

4.33 The right-hand engine mounting bolts are behind plugs in the wheelarch liner

56 Refit the left-hand engine mounting with reference to Chapter 2A.

57 Reconnect the front and rear engine mountings with reference to Chapter 2A. On early models with a roll rod link, do not tighten the lower mounting bolt (located in the slotted hole) until all the remaining mountings have been tightened.

58 The remainder of the refitting procedure is a direct reversal of the removal sequence, with reference to the relevant Chapters and noting the following points:
  a) Ensure that the wiring harness is correctly routed and all connectors are correctly and securely reconnected.
  b) Prior to refitting the driveshafts to the transmission, renew the driveshaft oil seals as described in Chapter 7A or 7B (as applicable).
  c) Refill the transmission oil/fluid with reference to Chapter 7A or 7B (as applicable).
  d) Refill the engine with oil with reference to Chapter 1.
  e) Adjust the auxiliary drivebelts as described in Chapter 1.
  f) Adjust the accelerator cable as described in Chapter 4A.
  g) Refill the cooling system as described in Chapter 1.
  h) On completion, start the engine and check for leaks.

4.35 Lifting the engine/transmission out of the engine compartment

6.3a Compressing a valve spring to remove the split collets

6.3b Removing the spring retainer . . .

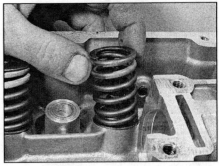

6.3c . . . valve spring . . .

5 Engine overhaul - dismantling sequence

1 It is much easier to dismantle and work on the engine if it is mounted on a portable engine stand. These stands can often be hired from a tool hire shop. Before the engine is mounted on a stand, the flywheel/driveplate should be removed, so that the stand bolts can be tightened into the end of the cylinder block/crankcase.

2 If a stand is not available, it is possible to dismantle the engine with it blocked up on a sturdy workbench, or on the floor. Be extra-careful not to tip or drop the engine when working without a stand.

3 If you are going to obtain a reconditioned engine, all the external components must be removed first, to be transferred to the replacement engine (just as they will if you are doing a complete engine overhaul yourself). These components include the following:

a) Alternator, power steering pump and/or air conditioning compressor mounting brackets (as applicable).

b) Distributor, HT leads and spark plugs (Chapters 1 and 5).

c) Coolant pump and thermostat/coolant outlet housing(s) (Chapter 3).

d) The carburettor or fuel injection system components (see Chapter 4A).

e) All electrical switches and sensors, and the engine wiring harness.

f) Inlet and exhaust manifolds (see Chapter 4A).

g) Engine mountings (Part A of this Chapter).

h) Flywheel/driveplate (Part A of this Chapter).

i) Engine rear plate

Note: When removing the external components from the engine, pay close attention to details that may be helpful or important during refitting. Note the fitted position of gaskets, seals, spacers, pins, washers, bolts, and other small items.

4 If you are obtaining a "short" engine (which consists of the engine cylinder block/crankcase, crankshaft, pistons and connecting rods all assembled), then the cylinder head, sump, oil pump, and timing belt will have to be removed as well.

5 If you are planning a complete overhaul, the engine can be dismantled, and the internal components removed, in the order given below, referring to Part A of this Chapter unless otherwise stated.

a) Inlet and exhaust manifolds (Chapter 4A).

b) Timing belt, sprockets and tensioner (see Part A).

c) Cylinder head (see Part A).

d) Flywheel/driveplate (see Part A).

e) Sump (see Part A).

f) Oil pump and rear oil seal housing (see Part A).

g) Piston/connecting rod assemblies (Section 9).

h) Crankshaft (Section 10).

6 Before beginning the dismantling and overhaul procedures, make sure that you have all of the correct tools necessary. Refer to "Tools and working facilities" at the end of this manual for further information.

6 Cylinder head - dismantling

Note: New and reconditioned cylinder heads can be obtained from the manufacturer and from engine overhaul specialists. Be aware that some specialist tools are required for the dismantling and inspection procedures, and new components may not be readily available. It may therefore be more practical and economical for the home mechanic to purchase a reconditioned head, rather than dismantle, inspect and recondition the original head.

1 Remove the cylinder head as described in Part A of this Chapter. This procedure includes removal of the inlet and exhaust manifolds.

2 Remove the rocker shafts and camshaft as described in Part A of this Chapter.

3 Using a valve spring compressor, compress each valve spring in turn until the split collets can be removed. Release the compressor, and lift off the spring retainer, spring and spring seat. Using a pair of pliers or special removal tool, carefully extract the valve stem seal from the top of the guide **(see illustrations)**.

4 If, when the valve spring compressor is screwed down, the spring retainer refuses to free and expose the split collets, gently tap the top of the tool, directly over the retainer, with a light hammer. This will free the retainer.

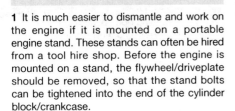

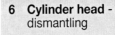

6.3d . . . spring seat . . .

6.3e . . . and valve stem seal

6.3f Valve components

6.5 Removing a valve

6.6 Place each valve and its associated components in a labelled polythene bag

6.7 Removing the jet valves using the special Hyundai tool no. 09222-21300

5 Withdraw the valve through the combustion chamber **(see illustration)**.
6 It is essential that each valve is stored together with its collets, retainer, spring, and spring seat. The valves should also be kept in their correct sequence, unless they are so badly worn that they are to be renewed. If they are going to be kept and used again, place each valve assembly in a labelled polythene bag or similar small container. Note that No 1 valve is nearest to the timing belt end of the engine **(see illustration)**.
7 Where fitted, remove the jet valves from the cylinder head using the special Hyundai tool or a deep socket **(see illustration)**.

HAYNES HINT *When unscrewing the jet valve, make sure that the socket is not tilted, otherwise the valve stem may be bent, resulting in defective jet valve operation.*

8 To dismantle the jet valve, compress the spring and remove the valve spring retainer lock, the retainer and spring, and the valve. Hyundai technicians use a special tool to compress the spring, however it should be possible to fabricate a tool or use a valve spring compressor. Keep all the jet valve components identified for location to ensure correct reassembly. Pull off the valve stem seals with pliers and discard them.

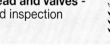
7 Cylinder head and valves - cleaning and inspection

1 Thorough cleaning of the cylinder head and valve components, followed by a detailed inspection, will enable you to decide how much valve service work must be carried out during the engine overhaul. **Note:** *If the engine has been severely overheated, it is best to assume that the cylinder head is warped - check carefully for signs of this.*

Cleaning

2 Scrape away all traces of old gasket material from the cylinder head.
3 Scrape away the carbon from the combustion chambers and ports, then wash

the cylinder head thoroughly with paraffin or a suitable solvent.
4 Scrape off any heavy carbon deposits that may have formed on the valves, then use a power-operated wire brush to remove the remaining deposits from the valve heads and stems.

Inspection

Note: *Be sure to perform all the following inspection procedures before concluding that the services of a machine shop or engine overhaul specialist are required. Make a list of all items that require attention.*

Cylinder head

5 Inspect the head very carefully for cracks, evidence of coolant leakage, and other damage. If cracks are found, a new cylinder head should be obtained.
6 Use a straight-edge and feeler blade to check that the cylinder head surface is not distorted. If it is, it may be possible to have it machined by an engine overhaul specialist.
7 Examine the valve seats in each of the combustion chambers. If they are severely pitted, cracked, or burned, they will need to be renewed or re-cut by an engine overhaul specialist. If they are only slightly pitted, this can be removed by grinding-in the valve heads and seats with fine valve-grinding compound, as described below.
8 Check the valve guides for wear by inserting the relevant valve, and checking for side-to-side movement of the valve. A very small amount of movement is acceptable, however, if excessive remove the valve and measure the valve stem diameter (see below) and renew the valve if it is worn. If the valve stem is not worn, the wear must be in the valve guide, and the guide must be renewed. The renewal of valve guides is best carried out by a Hyundai dealer or engine overhaul specialist, who will have the necessary tools available.
9 If renewing the valve guides, the valve seats must be re-cut or re-ground only *after* the new guides have been fitted.

Valves

10 Examine the head of each valve for pitting, burning, cracks, and general wear. Check the valve stem for scoring and wear

ridges. Rotate the valve, and check for any obvious indication that it is bent. Look for pits and excessive wear on the tip of each valve stem. Renew any valve that shows any signs of wear or damage.
11 If the valve appears satisfactory at this stage, measure the valve stem diameter at several points using a micrometer **(see illustration)**. Any significant difference in the readings obtained indicates wear of the valve stem. Should any of these conditions be apparent, the valve(s) must be renewed.
12 If the valves are in satisfactory condition, they should be ground (lapped) into their respective seats, to ensure a smooth, gas-tight seal. If the seat is only lightly pitted, or if it has been re-cut, fine grinding compound *only* should be used to produce the required finish. Coarse valve-grinding compound should *not* be used, unless a seat is badly burned or deeply pitted. If this is the case, the cylinder head and valves should be inspected by an expert, to decide whether seat re-cutting, or even the renewal of the valve or seat insert is required.
13 Valve grinding is carried out as follows. Place the cylinder head upside-down on a bench.
14 Smear a trace of the appropriate grade of valve-grinding compound on the seat face, and press a suction grinding tool onto the valve head. With a semi-rotary action, grind the valve head to its seat, lifting the valve occasionally to redistribute the grinding compound. A light spring placed under the valve head will greatly ease this operation.

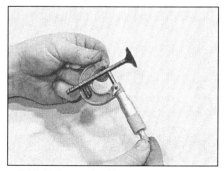

7.11 Using a micrometer to measure a valve stem diameter

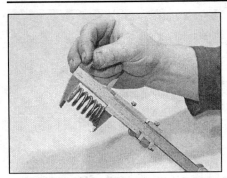

7.17 Measuring valve spring free length

15 If coarse grinding compound is being used, work only until a dull, matt even surface is produced on both the valve seat and the valve, then wipe off the used compound, and repeat the process with fine compound. When a smooth unbroken ring of light grey matt finish is produced on both the valve and seat, the grinding operation is complete. *Do not* grind-in the valves any further than absolutely necessary.
16 When all the valves have been ground-in, carefully wash off *all* traces of grinding compound using paraffin or a suitable solvent, before reassembling the cylinder head.

Valve components

17 Examine the valve springs for signs of damage and discoloration. Measure the free length of each spring and compare it to the measurements given in the *Specifications* **(see illustration)**.
18 Stand each spring on a flat surface, and check it for squareness. If any of the springs are damaged, distorted or have lost their tension, obtain a complete new set of springs. It is normal to renew the valve springs as a matter of course if a major overhaul is being carried out.
19 Renew the valve stem oil seals regardless of their apparent condition.

Rocker arm components

20 Refer to Chapter 2A for the rocker arm and shaft inspection procedures.

Jet valves

21 Make sure each jet valve slides smoothly

in the jet valve body with no play. Do not interchange parts between jet valves. If any parts are worn or damaged, renew the complete jet valve assembly.
22 Check the valve head and valve seat for damage and evidence of seizure. Check the spring for distortion and damage. Renew the components as necessary.

8 Cylinder head - reassembly

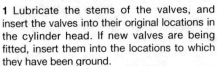

1 Lubricate the stems of the valves, and insert the valves into their original locations in the cylinder head. If new valves are being fitted, insert them into the locations to which they have been ground.
2 Refit the spring seat then, working on the first valve, dip the new valve stem seal in fresh engine oil. Carefully locate it over the valve and onto the guide. Take care not to damage the seal as it is passed over the valve stem. Use a socket or metal tube to press the seal firmly onto the guide.
3 Locate the valve spring on top of its seat, then refit the spring retainer.
4 Compress the valve spring, and locate the split collets in the recess in the valve stem. Release the compressor, then repeat the procedure on the remaining valves.

Use a little dab of grease to hold the collets in position on the valve stem while the spring compressor is released.

5 With all the valves installed, place the cylinder head flat on the bench and, using a hammer and interposed block of wood, tap the end of each valve stem to settle the components.
6 To reassemble the jet valves, first drive the stem seal onto the body using a suitable tool such as a deep socket. Lubricate the valve and insert it in the body, then refit the spring and retainer and compress the spring with the tool before refitting the retainer lock.
7 Locate new O-rings to the jet valve bodies, then lightly lubricate the O-rings, valve threads and seatings. Refit the jet valves and tighten them to the specified torque.
8 Refit the camshaft and rocker shafts as described in Part A of this Chapter.
9 The cylinder head (and inlet and exhaust manifolds) can then be refitted as described in Part A of this Chapter.

9 Piston/connecting rod assembly - removal

1 Remove the cylinder head and sump as described in Part A of this Chapter.
2 If there is a pronounced wear ridge at the top of any bore, it may be necessary to remove it with a scraper or ridge reamer, to avoid piston damage during removal. Such a ridge indicates excessive wear of the cylinder bore.
3 Prior to removal, using feeler blades, measuring the connecting rod big-end side clearance of each rod **(see illustration)**. If any rod exceeds the specified clearance, it must be renewed.
4 Using a hammer and centre-punch, paint or similar, mark each connecting rod and its bearing cap with its respective cylinder number on the flat machined surface provided; if the engine has been dismantled before, note carefully any identifying marks made previously **(see illustration)**. Note that No 1 cylinder is at the timing belt end of the engine.
5 Turn the crankshaft to bring pistons 1 and 4 to BDC (bottom dead centre).
6 Unscrew the nuts from No 1 piston big-end bearing cap. Take off the cap and recover the bottom half bearing shell. If the bearing shells are to be re-used, tape the cap and the shell together.
7 Using a hammer handle, push the piston up through the bore, and remove it from the top of the cylinder block. Recover the bearing shell, and tape it to the connecting rod for safe-keeping.
8 Loosely refit the big-end cap to the connecting rod, and secure with the nuts - this will help to keep the components in their correct order.
9 Remove No 4 piston assembly in the same way.
10 Turn the crankshaft through 180° to bring pistons 2 and 3 to BDC (bottom dead centre), and remove them in the same way.

9.3 Measuring connecting rod big-end side clearance

9.4 Make identification marks on the connecting rod and cap prior to removal (cylinder No 3 shown)

10 Crankshaft - removal

1 Remove the oil pump and the flywheel/driveplate as described in Part A of this Chapter. If the piston and connecting rod assemblies are also to be removed, remove the cylinder head.
2 Check the crankshaft endfloat as described in Section 13, then proceed as follows.
3 Remove the piston and connecting rod assemblies as described in Section 9. If no work is to be done on the pistons and connecting rods, unbolt the caps and push the pistons far enough up the bores so that the connecting rods are positioned clear of the crankshaft journals.
4 Slacken and remove the retaining bolts securing the crankshaft rear oil seal housing to the cylinder block and remove the housing from the crankshaft end along with its gasket. If the cover locating dowels are a loose fit, remove and store them with the cover for safe-keeping. Also, if required, unbolt and remove the engine rear plate.
5 The main bearing caps should be numbered 1 to 5 from the timing belt end of the engine and have an arrow stamped on them indicating the timing end of the engine **(see illustration)**. If not, mark them accordingly using a centre-punch or paint in the same way as the connecting rods.
6 Unscrew and remove the main bearing cap retaining bolts, and withdraw the caps. Recover the lower main bearing shells, and tape them to their respective caps for safe-keeping.
7 Carefully lift out the crankshaft, taking care not to displace the upper main bearing shells **(see illustration)**.
8 Recover the upper bearing shells from the cylinder block, and tape them to their respective caps for safe-keeping.

11 Cylinder block/crankcase - cleaning and inspection

Cleaning

1 Remove all external components and electrical switches/sensors from the block, and if necessary unbolt the mounting brackets.
2 For complete cleaning, the core plugs should ideally be removed. Drill a small hole in the plugs, then insert a self-tapping screw into the hole. Pull out the plugs by pulling on the screw with a pair of grips, or by using a slide hammer.
3 Scrape all traces of sealant from the cylinder block/crankcase, taking care not to damage the gasket/sealing surfaces.
4 Remove all oil gallery plugs (where fitted).

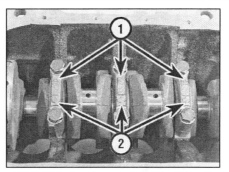

10.5 Main bearing cap location (1) and direction (2) identification markings

The plugs are usually very tight - they may have to be drilled out, and the holes re-tapped. Use new plugs when the engine is reassembled.
5 If the cylinder block is extremely dirty, it should be steam-cleaned.
6 Clean all oil holes and oil galleries and flush all internal passages with warm water until the water runs clear. Dry thoroughly, and apply a light film of oil to all mating surfaces and the cylinder bores, to prevent rusting. If you have access to compressed air, use it to speed up the drying process, and to blow out all the oil holes and galleries **(see illustration)**.

 Warning: Wear eye protection when using compressed air!

7 If the cylinder block is not very dirty, you can do an adequate cleaning job with hot (as hot as you can stand!), soapy water and a stiff brush. Take plenty of time, and do a thorough job. Regardless of the cleaning method used, be sure to clean all oil holes and galleries very thoroughly, and to dry all components well. Protect the cylinder bores as described above, to prevent rusting.
8 All threaded holes must be clean, to ensure accurate torque readings during reassembly. To clean the threads, run the correct-size tap into each of the holes to remove rust, corrosion, thread sealant or sludge, and to restore damaged threads. If possible, use compressed air to clear the holes of debris produced by this operation. An alternative is to inject aerosol-applied water-dispersant lubricant into each hole, using the long spout usually supplied, but be sure to soak up all traces of the lubricant prior to reassembly.

 Warning: Wear eye protection when cleaning out these holes in this way!

9 Apply suitable sealant to the new oil gallery plugs, and insert them into the holes in the block. Tighten them securely.
10 If the engine is not going to be reassembled right away, cover it with a large plastic bag to keep it clean; protect all mating surfaces and the cylinder bores as described above, to prevent rusting.

10.7 Removing the crankshaft

Inspection

11 Visually check the cylinder block for cracks and corrosion. Look for stripped threads in the threaded holes. If there has been any history of internal water leakage, it may be worthwhile having an engine overhaul specialist check the cylinder block/crankcase with special equipment. If defects are found, have them repaired if possible, or obtain a new block.
12 Check each cylinder bore for scuffing and scoring. Check for signs of a wear ridge at the top of the cylinder, indicating that the bore is excessively worn.
13 If the necessary measuring equipment is available, measure the bore diameter of each cylinder at the top (just under the wear ridge), centre, and bottom of the cylinder bore, parallel to the crankshaft axis.
14 Next, measure the bore diameter at the same three locations, at right-angles to the crankshaft axis. Compare the results with the figures given in the *Specifications*. If there is any doubt about the condition of the cylinder bores seek the advice of a Hyundai dealer or engine reconditioning specialist.
15 If the cylinder bores are worn, it is possible to have them rebored and fit oversize pistons. Oversize pistons are available in the following sizes; 0.25 mm, 0.50 mm, 0.75 mm and 1.00 mm oversize. Seek the advice of a Hyundai dealer or engine overhaul specialist for further information.

11.6 Clean out all the cylinder block oilways using compressed air

12 Piston/connecting rod assembly - inspection

1 Before the inspection process can begin, the piston/connecting rod assemblies must be cleaned, and the original piston rings removed from the pistons.

2 Carefully expand the old rings over the top of the pistons - note that the oil control ring assembly incorporates two rails and an expander. The use of two or three old feeler blades will be helpful in preventing the rings dropping into empty grooves (see illustration). Be careful not to scratch the piston with the ends of the ring. The rings are brittle, and will snap if they are spread too far. They're also very sharp - protect your hands and fingers. Always remove the rings from the top of the piston. Keep each set of rings with its piston if the old rings are to be re-used.

3 Scrape away all traces of carbon from the top of the piston. A hand-held wire brush (or a piece of fine emery cloth) can be used, once the majority of the deposits have been scraped away.

4 Remove the carbon from the ring grooves in the piston, using an old ring. Break the ring in half to do this (be careful not to cut your fingers - piston rings are sharp). Be careful to remove only the carbon deposits - do not remove any metal, and do not nick or scratch the sides of the ring grooves.

5 Once the deposits have been removed, clean the piston/connecting rod assembly with paraffin or a suitable solvent, and dry thoroughly. Make sure that the oil return holes in the ring grooves are clear.

6 If the pistons and cylinder bores are not damaged or worn excessively, and if the cylinder block does not need to be rebored, the original pistons can be refitted. Normal piston wear shows up as even vertical wear on the piston thrust surfaces, and slight looseness of the top ring in its groove. New piston rings should always be used when the engine is reassembled.

7 Carefully inspect each piston for cracks around the skirt, around the gudgeon pin holes, and at the piston ring "lands" (between the ring grooves).

8 Look for scoring and scuffing on the piston skirt, holes in the piston crown, and burned areas at the edge of the crown. If the skirt is scored or scuffed, the engine may have been suffering from overheating, and/or abnormal combustion which caused excessively high operating temperatures. The cooling and lubrication systems should be checked thoroughly. Scorch marks on the sides of the pistons show that blow-by has occurred. A hole in the piston crown, or burned areas at the edge of the piston crown, indicates that abnormal combustion (pre-ignition, knocking, or detonation) has been occurring. If any of the above problems exist, the causes must be investigated and corrected, or the damage will

12.2 Using a feeler blade to remove a piston ring

occur again. The causes may include incorrect ignition timing, or a faulty carburettor/injector (as applicable).

9 Corrosion of the piston, in the form of pitting, indicates that coolant has been leaking into the combustion chamber and/or the crankcase. Again, the cause must be corrected, or the problem may persist in the rebuilt engine.

10 Examine each connecting rod carefully for signs of damage, such as cracks around the big-end and small-end bearings. Check that the rod is not bent or distorted. Damage is highly unlikely, unless the engine has been seized or badly overheated. Detailed checking of the connecting rod assembly can only be carried out by a Hyundai dealer or engine repair specialist with the necessary equipment.

11 The gudgeon pins are an interference fit in the connecting rod small-end bearing. Therefore, piston and/or connecting rod renewal should be entrusted to a Hyundai dealer or engine repair specialist, who will have the necessary tooling to remove and install the gudgeon pins. If new pistons are to be fitted, ensure that the correct size pistons are fitted to each bore (see Section 11).

13 Crankshaft - inspection

Checking crankshaft endfloat

1 If the crankshaft endfloat is to be checked, this must be done when the crankshaft is still

13.2 Using a dial gauge to measure crankshaft endfloat

installed in the cylinder block, but is free to move (see Section 10).

2 Check the endfloat using a dial gauge in contact with the end of the crankshaft. Push the crankshaft fully one way, and then zero the gauge. Push the crankshaft fully the other way, and check the endfloat (see illustration). The result can be compared with the specified amount, and will give an indication as to whether new main bearing shells are required (endfloat is controlled by the centre main bearing shells).

3 If a dial gauge is not available, feeler blades can be used. First push the crankshaft fully towards the flywheel/driveplate end of the engine, then use feeler blades to measure the gap between the centre main bearing shell and the web of the crankshaft (see illustration).

Inspection

4 Clean the crankshaft using paraffin or a suitable solvent, and dry it, preferably with compressed air if available. Be sure to clean the oil holes with a pipe cleaner or similar probe, to ensure that they are not obstructed.

Warning: Wear eye protection when using compressed air.

5 Check the main and big-end bearing journals for uneven wear, scoring, pitting and cracking.

6 Big-end bearing wear is accompanied by distinct metallic knocking when the engine is running (particularly noticeable when the engine is pulling from low speed) and some loss of oil pressure.

7 Main bearing wear is accompanied by severe engine vibration and rumble - getting progressively worse as engine speed increases - and again by loss of oil pressure.

8 Check the bearing journal for roughness by running a finger nail lightly over the bearing surface. Any roughness (which will be accompanied by obvious bearing wear) indicates that the crankshaft requires regrinding (where possible) or renewal.

9 If the crankshaft has been reground, check for burrs around the crankshaft oil holes (the holes are usually chamfered, so burrs should not be a problem unless regrinding has been carried out carelessly). Remove any burrs with a fine file or scraper, and thoroughly clean the oil holes as described previously.

13.3 Using feeler blades to check crankshaft endfloat

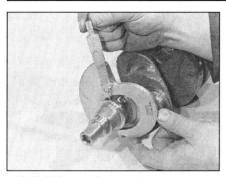

13.10 Using a micrometer to measure a crankshaft journal

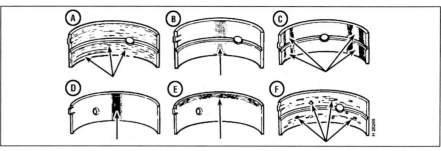

14.2 Typical bearing failures

A Scratched by dirt; dirt embedded in bearing material
B Lack of oil; overlay wiped out
C Improper seating; bright (polished) sections

D Tapered journal; overlay gone from entire surface
E Radius ride
F Fatigue failure; craters or pockets

10 Using a micrometer, measure the diameter of the main and big-end bearing journals, and compare the results with the *Specifications* (see illustration). By measuring the diameter at a number of points around each journal's circumference, you will be able to determine whether or not the journal is out-of-round. Take the measurement at each end of the journal, near the webs, to determine if the journal is tapered. Compare the results obtained with those given in the *Specifications*.
11 Check the oil seal contact surfaces at each end of the crankshaft for wear and damage. If the seal has worn a deep groove in the surface of the crankshaft, consult an engine overhaul specialist; repair may be possible, but otherwise a new crankshaft will be required.
12 If the crankshaft journals have not already been reground, it may be possible to have the crankshaft reconditioned, and to fit undersize shells; big-end and main bearing shells are available in the following sizes; 0.25 mm, 0.50 mm and 0.75 mm undersize.

14 Main and big-end bearings - inspection

1 Even though the main and big-end bearings should be renewed during the engine overhaul, the old bearings should be retained for close examination, as they may reveal valuable information about the condition of the engine.
2 Bearing failure can occur due to lack of lubrication, the presence of dirt or other foreign particles, overloading the engine, or corrosion. Regardless of the cause of bearing failure, the cause must be corrected (where applicable) before the engine is reassembled, to prevent it from happening again (see illustration).
3 When examining the bearing shells, remove them from the cylinder block/crankcase, the main bearing caps, the connecting rods and the connecting rod big-end bearing caps. Lay them out on a clean surface in the same general position as their location in the engine. This will enable you to match any bearing problems with the corresponding crankshaft journal.

4 Dirt and other foreign matter gets into the engine in a variety of ways. It may be left in the engine during assembly, or it may pass through filters or the crankcase ventilation system. It may get into the oil, and from there into the bearings. Metal chips from machining operations and normal engine wear are often present. Abrasives are sometimes left in engine components after reconditioning, especially when parts are not thoroughly cleaned using the proper cleaning methods. Whatever the source, these foreign objects often end up embedded in the soft bearing material, and are easily recognised. Large particles will not embed in the bearing, and will score or gouge the bearing and journal. The best prevention for this cause of bearing failure is to clean all parts thoroughly, and keep everything spotlessly-clean during engine assembly. Frequent and regular engine oil and filter changes are also recommended.
5 Lack of lubrication (or lubrication breakdown) has a number of interrelated causes. Excessive heat (which thins the oil), overloading (which squeezes the oil from the bearing face) and oil leakage (from excessive bearing clearances, worn oil pump or high engine speeds) all contribute to lubrication breakdown. Blocked oil passages, which usually are the result of misaligned oil holes in a bearing shell, will also oil-starve a bearing, and destroy it. When lack of lubrication is the cause of bearing failure, the bearing material is wiped or extruded from the steel backing of the bearing. Temperatures may increase to the point where the steel backing turns blue from overheating.
6 Driving habits can have a definite effect on bearing life. Full-throttle, low-speed operation (labouring the engine) puts very high loads on bearings, tending to squeeze out the oil film. These loads cause the bearings to flex, which produces fine cracks in the bearing face (fatigue failure). Eventually, the bearing material will loosen in pieces, and tear away from the steel backing.
7 Short-distance driving leads to corrosion of bearings, because insufficient engine heat is produced to drive off the condensed water and corrosive gases. These products collect in the engine oil, forming acid and sludge. As the

oil is carried to the engine bearings, the acid attacks and corrodes the bearing material.
8 Incorrect bearing installation during engine assembly will lead to bearing failure as well. Tight-fitting bearings leave insufficient bearing running clearance, and will result in oil starvation. Dirt or foreign particles trapped behind a bearing shell result in high spots on the bearing, which lead to failure.
9 As mentioned at the beginning of this Section, the bearing shells should be renewed as a matter of course during engine overhaul; to do otherwise is false economy.

15 Engine overhaul - reassembly sequence

1 Before reassembly begins, ensure that all new parts have been obtained, and that all necessary tools are available. Read through the entire procedure, to familiarise yourself with the work involved, and to ensure that all items necessary for reassembly of the engine are at hand. In addition to all normal tools and materials, thread-locking fluid will be needed. A tube of liquid sealant will also be required for the joint faces that are fitted without gaskets.
2 In order to save time and avoid problems, engine reassembly can be carried out in the following order:
  a) Crankshaft (Section 16).
  b) Piston/connecting rod assemblies (Sections 17 and 18).
  c) Oil pump and rear oil seal housing (see Part A).
  d) Sump (see Part A).
  e) Flywheel/driveplate (see Part A).
  f) Cylinder head (see Part A).
  g) Timing belt, sprockets and tensioner (see Part A).
  h) Inlet and exhaust manifolds (Chapter 4A).
  i) Engine external components.
3 At this stage, all engine components should be absolutely clean and dry, with all faults repaired. The components should be laid out (or in individual containers) on a completely clean work surface.

16.2 Typical marking on the back of a bearing shell

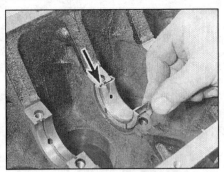

16.5a Fit the bearing shells ensuring that their tabs are correctly aligned with the notches in the cylinder block/caps

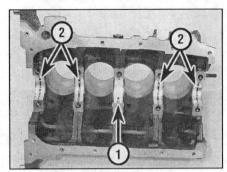

16.5b The centre main bearing shells (1) are flanged whilst the other upper bearing shells (2) are grooved . . .

16 Crankshaft - refitting and main bearing running clearance check

Note: *It is recommended that new main bearing shells are fitted regardless of the condition of the original ones.*

Selection of bearing shells

1 There are four different sizes of bearing shell available; the standard size shell for use with an original crankshaft and three different undersizes for use once the crankshaft has been reground.

2 The relevant set of bearing shells required can be obtained by measuring the diameter of the crankshaft main bearing journals (see Section 13). This will show if the crankshaft is original or whether its journals have been reground, identifying if either standard or undersize bearing shells are required. If the measuring equipment is unavailable, the size of the bearing shells can be identified by the markings stamped on the rear of each shell **(see illustration)**. Details of these markings should be supplied to your Hyundai dealer who will then be able to identify the size of shell fitted.

3 Whether the original shells or new shells are being fitted, it is recommended that the running clearance is checked as follows prior to installation.

Main bearing running clearance check

4 Clean the backs of the bearing shells and the bearing locations in both the cylinder block and the main bearing caps.

5 Press the bearing shells into their locations, ensuring that the tab on each shell engages in the notch in the cylinder block or main bearing cap. Ensure that the flanged bearing shells are fitted to the centre (No 3) main bearing (both upper and lower bearings) and that the four grooved bearing shells are fitted in the upper (No 1, 2, 4 and 5) locations in the block and the plain bearing shells to the (No 1, 2, 4 and 5) bearing caps **(see illustrations)**. If the original bearing shells are being used for the check ensure that they are refitted in their original locations. The clearance can be checked in either of two ways.

6 One method (which will be difficult to achieve without a range of internal micrometers or internal/external expanding calipers) is to refit the main bearing caps to the cylinder block, with bearing shells in place. With the cap retaining bolts correctly tightened, measure the internal diameter of each assembled pair of bearing shells. If the diameter of each corresponding crankshaft journal is measured and then subtracted from the bearing internal diameter, the result will be the main bearing running clearance.

7 The second (and more accurate) method is to use a product known as Plastigauge. This

consists of a fine thread of perfectly round plastic which is compressed between the bearing shell and the journal. When the shell is removed, the plastic is deformed and can be measured with a special card gauge supplied with the kit. The running clearance is determined from this gauge. Plastigauge is sometimes difficult to obtain but enquiries at one of the larger specialist quality motor factors should produce the name of a stockist in your area. The procedure for using Plastigauge is as follows.

8 With the main bearing upper shells in place, carefully lay the crankshaft in position. Do not use any lubricant; the crankshaft journals and bearing shells must be perfectly clean and dry.

9 Cut several lengths of the appropriate size Plastigauge (they should be slightly shorter than the width of the main bearings) and place one length on each crankshaft journal axis **(see illustration)**.

10 With the main bearing lower shells in position, refit the main bearing caps, tightening their retaining bolts to the specified torque. Take care not to disturb the Plastigauge and **do not** rotate the crankshaft at any time during this operation. Remove the main bearing caps again taking great care not to disturb the Plastigauge or rotate the crankshaft **(see illustration)**.

11 Compare the width of the crushed Plastigauge on each journal to the scale printed on the Plastigauge envelope to obtain

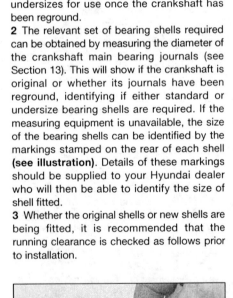
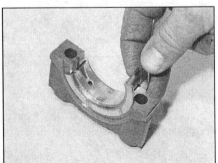

16.5c . . . all the lower bearing shells are plain with the flanged bearing (shown) being fitted to the centre cap

16.9 Lay a strip of Plastigauge on the clean journal then refit the bearing cap and tighten its bolts to the specified torque

16.10 Remove the bearing cap carefully to reveal the crushed Plastigauge . . .

16.11 . . . then determine the running clearance by measuring the Plastigauge using the scale provided

16.18 Lubricate the bearing shells with clean engine oil before fitting the crankshaft

16.20a Refit the bearing caps . . .

the main bearing running clearance **(see illustration)**. Compare the clearance measured with that given in the *Specifications*.

12 If the clearance is significantly different from that expected, the bearing shells may be the wrong size (or excessively worn if the original shells are being re-used). Before making a final decision, make sure that no dirt or oil was trapped between the bearing shells and the caps or block when the clearance was measured. If the Plastigauge was wider at one end than at the other, the crankshaft journal may be tapered.

13 Before condemning the components concerned, seek the advice of your Hyundai dealer or engine repair specialist. They will be able to inform as to the best course of action

and whether it is possible to have the crankshaft journals reground (where possible) or whether renewal will be necessary.

14 Where necessary, obtain the correct size of bearing shell and repeat the running clearance checking procedure as described above.

15 On completion, carefully scrape away all traces of the Plastigauge material from the crankshaft and bearing shells using a fingernail or other object which is unlikely to score the bearing surfaces.

Final crankshaft refitting

16 Carefully lift the crankshaft out of the cylinder block once more.

17 Place the bearing shells in their locations as already described. If new shells are being

fitted, ensure that all traces of the protective grease are cleaned off using paraffin. Wipe dry the shells and caps with a lint-free cloth.

18 Liberally lubricate each bearing shell in the cylinder block with clean engine oil then lower the crankshaft into position ensuring that the bearing shells remain correctly seated **(see illustration)**.

19 Check the crankshaft endfloat as described in Section 13.

20 Ensure that the bearing shells are correctly located in the caps and refit the caps to the cylinder block. Ensure that the caps are fitted in their correct locations with No 1 cap at the timing belt end, and are fitted the correct way around so that all the arrows point towards the timing belt end of the engine. Insert the bearing cap bolts and tighten them to the specified torque setting **(see illustrations)**.

21 Fit a new oil seal to the rear oil seal housing and fit it together with a new gasket with reference to Chapter 2A **(see illustrations)**.

22 Refit/reconnect the piston connecting rod assemblies to the crankshaft as described in Section 18.

23 If removed, refit the engine rear plate and tighten the bolts to the specified torque (see Chapter 2A).

24 Refit the oil pump, flywheel/driveplate and cylinder head (if removed) as described in Part A.

16.20b . . . and tighten the main bearing bolts to the specified torque setting

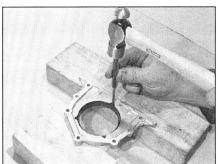

16.21a Support the housing and tap out the rear oil seal using a hammer and punch

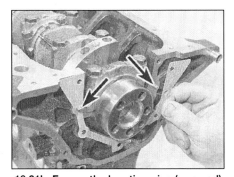

16.21b Ensure the locating pins (arrowed) are in position and fit the new gasket

16.21c Carefully ease the housing into position, taking care not to damage the oil seal lip . . .

16.21d . . . and securely tighten its retaining bolts

17.4 Checking a piston ring end gap

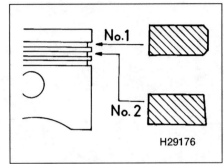

17.9a Ensure the top and second compression rings are fitted in the correct locations . . .

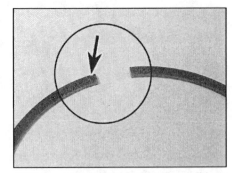

17.9b . . . with their identification markings (arrowed) uppermost

17 Piston rings - refitting

1 Before fitting new piston rings, the ring end gaps must be checked as follows.
2 Lay out the piston/connecting rod assemblies and the new piston ring sets, so that the ring sets will be matched with the same piston and cylinder during the end gap measurement and subsequent engine reassembly.
3 Insert the top ring into the first cylinder, and push it down the bore using the top of the piston. This will ensure that the ring remains square with the cylinder walls. Push the ring down into the bore until the piston skirt is level with the block mating surface, then withdraw the piston.
4 Measure the end gap using feeler blades, and compare the measurements with the figures given in the *Specifications* (see illustration).
5 If the gap is too small (unlikely if genuine parts are used), it must be enlarged, or the ring ends may contact each other during

engine operation, causing serious damage. Ideally, new piston rings providing the correct end gap should be fitted. As a last resort, the end gap can be increased by filing the ring ends very carefully with a fine file. Mount the file in a vice with soft jaws, slip the ring over the file with the ends contacting the file face, and slowly move the ring to remove material from the ends. Take care, as piston rings are sharp, and are easily broken.
6 With new piston rings, it is unlikely that the end gap will be too large. If the gaps are too large, check that you have the correct rings for your engine and for the particular cylinder bore size.
7 Repeat the checking procedure for each ring in the first cylinder, and then for the rings in the remaining cylinders. Remember to keep rings, pistons and cylinders matched up.
8 Once the ring end gaps have been checked and if necessary corrected, the rings can be fitted to the pistons.
9 Fit the piston rings using the same technique as for removal. Fit the bottom (oil control) spacer first then install both the side rails, noting that both the spacer and side rails can be installed either way up. Fit the second

and top compression rings ensuring that each ring is fitted the correct way up with its identification mark uppermost (see illustrations). **Note:** *Always follow any instructions supplied with the new piston ring sets - different manufacturers may specify different procedures. Do not mix up the top and second compression rings, as they have different cross-sections.*
10 With the piston rings correctly installed, check that each ring is free in its groove. Position the ring end gaps as shown (see illustration).

18 Piston/connecting rod assembly - refitting and big-end bearing clearance check

Note: *It is recommended that new piston rings and big-end bearing shells are fitted regardless of the condition of the original ones.*

Selection of bearing shells

1 See Section 16.

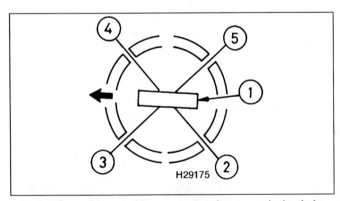

17.10 Ring end gap positions - arrow points towards the timing belt end of the engine

1 Gudgeon pin
2 Oil control (bottom) ring lower side rail gap
3 Second compression ring and oil control (bottom) ring spacer gap
4 Oil control (bottom) ring upper side rail gap
5 Top compression ring gap

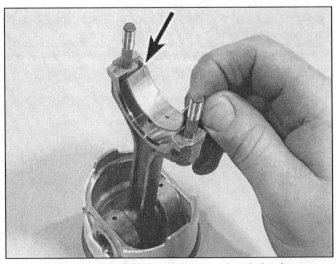

18.3 Fit the bearing shells making sure that their tabs are correctly engaged with the rod/cap notch (arrowed)

18.9a Arrow on the piston crown indicating the timing belt end of the engine

18.9b Insert the piston/connecting rod assembly, ensuring that the piston marking (arrowed) is pointing towards the timing belt end of the engine . . .

Big-end bearing running clearance check

2 Clean the backs of the bearing shells and the bearing locations in both the connecting rods and bearing caps.

3 Press the bearing shells into their locations, ensuring that the tab on each shell engages in the notch in the connecting rod and cap **(see illustration)**. If the original bearing shells are being used for the check ensure that they are refitted in their original locations. The clearance can be checked in either of two ways.

4 One method is to refit the big-end bearing cap to the connecting rod, with bearing shells in place. With the cap retaining nuts correctly tightened, use an internal micrometer or vernier caliper to measure the internal diameter of each assembled pair of bearing shells. If the diameter of each corresponding crankpin is measured and then subtracted from the bearing internal diameter, the result will be the big-end bearing running clearance.

5 The second method is to use Plastigauge as described in Section 16. Place a strand of Plastigauge on each (cleaned) crankpin journal and refit the (clean) piston/connecting

rod assemblies, shells and big-end bearing caps. Tighten the nuts to the specified torque wrench setting. Take care not to disturb the Plastigauge. Dismantle the assemblies without rotating the crankshaft and use the scale printed on the Plastigauge envelope to obtain the big-end bearing running clearance. On completion of the measurement, carefully scrape off all traces of Plastigauge from the journal and shells using a fingernail or other object which will not score the components.

Final piston/connecting rod assembly refitting

6 Ensure that the bearing shells are correctly refitted as described above. If new shells are being fitted, ensure that all traces of the protective grease are cleaned off using paraffin. Wipe dry the shells and connecting rods with a lint-free cloth.

7 Lubricate the bores, the pistons and piston rings then lay out each piston/connecting rod assembly in its respective position.

8 Starting with assembly number 1, make sure that the piston rings are still spaced as described in Section 17, then clamp them in position with a piston ring compressor.

9 Insert the piston/connecting rod assembly into the top of cylinder No 1, ensuring that the arrow marking on the piston crown is pointing towards the timing belt end of the engine. Using a block of wood or hammer handle against the piston crown, tap the assembly into the cylinder until the piston crown is flush with the top of the cylinder **(see illustrations)**.

10 Taking care not to mark the cylinder bore, liberally lubricate the crankpin and both bearing shells, then pull the piston/connecting rod assembly down the bore and onto the crankpin and refit the big-end bearing cap using the markings to ensure it is fitted the correct way around (the upper and lower bearing shells locating tabs should be on the same side) **(see illustration)**.

11 Refit the bearing cap nuts and tighten them evenly and progressively to the specified torque setting **(see illustration)**.

12 Refit the remaining three piston and connecting rod assemblies in the same way.

13 Rotate the crankshaft, and check that it turns freely, with no signs of binding or tight spots.

14 Refit the sump and cylinder head as described in Part A of this Chapter.

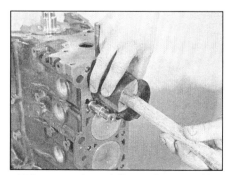

18.9c . . . and carefully tap the assembly into the cylinder using a hammer handle

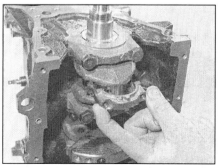

18.10 Pull the connecting rod down onto the crankshaft and refit the bearing cap

18.11 Tightening the big-end bearing cap nuts with a torque wrench

19 Engine -
initial start-up after overhaul

1 With the engine refitted in the vehicle, double-check the engine oil and coolant levels. Make a final check that everything has been reconnected, and that there are no tools or rags left in the engine compartment.

2 Remove the spark plugs. Disable the ignition system by disconnecting the ignition HT coil lead from the distributor cap and earthing it on the cylinder block. Use a jumper lead or similar wire to make a good connection.

3 Turn the engine on the starter until the oil pressure warning light goes out. Refit the spark plugs, and reconnect the spark plug (HT) leads, referring to Chapter 1 for further information. Reconnect the ignition HT coil lead to the distributor cap.

4 Start the engine, noting that this may take a little longer than usual, due to the fuel system components having been disturbed.

5 While the engine is idling, check for fuel, water and oil leaks. Don't be alarmed if there are some odd smells and smoke from parts getting hot and burning off oil deposits.

6 Assuming all is well, keep the engine idling until hot water is felt circulating through the top hose, then switch off the engine.

7 Check the ignition timing, and the idle speed settings (as appropriate), then switch the engine off. Remove the cylinder head cover and recheck the valve clearances with the engine "hot" (see Chapter 1).

8 After a few minutes, recheck the oil and coolant levels as described in "Weekly checks", and top-up as necessary.

9 If new pistons, rings or crankshaft bearings have been fitted, the engine must be treated as new, and run-in for the first 500 miles (800 km). Do not operate the engine at full-throttle, or allow it to labour at low engine speeds in any gear. It is recommended that the oil and filter be changed at the end of this period.

Chapter 3
Cooling, heating and ventilation systems

Contents

Air conditioning system - general information and precautions 10
Air conditioning system - refrigerant level check .... see Chapter 1
Air conditioning system components - removal and refitting 11
Auxiliary cooling fan - removal and refitting 5
Coolant level check .... see "Weekly Checks"
Coolant pump - removal, inspection and refitting 7
Coolant renewal .... see Chapter 1

Cooling fan switch - testing, removal and refitting 6
Cooling system hoses - disconnection and renewal 2
General information and precautions 1
Heater/ventilation components - removal and refitting 9
Radiator - removal, inspection and refitting 3
Temperature gauge coolant sensor - testing, removal and refitting . 8
Thermostat - removal, testing and refitting 4

Degrees of difficulty

Easy, suitable for novice with little experience	Fairly easy, suitable for beginner with some experience	Fairly difficult, suitable for competent DIY mechanic	Difficult, suitable for experienced DIY mechanic	Very difficult, suitable for expert DIY or professional 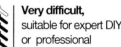

Specifications

General

Radiator cap relief valve opening pressure	0.83 - 1.1 bar
Radiator cap vacuum valve opening depression	< 0.07 bar
Coolant pump/alternator drivebelt deflection (tension):	
New belt	5.5 - 7.0 mm
Used belt	7.5 - 9.0 mm

Thermostat

Opening temperature:	
Starts to open at:	
Engines with unleaded fuel	88 °C
Engines with leaded fuel	82 °C
Fully open at:	
Engines with unleaded fuel	100 °C
Engines with leaded fuel	95 °C
Valve lift when fully open	8 mm (minimum)

Electric cooling fan

Cut-in temperature	82 to 88 °C
Cut-out temperature	78 °C
Thermo sensor resistance at 115 °C	21.3 to 26.3 Ω

Temperature gauge coolant sensor

Electrical resistance:	
At 70 °C	90.5 to 117.5 Ω
At 100 °C	38 Ω

Temperature switch (automatic transmission models)

Cut-in temperature	50 °C

Torque wrench settings

	Nm	lbf ft
Alternator bracing bracket (through coolant pump) to cylinder block ..	23	17
Alternator brace bolt	14	10
Coolant pump to cylinder block bolts:		
Bolt head mark "4"	14	10
Bolt head mark "7" (alternator brace mounting)	24	18
Coolant pump pulley securing bolts	9	7
Coolant temperature gauge sensor	30	22
Thermostat housing cover bolts	19	14
Temperature switch (automatic transmission models)	8	6

1 General information and precautions

General information

The engine cooling system is of the pressurised type, comprising a centrifugal coolant pump driven by the auxiliary belt, a crossflow radiator, a coolant expansion tank, an electric cooling fan, a thermostat, heater matrix, and all associated hoses and switches.

The system functions as follows: the coolant pump circulates cold water around the engine cylinder block and head passages, and through the inlet manifold, heater matrix and throttle body to the thermostat housing.

When the engine is cold, the thermostat remains closed and prevents coolant from circulating through the radiator. When the coolant reaches a predetermined temperature, the thermostat opens, and the coolant passes through the top hose to the radiator. As the coolant circulates through the radiator, it is cooled by the in-rush of air when the car is in forward motion. The airflow is supplemented by the action of the electric cooling fan, when necessary. The coolant reaches the bottom of the radiator and passes out through the bottom hose to the coolant pump - the cycle is then repeated.

When the engine is at normal operating temperature, the coolant expands, and some of it is displaced into the expansion tank. Coolant collects in the tank, and is returned to the radiator when the system cools. The tank is a separate unit to the radiator, mounted on the right hand side of the engine compartment and is not pressurised.

The electric cooling fan, which is mounted on the engine side of the radiator, is controlled by a thermostatic switch. At a predetermined coolant temperature, the switch/sensor actuates the fan to provide additional airflow through the radiator. The switch cuts the electrical supply to the fan when the coolant temperature has dropped below a preset threshold (see Specifications). An additional cooling fan is fitted on automatic transmission models.

Precautions

⚠️ *Warning: Do not attempt to remove the radiator pressure cap, or to disturb any part of the cooling system, while the engine is hot, as there is a high risk of scalding. If the radiator pressure cap must be removed before the engine and radiator have fully cooled (even though this is not recommended), the pressure in the cooling system must first be relieved. Cover the cap with a thick layer of cloth, to avoid scalding, and slowly unscrew the pressure cap until a hissing sound is heard. When the hissing stops, indicating that the* pressure has reduced, slowly unscrew the pressure cap until it can be removed; if more hissing sounds are heard, wait until they have stopped before unscrewing the cap completely. At all times, keep your face well away from the pressure cap opening, and protect your hands.

⚠️ *Warning: Do not allow antifreeze to come into contact with your skin, or with the painted surfaces of the vehicle. Rinse off spills immediately, with plenty of water. Never leave antifreeze lying around in an open container, or in a puddle in the driveway or on the garage floor. Children and pets are attracted by its sweet smell, but antifreeze can be fatal if ingested.*

⚠️ *Warning: If the engine is hot, the electric cooling fan may start rotating, even if the engine and ignition are switched off. Be careful to keep your hands, hair, and any loose clothing well clear when working in the engine compartment.*

2 Cooling system hoses - disconnection and renewal

1 The routing and pattern of hoses will vary slightly according to the model year, but the same basic procedure applies. Before commencing work, make sure that the new hoses are to hand, along with new hose clips if needed. It is good practice to renew the hose clips at the same time as the hoses.
2 Drain the cooling system, as described in Chapter 1, saving the coolant if it is fit for re-use. Squirt a little penetrating oil onto the hose clips if they are corroded.
3 Loosen the hose clips on the hose concerned and position the clips away from the hose stub.
4 Unclip any wires, cables or other hoses which may be attached to the hose being removed. Make notes for reference when reassembling if necessary.
5 Release the hose from its stubs with a twisting motion. Be careful not to damage the stubs on delicate components such as the radiator, or thermostat housings. If the hose is stuck fast, the best course is often to cut it off using a sharp knife, but again be careful not to damage the stubs.
6 Before fitting the new hose, smear the stubs with washing-up liquid or a suitable rubber lubricant to aid fitting. Do not use oil or grease, which may attack the rubber.
7 Fit the hose clips over the ends of the hose, then fit the hose over its stubs. Work the hose into position. When satisfied, locate and tighten the hose clips.
8 Refill the cooling system as described in Chapter 1. Run the engine, and check that there are no leaks.
9 Recheck the tightness of the hose clips on any new hoses after a few hundred miles.
10 Top-up the coolant level, if necessary.

3 Radiator - removal, inspection and refitting

Removal

Note: *If leakage is the reason for removing the radiator, bear in mind that minor leaks can often be cured using a proprietary radiator sealing product, with the radiator in situ.*
1 Disconnect the battery negative lead.
Caution: If the radio/cassette in your vehicle is equipped with an anti-theft system, make sure you have the correct activation code before disconnecting the battery.
2 Unplug the electrical wiring from the auxiliary cooling fan at the connector - see Section 6 for details, and note that on models with air conditioning, there are two fans.
3 At the heater control panel, set the temperature control lever to the 'HOT' position, then drain the cooling system as described in Chapter 1.
4 Slacken the clips and disconnect the top, bottom and overflow coolant hoses from the radiator **(see illustration)**.
5 On automatic transmission models position a suitable container beneath the radiator, then identify the transmission fluid cooler hose locations on the radiator and disconnect them. Tape over or plug them to prevent entry of dust and dirt.

3.4 Top hose connection to the radiator

3.6 On early models, the radiator mounting bolts are located behind the radiator grille

6 On early models, remove the radiator grille as described in Chapter 11 then support the radiator and unscrew the upper and lower mounting bolts gaining access from the front of the vehicle. Carefully lift the radiator from the engine compartment complete with the cooling fan(s) and motor(s) **(see illustration)**.

7 On later models, unbolt the upper mounting brackets from the engine compartment front crossmember, and remove the brackets from the stubs on the top of the radiator. Carefully tilt the radiator back towards the engine, then lift it from the lower mounting brackets, complete with the cooling fan(s) and motor(s) **(see illustrations)**.

8 If necessary, remove the fan(s) from the radiator as described in Section 5. On later models, the lower mounting brackets may also be unbolted from the front valance at this stage if required.

Inspection

9 If the radiator has been removed due to suspected blockage, it may be flushed out as described in the coolant renewal procedure (see Chapter 1).

10 Leaves, dust and insects lodged between the cooling fins will impede the air flow through the radiator and reduce its cooling efficiency. Clean out all traces of dirt and debris using a soft brush or a compressed air supply. Note that the cooling fins are quite fragile and can easily be damaged by rough treatment.

 Warning: Eye protection should be worn, if compressed air is used to clean the radiator. Be careful, as the edges of the cooling fins are sharp enough to cause injury.

11 If necessary, a radiator specialist can perform a "flow test" on the radiator, to establish whether an internal blockage exists.

12 A leaking radiator must be referred to a specialist for permanent repair. Do not attempt to weld or solder a leaking radiator.

Note: *In an emergency, minor leaks from the radiator can often be cured by using a suitable radiator sealing product, in accordance with its manufacturer's instructions, with the radiator in situ.*

13 Inspect the radiator mounting brackets and/or bolts. Renew them if necessary.

Refitting

14 Refitting is a reversal of removal. On completion, refill the cooling system as described in Chapter 1. Where necessary, check the automatic transmission fluid level as described in Chapter 1.

4 Thermostat - removal, testing and refitting

1 The thermostat housing is integral with the inlet manifold and is located at the right hand end of the manifold casting.

3.7a Radiator upper mounting bracket . . .

Removal

2 Refer to Chapter 1 and drain approximately one third of the coolant from the cooling system. Provided that the coolant is in good condition (free from corrosion deposits) it can be retained and re-used later.

3 Slacken the clip and detach the coolant hose from the thermostat housing cover.

4 Unscrew the securing bolts, and remove the cover from the thermostat housing. If it sticks, tap it *gently* with a soft-faced mallet, first on one side and then the other to free it - **do not** lever between the mating faces. Recover the old gasket **(see illustration)**.

5 Lift the thermostat from its housing **(see illustration)**.

Testing

6 A rough test of the thermostat may be made by suspending it with a piece of string in a container full of water. Heat the water to bring it to the boil and observe the movement of the thermostat valve.

7 As a rough guide, the thermostat valve must be fully open by the time the water boils. If a thermometer is available, the opening temperature of the thermostat may be determined more precisely. With the valve fully open, measure the valve lift with a ruler. Compare the opening temperature and valve lift figures with those given in the *Specifications*. Renew the thermostat if its operation is suspect.

8 Remove the thermostat from the water, allow it to cool and check that the valve fully closes. Renew the thermostat if the valve fails to close completely.

4.4 Thermostat housing cover retaining bolts

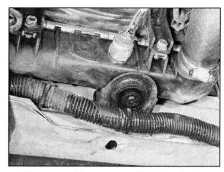

3.7b . . . and lower mounting bracket on later models

Refitting

9 Ensure that the thermostat housing and cover mating surfaces are completely clean and free from all traces of the old gasket.

10 Locate the thermostat into its housing, observing the correct orientation - the compression spring side of the thermostat must face downwards. Note that the bottom of the thermostat will touch the rib inside the inlet manifold if it is incorrectly orientated.

11 Lay a new gasket in position on the inlet manifold. Fit the thermostat housing cover in position, then insert the retaining bolts, and tighten to the specified torque.

Caution: Take care to avoid over-tightening the retaining bolts, as the alloy casting could easily be damaged.

12 Refit the coolant hose to the thermostat housing cover and tighten the hose clip securely.

13 Refill the cooling system as described in Chapter 1.

5 Auxiliary cooling fan - removal and refitting

Removal

1 Drain the cooling system, with reference to Chapter 1.

2 Refer to Section 3 and remove the radiator/cooling fan assembly.

3 Remove the securing bolts, then lift the cooling fan and shroud assembly away from the radiator **(see illustration)**.

4.5 Lifting the thermostat from its housing

5.3 Auxiliary cooling fan mounting bolts

6.7 Cooling fan switch wiring connector

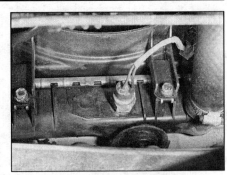

6.8 Cooling fan switch in the bottom of the radiator

4 Slacken and withdraw the nut from the end of the motor shaft, to release the fan blades.

5 Unscrew the mounting bolts, then remove the fan motor from the shroud. Remove the screws and detach the wiring clips from the shroud support struts.

Refitting

6 Refitting is reversal of removal with reference to Section 3. On completion, refill the cooling system, as described in Chapter 1.

6 Cooling fan switch - testing, removal and refitting

Testing

1 The switch is threaded into the lower tank of the radiator. On early models it is on the left-hand side and on later models it is on the right-hand side.

2 If the motor does not operate at the specified cut-in temperature, unplug the motor connector and use a bridging wire to connect the two wire terminals together. If the motor runs with the ignition switched on, the switch is probably faulty. To confirm this, connect an ohmmeter across the switch terminals and check for continuity with the coolant at the cut-in temperature.

3 To test the switch comprehensively, remove it from the radiator and check that the switching action occurs at the correct temperature, as follows. Connect a continuity tester or ohmmeter across the switch terminals. Heat the sensor in a container of water, whilst monitoring the temperature of the water with a thermometer.

4 There should only be continuity between the switch terminals when the cooling fan cut-in temperature is reached (see *Specifications*). If the switch operates at a much lower temperature, or fails to operate at all, it must be renewed.

Removal

5 Disconnect the battery negative lead.
Caution: If the radio/cassette in your vehicle is equipped with an anti-theft system, make sure you have the correct activation code before disconnecting the battery.

6 Ensure that the engine has cooled completely, then drain the cooling system, with reference to Chapter 1.

7 Disconnect the cooling fan switch wiring at the connector **(see illustration)**.

8 Carefully unscrew and remove the switch from the radiator **(see illustration)**.

Refitting

9 Refitting is a reversal of removal, but clean the switch threads thoroughly and coat them with sealing compound before inserting and tightening the switch. Refill the cooling system as described in Chapter 1. On completion, start the engine and run it until it reaches its normal operating temperature. Allow the engine to idle and verify that the cooling fan cuts in and out correctly, as the coolant temperature rises and falls.

7 Coolant pump - removal, inspection and refitting

Note: *The coolant pump body incorporates a "weep" hole for the escape of coolant passing the internal seal. If coolant is leaking from the left-hand end of the engine, check this hole for leakage and renew the pump as necessary.*

Removal

1 Disconnect the battery negative lead.
Caution: If the radio/cassette in your vehicle

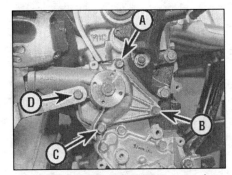

7.8 Unscrew the coolant pump securing bolts (arrowed)

A 28 mm	C 28 mm
B 28 mm	D 65 mm

is equipped with an anti-theft system, make sure you have the correct activation code before disconnecting the battery.

2 Drain the cooling system as described in Chapter 1.

3 Remove the left-hand engine mounting as described in Chapter 2A.

4 On models with power steering, refer to Chapter 10 and remove the power steering pump drivebelt from the outer coolant pump pulley.

5 Relieve the tension on the coolant pump/alternator drivebelt as follows. Slacken the alternator lower mounting bolt, then slacken the alternator tensioning lockbolt (refer to Chapter 5 for details). Turn the tensioning bolt anticlockwise until the belt becomes loose, then remove the belt from the coolant pump pulley. **Note:** *Some early models may not be fitted with an alternator tensioning bolt, in which case it will be necessary to swivel the alternator towards the engine by hand to remove the drivebelt.*

6 Counterhold the coolant pump pulley, then unscrew the securing bolts, and remove the pulley from the pump shaft. **Note:** *This is most easily achieved by wrapping an old drivebelt (or a length of old rubber hose) tightly around the pulley, to act as a strap wrench. Alternatively, a screwdriver can be braced between two of the pulley bolts, whilst the others are slackened.* On models with power steering, remove the additional pulley from the coolant pump.

7 Remove the timing belt and tensioner pulley as described in Chapter 2A.

8 Unscrew the coolant pump securing bolts - note the fitted position of each bolt, as some are of different lengths. Recover the alternator adjustment link bracket from the front bolt **(see illustration)**.

9 Withdraw the coolant pump from the cylinder block and remove the gasket. If the pump sticks to the block, tap on the upper and lower surfaces of the pump casting *gently*, using a soft-faced mallet, to free it. **Do not** lever between the pump and cylinder block mating faces. As the pump is withdrawn, release it from the water inlet pipe on its rear face and recover the O-ring seal. Note that a new O-ring must be used on refitting **(see illustration)**.

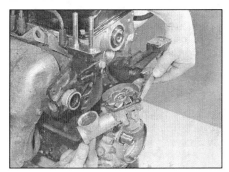

7.9 Removing the coolant pump from the cylinder block

7.15 Fit a new O-ring seal to the end of the water inlet pipe

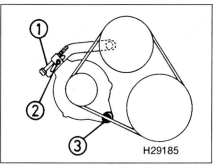

H29185

7.20 Coolant pump/alternator drivebelt tensioning

1 Adjuster bolt
2 Lock bolt
3 Lower mounting/pivot bolt

Inspection

10 Examine the pump body and impeller for signs of excessive corrosion, or damage.
11 Turn the impeller and check its rotation. Note that a certain amount of stiffness is to be expected, however, if the shaft is difficult to turn, or feels rough in rotation, it should be renewed.
12 Grasp the impeller and attempt to slide the pump shaft backwards and forwards in its bushing. If excessive end play is evident, the pump must be renewed. Similarly, if the shaft spins easily, with little or no resistance, this indicates that the bearings and seal are worn. If this is case, then the pump must be renewed.
13 No spare components are available; the coolant pump can only be renewed as a complete assembly.

Refitting

14 Commence refitting by thoroughly cleaning the mating faces of the pump and cylinder block, to remove all traces of old gasket material.
15 Fit a new O-ring seal to the end of the water inlet pipe and lubricate it with clean water **(see illustration)**.
16 Locate a new gasket on the coolant pump and hold it in place by temporarily inserting two of the mounting bolts through the pump body.
17 Fit the coolant pump to the cylinder block and at the same time locate it on the water inlet pipe taking care not to displace the O-ring seal. Insert the mounting bolts and progressively tighten them to the specified torque. **Note:** *The bolts are of different lengths - ensure that they are fitted in the correct positions and that the alternator adjustment link bracket is in position on the front bolt.* When locating the pump on the inlet pipe, hold the pipe at the front of the engine to ensure the pipe enters the pump fully.
18 Refit the timing belt and tensioner as described in Chapter 2A.
19 Refit the pump pulley(s) and tighten the bolts to the specified torque while counterholding the pulley using the method described in paragraph 6.
20 Refit and tension the coolant pump/ alternator and power steering pump drivebelts with reference to Chapter 1 **(see illustration)**.

21 Refit the left-hand engine mounting as described in Chapter 2A.
22 Reconnect the battery negative lead.
23 Refill the cooling system, as described in Chapter 1.

8 Temperature gauge coolant sensor - testing, removal and refitting

Testing

1 The temperature gauge coolant sensor is threaded into the right-hand end of the inlet manifold. On early models the sensor is located in the bottom of the inlet manifold, behind the distributor **(see illustration)**. On later models, the sensor is located nearest to the thermostat on the MPi models and nearest to the cylinder head on carburettor models.
2 Run the engine until it reaches normal operating temperature. Switch off the engine and turn the ignition switch to the 'Off' position.
3 Unplug the wiring from the sensor terminal, and connect the probes of an ohmmeter between the sensor terminal and a good earth point on the engine.
4 The resistance of the sensor should be as given in the *Specifications* with the coolant at the specified temperature. If the tester indicates a much different figure, then the sensor is faulty and must be renewed. Note that a sensor which reads open circuit or

8.1 Temperature gauge sensor located in the bottom of the inlet manifold (distributor removed)

short circuit will give a permanent 'fully hot' or 'fully cold' reading on the gauge, with the ignition switched on.

Removal

5 Ensure that the engine has cooled completely, then drain the cooling system, with reference to Chapter 1.
6 Disconnect the wiring plug from the coolant sensor.
7 Unscrew and remove the sensor from the inlet manifold. Where applicable, recover the sealing ring.

Refitting

8 Refitting is a reversal of removal, noting the following points:
  a) *If the sensor was originally fitted using sealing compound (visible as coloured deposits on the switch threads), clean the switch threads thoroughly, and coat them with fresh sealing compound.*
  b) *Where applicable, use a new sealing ring.*
  c) *Refill the cooling system, as described in Chapter 1.*

9 Heater/ventilation components - removal and refitting

Heater control unit

Removal

1 Disconnect the battery negative lead.
Caution: If the radio/cassette in your vehicle is equipped with an anti-theft system, make sure you have the correct activation code before disconnecting the battery.
2 Remove the glovebox and the trim panels on either side of the console beneath the facia as described in Chapter 11.
3 On later models, remove the ashtray then unscrew and remove the retaining screws and carefully withdraw the surround from the facia. Disconnect the wiring from the surround.
4 On early models, prise off the radio/ cassette cover then remove the screws and prise off the surround from the facia.

9.6 Heater control unit on the facia

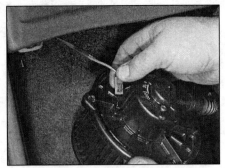

9.24 Heater blower motor wiring

5 On the lever-type heater, disconnect the control cables at the heater by releasing the clamps and separating the cables from the pins on the operating levers. Note the positions of the cables to ensure correct refitting.

6 Unscrew the control unit mounting screws and carefully withdraw the unit from the facia together with the control cables. Disconnect the wiring from the blower motor control and temperature control. On the vacuum-type heater, disconnect the vacuum motor wiring and vacuum lines (see illustration).

Refitting

7 Refitting is a reversal of removal, but where applicable on the lever-type heater, adjust the control cables so that the relevant controls operate correctly. This is best achieved by moving the relevant heater flap fully in one direction, then moving the control fully in the same direction and refitting the clamp.

Complete heater assembly

Note: This Section does not apply to models fitted with air conditioning, where removal of the cooling unit entails disconnection of refrigerant fluid pipes. This task requires access to specialist equipment (refer to the precautions given in Section 11) and should, therefore, be entrusted to a Hyundai dealer, or an air conditioning specialist.

Removal

Note: This is an involved procedure, and it is recommended that the following Section is read through thoroughly before commencing work. Plenty of time should be allowed to complete the operation. During dismantling,

make notes on the routing of all wiring and cables, and the locations of all fixings, to aid correct reassembly.

8 Disconnect the battery negative lead.
Caution: If the radio/cassette in your vehicle is equipped with an anti-theft system, make sure you have the correct activation code before disconnecting the battery.

9 Set the heater control to 'HOT', then drain the cooling system as described in Chapter 1.

10 Refer to Chapter 11 and remove the facia assembly from the vehicle bulkhead together with the glovebox and lower crashpad. Rest the assembly on the front seats.

11 Working in the engine compartment, slacken the clips and detach the hoses from the heater matrix tubes at the bulkhead. Identify each hose for position to ensure correct refitting.

12 Loosen the heating duct mounting screws and remove the lower heating ducts.

13 As applicable, disconnect the heater control cables or vacuum lines from the heater.

14 Unscrew the mounting bolts and withdraw the heater assembly from inside the vehicle. Be prepared for some loss of coolant by placing cloth rags in the front footwells, but tilt the assembly so that the matrix tubes are uppermost as a precaution.

15 To remove the heater matrix core, refer to the information given in the next sub-section.

Refitting

16 Refit the heater assembly by following the removal procedure in reverse, noting the following points:

a) Make sure that all wiring, cables and vacuum lines are routed as noted during dismantling.
b) Make sure that the air ducting is securely reconnected.
c) Reconnect the heater panel control cables, with reference to the previous sub-section.
d) Refit the facia components with reference to Chapter 11.
e) On completion, refill the cooling system as described in Chapter 1.

Heater matrix

Removal

17 Remove the complete heater assembly, as described in the previous sub-section.

18 On early models, unbolt the inlet and outlet tubes and brackets and recover the sealing O-rings. Unscrew the retaining screws and withdraw the matrix from the side of the heater assembly.

19 On later models, remove the screws and clips and separate the two halves of the heater assembly. Withdraw the matrix from its location at the front of the heater. Exercise caution, as the edges of the matrix core cooling fins are sharp enough to cause personal injury.

Refitting

20 Refitting is a reversal of removal; refit the heater assembly as described previously in this Section.

Heater blower motor

Removal

21 Disconnect the battery negative lead.
Caution: If the radio/cassette in your vehicle is equipped with an anti-theft system, make sure you have the correct activation code before disconnecting the battery.

22 With reference to Chapter 11, remove the glovebox from the passenger side of the facia.

23 Remove the lower facia panel below the glovebox location with reference to Chapter 11.

24 Unplug the wiring from the bottom of the blower motor (see illustration).

25 Disconnect the motor cooling duct, then unscrew the mounting screws and lower the heater blower motor assembly from the air duct housing. Where applicable, disconnect the vacuum line (see illustrations).

9.25a Disconnect the motor cooling duct . . .

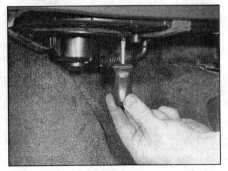

9.25b . . . then unscrew the mounting screws . . .

9.25c . . . and withdraw the motor

26 If necessary, release the clip and detach the fan from the motor shaft **(see illustration)**.

Refitting

27 Refitting is a reversal of removal, but reconnect the battery and check the operation of the blower motor before refitting the glovebox.

Blower motor resistor

Removal

28 It is located on the top of the air duct housing above the heater blower motor. For access to the resistor, remove the glovebox as described in Chapter 11.

29 With the ignition switched off, disconnect the wiring then unscrew the mounting screws and withdraw the resistor **(see illustrations)**.

Refitting

30 Refitting is a reversal of removal.

---

10 Air conditioning system -
general information and precautions

General information

Air conditioning is fitted as an optional extra on certain models. The function of the air conditioning system is to enable air entering the passenger compartment via the heater/ventilation ducts to be cooled and dehumidified. This allows the interior temperature to be controlled at a comfortable level, whilst driving in high ambient temperatures. In addition, the dehumidified air aids rapid windscreen demisting.

The cooling side of the system works in the same way as a domestic refrigerator. Refrigerant gas is drawn into a belt-driven compressor where the increase in pressure

9.26 The heater blower motor fan is secured by a clip to the shaft

causes the refrigerant gas to turn to liquid. It then passes through a condenser, mounted adjacent to the radiator, where it is cooled. The liquid then passes through an expansion valve to an evaporator, where it changes from liquid under high pressure to gas under low pressure. This change of state is accompanied by a drop in temperature, which cools the evaporator and the air passing through it. The refrigerant returns to the compressor, and the cycle begins again.

Fresh air is drawn from outside the vehicle, through the evaporator. The cooled air then passes to the air distribution housing where it is mixed, if required, with hot air blown through the heater matrix to achieve the desired temperature in the passenger compartment.

The heating side of the system works in the same way as that found on models without air conditioning.

The air conditioning system is electronically-controlled. The diagnosis of problems related to the control system requires access to dedicated test equipment and so should be referred to a Hyundai dealer or air conditioning specialist.

9.29a Disconnect the wiring . . .

Precautions

Special precautions must be observed, when working on any part of the air conditioning system and its associated components, as described in the following Warning.

⚠️ *Warning: The refrigeration circuit contains a Freon-based liquid refrigerant. The refrigerant is potentially very dangerous, and should only be handled by qualified persons. If it is splashed onto the skin, it can cause severe frostbite. It is not actually poisonous, but in the presence of a naked flame (such as a lighted cigarette), it forms a poisonous gas. The air conditioning refrigerant system is sealed at the factory. Uncontrolled discharging of the refrigerant is dangerous, as well as being extremely damaging to the environment. For all these reasons, it is dangerous and irresponsible to disconnect any part of the system without specialist knowledge and equipment.*
Caution: Do not operate the air conditioning system if it is known to be short of refrigerant, as this may damage the compressor.

9.29b . . . then unscrew the mounting screws . . .

9.29c . . . and withdraw the heater blower motor resistor

11 Air conditioning system components - removal and refitting

⚠️ *Warning: Do not attempt to open the refrigerant circuit. Refer to the precautions given in Section 10.*

The only operation which can be carried out easily without discharging the refrigerant is the renewal of the compressor drivebelt - this procedure is described in Chapter 1. All other operations must be referred to a Hyundai dealer or an air conditioning specialist.

If necessary for access to other components, the compressor can easily be unbolted and moved aside, *without disconnecting its flexible hoses*, after removing the drivebelt.

Chapter 4 Part A:
Fuel and exhaust systems - carburettor engines

Contents

Accelerator cable - removal, refitting and adjustment 7
Accelerator pedal - removal and refitting 8
Air cleaner air temperature control system - general information . . . 3
Air cleaner assembly - removal and refitting 2
Air cleaner filter element renewal . . . . .See Chapter 1
Carburettor - fault diagnosis, overhaul and adjustments 13
Carburettor - general information 11
Carburettor - removal and refitting 12
Choke cable - removal, refitting and adjustment 9
Exhaust manifold - removal and refitting 15
Exhaust system - general information, removal and refitting 16

Exhaust system check . . . . .See Chapter 1
Fuel filter - renewal . . . . .See Chapter 1
Fuel gauge sender unit - removal and refitting 5
Fuel pump - testing, removal and refitting 4
Fuel tank - removal and refitting 6
General fuel system checks .See Chapter 1
General information and precautions 1
Idle speed and mixture adjustment . . . . .See Chapter 1
Inlet manifold - removal and refitting 14
Unleaded petrol - general information and usage 10

Degrees of difficulty

Easy, suitable for novice with little experience	**Fairly easy,** suitable for beginner with some experience	**Fairly difficult,** suitable for competent DIY mechanic	**Difficult,** suitable for experienced DIY mechanic	**Very difficult,** suitable for expert DIY or professional

Specifications

Fuel pump
Type . . . . Mechanical, driven by pushrod from eccentric on camshaft

Carburettor
Type . . . . Changwon or Aisan
Choke type . . . . Manual (Changwon) or Automatic (Aisan)

Changwon Carburettor (1985-1991) data	Primary	Secondary
Throttle valve diameter	28 mm	32 mm
Main jet	100	150
Idle jet	48	80
Idle air jet	80	120
Enrichment jet	55	
Float height setting (see text):		
Sight glass	± 1.0 mm	
Float rib to gasket face	22.0 mm	
Choke valve opening angle with throttle fully open . . .	30°	
Choke	Manual	
Idle speed:		
Manual transmission models	750 ± 30 rpm	
Automatic transmission models	850 ± 30 rpm	
Idle mixture CO content	1.5%	

Aisan FBC Carburettor (1991-on) data

	Primary	Secondary
Throttle bore	30 mm	32 mm
Main jet	83.8	145
Main air jet:		
First	80 (1.5 litre), 70 (1.3 litre)	70
Second	70	70
Pilot jet	46.3 (1.5 litre), 47.5 (1.3 litre)	70 (1.5 litre), 72.5 (1.3 litre)
Pilot air jet:		
First	120	100
Second	200	100
Main nozzle	2.6 mm	2.8 mm
Enrichment jet	50	
Slow air jet	110	
SCSV resistance	48 to 60 ohms	
FBSV resistance	54 to 66 ohms	
Fast idle throttle opening:		
Manual transmission models	0.93 mm	
Automatic transmission models	1.02 mm	
Choke	Automatic	
Choke pull-down setting	1.9 to 2.1 mm	
Choke opener setting:		
1st stage	1.4 to 1.6 mm	
2nd stage	2.9 to 3.1 mm	
Fast idle speed:		
Manual transmission models	2800 rpm	
Automatic transmission models	2700 rpm	
Idle-up rpm	800 ± 50 rpm	
Air conditioning idle-up rpm	900 ± 50 rpm	
Idle speed	700 ± 50 rpm	
Idle mixture CO content	1.0 ± 0.5%	

Aisan CONV Carburettor (1991-on) data

	Primary	Secondary
Throttle bore	30 mm	32 mm
Main jet:		
1.3 litre engine	83.8	153.8
1.5 litre engine	85	155
Pilot jet:		
1.3 litre engine	51.3	57.5
1.5 litre engine	51.3	57.5
Enrichment jet:		
1.3 litre engine	60	
1.5 litre engine	60	
Choke	Automatic	
Dashpot adjustment engine speed	1800 rpm	
Fast idle setting	0.93 mm	
Idle speed:		
1.3 and 1.5 litre engines with manual transmission	800 ± 30 rpm	
1.5 litre engine with automatic transmission	850 ± 30 rpm	
Idle mixture CO content	1.0 ± 0.25%	

Recommended fuel

Minimum octane rating:	
Models without a catalytic converter	95 RON unleaded (UK unleaded premium) or 97 RON leaded (UK "4-star")
Models with a catalytic converter	95 RON unleaded (UK unleaded premium) **only**

Torque wrench settings

	Nm	lbf ft
Carburettor mounting nuts/bolts	18	13
Oxygen sensor	45	33
Fuel tank drain plug	90	66
Fuel pump	12	9
Exhaust manifold	18	13
Inlet manifold support bracket	22	16
Hot-air shroud to exhaust manifold	30	22
Front exhaust downpipe bracket bolt	35	26
Front pipe to catalytic converter	50	37
Front pipe to tailpipe	35	26
Tailpipe to catalytic converter	35	26
Tailpipe mounting bolt	13	10

1 General information and precautions

The fuel system consists of a fuel tank mounted under the rear of the car, a mechanical fuel pump, and a carburettor. The fuel pump is operated by pushrod from an eccentric on the camshaft, and is mounted on the rear of the cylinder head. The air cleaner contains a disposable paper filter element, and incorporates a flap valve air temperature control system; this allows cold air from the outside of the car, and warm air from the exhaust manifold, to enter the air cleaner in the correct proportions.

The fuel pump lifts fuel from the fuel tank via a filter, which is mounted on the engine compartment bulkhead, and supplies it to the carburettor. Excess fuel is returned from the pump to the fuel tank.

A fixed twin-venturi Changwon or Aisan carburettor is fitted. Mixture enrichment for cold starting is controlled by a manual choke on the Changwon carburettor and by an automatic choke on the Aisan carburettor. The manual choke incorporates a bi-metallic unload system which gradually opens the choke valve as the engine temperature increases.

On non-catalytic converter engines with the Changwon and conventional (CONV) Aisan carburettor, the exhaust system consists of two sections; the front pipe section, incorporating the front silencer box, and the tailpipe section incorporating the main silencer box. Where the Aisan feedback (FBC) carburettor is fitted, the exhaust system consists of three sections; the front pipe, the catalytic converter, and the tailpipe section which incorporates the main silencer box. The system is suspended throughout its entire length by rubber mountings.

 Warning: Many of the procedures in this Chapter require the removal of fuel lines and connections, which may result in some fuel spillage. Before carrying out any operation on the fuel system, refer to the precautions given in "Safety first!" at the beginning of this manual, and follow them implicitly. Petrol is a highly-dangerous and volatile liquid, and the precautions necessary when handling it cannot be overstressed.

2 Air cleaner assembly - removal and refitting

Removal

1 Disconnect the breather hose from the air cleaner housing cover on early models, or from the bottom air cleaner housing on later models.

2 Unscrew the wing nut then release the retaining clips and remove the air cleaner housing cover and filter element **(see illustration)**.

3 On later models, release the retaining clip and detach the inlet duct from the end of the air cleaner housing body or from the side and front of the engine compartment **(see illustration)**.

4 Slacken and remove the mounting nuts and washers and lift the air cleaner housing body away from the carburettor, disconnecting the vacuum hose as it becomes accessible. Recover the warm air duct from between the air cleaner and exhaust manifold.

5 Recover the spacers from the housing mounting rubbers and remove the sealing ring from the top of the carburettor. Inspect the mounting rubbers and sealing ring for signs of damage or deterioration and renew if needed.

Refitting

6 Refitting is a reversal of the removal procedure, ensuring that all the air cleaner housing seals are air tight and that all hoses are correctly and securely reconnected.

3 Air cleaner air temperature control system - general information

Early models (wax-type)

1 On early models the system is controlled by a wax-filled pellet in the air cleaner inlet duct. When the engine is cold the pellet holds a flap across the inlet duct so that hot air from the inlet manifold shroud is drawn into the engine. When the engine warms up, the pellet opens the flap to admit air from the front of the vehicle only.

2 To check the system, allow the engine to cool down completely, then check that the flap in the air cleaner inlet duct is positioned to admit hot air from the exhaust manifold shroud. Run the engine until it is at normal operating temperature, then check that the flap has moved to admit air from the main cold air inlet duct.

3 If the system does not operate correctly, check with your Hyundai dealer if individual components or the complete assembly are available.

Later models (vacuum-type)

4 On later models the system is controlled by a heat-sensitive vacuum switch in the air cleaner housing. When the engine is started from cold, the switch is open, allowing inlet manifold depression to act on the air temperature control valve diaphragm in the inlet duct. This vacuum causes the diaphragm to rise, drawing a flap valve across the cold-air inlet, thus allowing only (hot) air from the exhaust manifold shroud to enter the air cleaner. As the temperature of the air in the air cleaner rises, the wax capsule in the vacuum switch deforms and closes the switch, cutting off the vacuum supply to the air temperature control valve assembly. As the vacuum supply is cut, the flap is gradually lowered across the hot-air inlet until, when the engine is fully warmed-up (air cleaner temperature above 45°C), only cold air from the front of the car is entering the air cleaner.

5 To check the system, allow the engine to cool down completely, then slacken the retaining clip and disconnect the inlet duct from the air cleaner assembly; the flap valve in the duct should be seated across the hot-air inlet. Start the engine; the flap should immediately rise to close off the main cold air inlet, and should then lower steadily as the engine warms up, until it is eventually seated across the hot-air inlet again.

6 To check the vacuum switch, disconnect the vacuum pipe from the control valve when the engine is running, and place a finger over the pipe end. When the engine is cold (air cleaner temperature below 30°C), full inlet manifold vacuum should be present in the pipe, and when the engine is at normal operating temperature (air cleaner temperature above 45°C), there should be no vacuum in the pipe.

7 To check the air temperature control valve assembly, slacken the retaining clip and disconnect the inlet duct from the front of the valve assembly; the flap valve should be securely seated across the hot-air inlet. Disconnect the vacuum pipe, and suck hard at the control valve stub; the flap should rise to shut off the cold-air inlet.

8 If either component is faulty, it must be renewed. Check with your Hyundai dealer if individual components or the complete assembly are available.

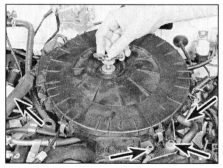

2.2 Unscrew the wing nut and release the air cleaner cover clips

2.3 Detaching the air cleaner duct from the side of the engine compartment

4.1 Check the fuel pump breather hole (arrowed) for signs of oil leakage

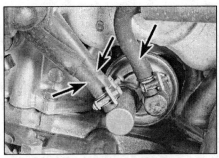

4.4 Working beneath the inlet manifold, disconnect the fuel inlet, outlet and return hoses from the fuel pump

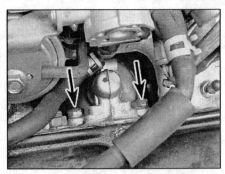

4.5 Fuel pump mounting bolts

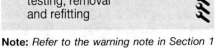

4 Fuel pump - testing, removal and refitting

Note: Refer to the warning note in Section 1 before proceeding.

Testing

1 To test the fuel pump on the engine, disconnect the outlet pipe which leads to the carburettor. Hold a wad of rag by the pump outlet while an assistant spins the engine on the starter. *Keep your hands away from the electric cooling fan.* Regular spurts of fuel should be ejected as the engine turns. Be careful not to spill fuel onto hot engine components. Check the fuel pump breather hole for signs of oil leakage; if evident renew the pump **(see illustration).**

2 The pump can also be tested by removing it. With the pump outlet pipe disconnected

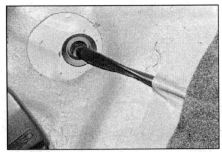

5.2 The wiring to the sender unit is located under the rear seat cushion

but the inlet pipe still connected, hold the wad of rag by the outlet. Operate the pump lever by hand, moving it in and out; if the pump is in a satisfactory condition, the lever should move and return smoothly, and a strong jet of fuel should be ejected.

Removal

3 Remove the air cleaner housing as described in Section 2. To gain access to the pump hoses from underneath, firmly apply the handbrake then jack up the front of the vehicle and support it on axle stands (see *"Jacking and Vehicle Support"*).

4 Identify the pump inlet, outlet and return hoses then slacken the retaining clips. Place wads of rag beneath the hose unions to catch any spilled fuel, then disconnect the hoses from the pump; plug the hose ends to minimise fuel loss **(see illustration).**

5 Slacken and remove the bolts securing the pump to the rear of the cylinder head. Remove the pump, along with its insulating spacer and gaskets, and withdraw the pump pushrod from the cylinder head. Discard the gaskets, new ones must be used on refitting **(see illustration).**

Refitting

6 Ensure that the pump, cylinder head and insulating spacer mating surfaces are clean and dry.

7 Insert the pushrod into the cylinder, then position a new gasket on each side of the spacer and refit the pump to the cylinder head. Refit the pump mounting bolts and tighten them to the specified torque setting. **Note:** *Where the*

pushrod is located on the apex of the camshaft eccentric, it will be difficult to insert and tighten the mounting bolts. Where this is the case, position the engine with No 1 cylinder piston at TDC (see Chapter 2A) before refitting the pump.

8 Reconnect the inlet, outlet and return hoses, and securely tighten their retaining clips. Refit the air cleaner housing (Section 2) and lower the vehicle to the ground.

5 Fuel gauge sender unit - removal and refitting

Note: Refer to the warning note in Section 1 before proceeding.

Removal

1 Disconnect the battery negative lead. *Caution: If the radio/cassette in your vehicle is equipped with an anti-theft system, make sure you have the correct activation code before disconnecting the battery.*

2 For access to the sender unit, remove the rear seat cushion as described in Chapter 11 on early models, or remove the spare wheel on later models. The wiring to the sender unit is located beneath the rear seat cushion **(see illustration).**

3 Remove the screws and lift the cover from the floor to expose the sender unit **(see illustrations).**

4 Disconnect the wiring from the sender unit, and tape it to the vehicle body to prevent it dropping through the hole **(see illustration).**

5.3a Unscrew the screws . . .

5.3b . . . and lift the cover to expose the sender unit (later models shown)

5.4 Showing the wiring to the sender unit (later models shown)

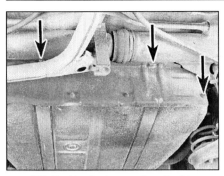

6.7 Fuel tank strap and protector mounting bolts

6.8 Location of the fuel tank straps in the underbody

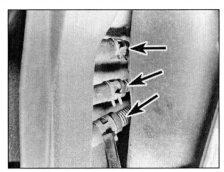

6.9a Fuel tank feed, return and breather hoses

5 Make alignment marks between the sender unit and tank then slacken and remove the retaining bolts securing the sender unit in position.
6 Carefully lift the sender unit from the top of the fuel tank, taking great care not to bend the sender unit float arm, or to spill fuel onto the interior of the vehicle. Recover the sender unit gasket and discard it - a new one must be used on refitting.

Refitting

7 Ensure that the sender unit and tank mating surfaces are clean and dry and fit a new gasket to the tank.
8 Manoeuvre the sender unit into position, taking great care not to damage the float arm, then refit the washers and retaining nuts tightening them securely.
9 Reconnect the wiring to the sender unit then refit the cover and tighten the screws.
10 Refit the spare wheel or rear seat cushion (as applicable) and reconnect the battery.

6 Fuel tank - removal and refitting

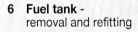

Note: *Refer to the warning note in Section 1 before proceeding.*

Removal

1 Before removing the fuel tank, all fuel must be drained from it. A drain plug is provided on the base of the tank for this operation. First, disconnect the battery negative lead.
Caution: If the radio/cassette in your vehicle is equipped with an anti-theft system, make sure you have the correct activation code before disconnecting the battery.
2 Chock the front wheels then jack up the rear of the vehicle and support it on axle stands (see "*Jacking and Vehicle Support*"). Remove the left-hand rear roadwheel.
3 Position a suitable container beneath the fuel tank and remove the filler cap. Unscrew and remove the drain plug and sealing washer and allow the tank contents to drain. Once the fuel tank is drained fit a new sealing washer to the drain plug then refit the plug and tighten it securely. Store the drained fuel safely in suitable containers.

4 Disconnect the wiring from the fuel gauge sender unit as described in Section 5.
5 Working at the left-hand side of the fuel tank, release the retaining clips then disconnect the filler neck vent pipe and main filler neck hose from the fuel tank/filler neck. Where necessary also disconnect the breather hose.
6 Place a trolley jack with an interposed block of wood beneath the tank, then raise the jack until it is supporting the weight of the tank.
7 Unscrew and remove the fuel tank strap bolts and, if equipped, the protector from the front of the tank (see illustration).
8 Swing the fuel tank retaining straps down until they are hanging out of the way (see illustration).
9 Lower the tank enough to access the fuel hoses at the top front of the tank. Identify each hose for position then disconnect them. Also disconnect the overfill limiter hoses and unbolt the limiter from the tank. Plug or tape over the hoses and tank tubes (see illustrations).
10 Lower the tank to the ground and withdraw it from under the vehicle.
11 Loosen the clips and remove the filler and vent hoses from the tank. If necessary, loosen the screws and withdraw the filter and pick-up pipe assembly together with the gasket and separate the filter. Note the location of the check valve in the vent hose.
12 If the tank is contaminated with sediment or water, remove the drain plug and swill the tank out with clean fuel. The tank is injection-moulded from a synthetic material - if

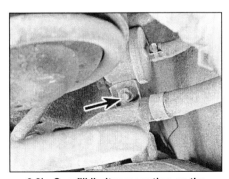

6.9b Overfill limiter mounting on the fuel tank

seriously damaged, it should be renewed. However, in certain cases, it may be possible to have small leaks or minor damage repaired. Seek the advice of a specialist before attempting to repair the fuel tank.

Refitting

13 Refitting is the reverse of the removal procedure, noting the following points:
 a) When fitting a new filter, make sure that it is held firmly by the retaining claws (see illustration).
 b) When lifting the tank back into position, take care to ensure that none of the hoses becomes trapped between the tank and vehicle body.
 c) Ensure that all pipes and hoses are correctly routed, and securely held in position with their retaining clips.
 d) On completion, refill the tank with a small amount of fuel, and check for signs of leakage prior to taking the vehicle out on the road.

7 Accelerator cable - removal, refitting and adjustment

Removal

1 Remove the air cleaner assembly as described in Section 2.
2 Loosen the cable adjusting nut half a turn and remove the outer cable from the support bracket (see illustration).

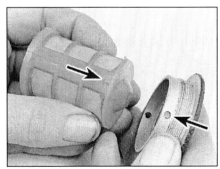

6.13 When fitting a new filter, engage the retaining claws in the holder (arrowed)

7.2 Accelerator cable adjusting nut on the support bracket

3 Release the inner cable from the carburettor throttle cam.
4 Working inside the vehicle, disconnect the inner cable from the top of the accelerator pedal.
5 Working in the engine compartment, unbolt the cable guide from the bulkhead **(see illustration)**.
6 Withdraw the cable through the bulkhead and release it from the clips in the engine compartment. Remove it from the vehicle.

Refitting

7 Refitting is a reversal of removal, but make sure that the cable run does not have sharp bends in it. Before refitting the air cleaner assembly adjust the free play as follows.

Adjustment

8 The accelerator cable must be adjusted so that there is a small amount of freeplay with the accelerator pedal released and the throttle cam against its stop on the carburettor. If adjustment is necessary, slacken the outer cable locknut then rotate the adjuster nut until only a small amount of freeplay is present in the inner cable. Once the cable is correctly adjusted, hold the adjuster nut stationary and securely tighten the locknut.
9 Have an assistant depress fully then release the accelerator pedal, and check that the throttle cam opens fully and returns smoothly to its stop. On models with automatic transmission, once the accelerator cable is correctly adjusted, check the kickdown cable adjustment as described in Chapter 7B.

8.5 Accelerator pedal bracket mounting bolts

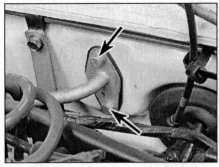

7.5 Accelerator cable guide mounting bolts on the bulkhead

8 Accelerator pedal -
removal and refitting

Removal

1 Reach up behind the facia and unhook the accelerator inner cable from the top of the pedal.
2 On automatic transmission models, disconnect the wiring from the accelerator switch then unscrew the nut and remove the switch from the bracket.
3 Using pliers unhook and remove the return spring from the upper end of the pedal.
4 Remove the split pin and outer washer then slide the pedal off from its mounting and remove the inner washer.
5 If necessary, the mounting bracket can be unbolted from the bulkhead **(see illustration)**.

Refitting

6 Refitting is a reversal of the removal procedure, applying a little multi-purpose grease to the pedal pivot point. To ensure a good seal from the engine compartment, apply a little sealant to the threads and heads of the mounting bracket bolts. On completion, adjust the accelerator cable as described in Section 7.

9 Choke cable -
removal, refitting and adjustment

Removal

1 Remove the air cleaner assembly as described in Section 2.
2 Unscrew the clamp bolt and release the choke outer cable from the support on the carburettor. **Note:** *On LHD models, the support also retains the heater hose.*
3 Unhook the inner cable from the choke lever.
4 Unscrew the knob from the end of the choke cable inside the vehicle.
5 Unscrew the nut and release the cable from the facia.
6 Disconnect the warning switch wiring from the end fitting.

7 Withdraw the cable through the bulkhead and remove it from inside the vehicle.

Refitting

8 Refitting is a reversal of removal, but make sure that the cable run does not have sharp bends in it and the bulkhead grommet is correctly fitted. Before refitting the air cleaner assembly adjust the free play as follows.

Adjustment

9 With the choke knob pushed in fully, check that there is approximately 2.0 to 3.0 mm free play before the choke lever on the carburettor moves. If adjustment is necessary, reposition the outer cable as required. Check that there is sufficient sliding resistance in the cable to keep it out in any position; if necessary the resistance can be adjusted by loosening or tightening the outer cable retaining nut at the facia.

10 Unleaded petrol -
general information and usage

Note: *The information given in this Chapter is correct at the time of writing. If updated information is thought to be required, check with a Hyundai dealer. If travelling abroad, consult one of the motoring organisations (or a similar authority) for advice on the fuel available.*

The fuel recommended is given in the *Specifications* of this Chapter, followed by the equivalent petrol currently on sale in the UK.

Both leaded and unleaded petrol can be used in models not fitted with a catalytic converter, however **only** unleaded petrol must be used in models with a catalytic converter.

11 Carburettor -
general information

The carburettor is of Changwon or Aisan manufacture and is a downdraught progressive twin venturi instrument, with a vacuum-controlled secondary throttle. The choke control is either manual on the Changwon carburettor or automatic on the Aisan carburettor. The manual choke is applied by the choke cable on the facia, however the system incorporates a bi-metallic unloader spring which gradually opens the choke valve as the temperature of the engine increases. The automatic choke utilises an electrically heated bi-metallic spring; when the engine is started from cold, the spring is electrically heated and gradually opens the choke valve until it is fully open.

During idling fuel from the float chamber passes into the idle channel through a metered idle jet. Here it is mixed with a small amount of air from a calibrated air bleed. The resulting mixture is drawn through a channel, to be discharged from the idle orifice under the primary throttle valve. On the FBC carburettor the mixture and idle speed is continuously adjusted by two solenoids controlled by the ECU. On the conventional carburettor a tapered mixture screw provides adjustment for the idle mixture, and a throttle valve adjustment screw provides adjustment for the idle speed.

12 Carburettor - removal and refitting

Note: *Refer to the warning note in Section 1 before proceeding.*

Removal

1 Disconnect the battery negative lead.
Caution: If the radio/cassette in your vehicle is equipped with an anti-theft system, make sure you have the correct activation code before disconnecting the battery.
2 Remove the air cleaner assembly as described in Section 2.
3 On engines fitted with the later conventional (CONV) carburettor, drain the cooling system as described in Chapter 1.
4 Loosen the accelerator cable adjusting nut half a turn and remove the outer cable from the support bracket. Disconnect the inner cable from the carburettor throttle cam.
5 On automatic transmission models, disconnect the kickdown cable. Refer to Chapter 7B if necessary.
6 On engines fitted with the early conventional carburettor, disconnect the choke cable by unscrewing the clamp bolt and disconnecting the cable from the choke lever.
7 Disconnect the wiring from the carburettor idle cut-off solenoid or solenoid valves and throttle position sensor (as applicable).
8 Remove and refit the fuel tank filler cap to relieve any pressure in the tank.
9 Release the retaining clip, and disconnect the fuel feed hose from the carburettor. Place wads of rag around the union to catch any spilled fuel, and plug the hose as soon as it is disconnected, to minimise fuel loss.
10 Make a note of the correct fitted positions of the vacuum, coolant and breather hoses to ensure that they are correctly positioned on refitting, then release the retaining clips (where fitted) and disconnect them from the carburettor.
11 Unscrew the four nuts or bolts (as applicable) securing the carburettor to the inlet manifold. Withdraw the carburettor assembly from the engine compartment and recover the insulating spacer and gaskets. Discard the gaskets; new ones must be used on refitting. Plug the inlet manifold port with a wad of clean cloth, to prevent the possible entry of foreign matter.

Refitting

12 Refitting is the reverse of the removal procedure, noting the following points:
  a) *Ensure that the carburettor, inlet manifold and insulating spacer sealing faces are clean and flat.*
  b) *Position a gasket on each side of the insulating spacer then refit the carburettor and tighten its mounting bolts progressively to the specified torque.*
  c) *Use the notes made on dismantling to ensure that all hoses are refitted to their original positions and, where necessary, are securely held by their retaining clips.*
  d) *Refit and adjust the accelerator and choke cables as described in Sections 7 and 9.*
  e) *On automatic transmission models refit and if necessary adjust the kickdown cable with reference to Chapter 7B.*
  f) *Refit the air cleaner as described in Section 2.*
  g) *On engines fitted with the later conventional carburettor, refill the cooling system as described in Chapter 1.*
  h) *On completion, check and adjust (where applicable) the idle speed and mixture settings as described in Chapter 1.*

13 Carburettor - fault diagnosis, overhaul and adjustments

Fault diagnosis

1 If a carburettor fault is suspected, always check first that the ignition timing is correctly set, that the spark plugs are in good condition and correctly gapped, that the accelerator cable is correctly adjusted, and that the air cleaner filter element is clean; refer to the relevant Sections of Chapter 1, Chapter 5 or this Chapter. If the engine is running very roughly, first check the valve clearances as described in Chapter 1, then check the compression pressures as described in Chapter 2A. On the FBC carburettor check that all wiring and hoses are correctly fitted.
2 If careful checking of all the above produces no improvement, the carburettor must be removed for cleaning and overhaul.
3 Prior to overhaul, check the availability of component parts before starting work; note that most sealing washers, screws and gaskets are available in kits, as are some of the major sub-assemblies. In most cases, it will be sufficient to dismantle the carburettor and to clean the jets and passages. The main area which causes problems on a well worn carburettor is the throttle valve spindle; if this is worn to the extent that there is excessive movement in the carburettor body, check if it is possible to rebush the spindle. Where this is not possible, it will usually be better to obtain another carburettor rather than overhaul the rest of the carburettor.

Overhaul

Note: *Refer to the warning note in Section 1 before proceeding.*

4 Once its determined that the carburettor requires an overhaul, several options are available. If you are carrying out the overhaul yourself, first obtain an overhaul kit which will include all necessary gaskets, certain internal parts, and instructions. You will also require some special solvent and a means of blowing out the internal passages of the carburettor with air.
5 An alternative is to obtain a new or overhauled carburettor from a carburettor specialist. Make sure the exchange carburettor is identical to the original. A tag is usually attached to the top of the carburettor or a number is stamped on the float bowl.
6 After removing the carburettor, allow enough time to dismantle it carefully noting the location of each component. Note the number of turns necessary to remove any adjustment screws so that they can be set approximately on reassembly. Soak all the parts in the cleaning solvent before blowing them dry. Clean the jets, carburettor body assemblies, float chamber and internal drillings. An air line may be used to clear the internal passages once the carburettor is fully dismantled. Use a straight edge to check all carburettor body assembly mating surfaces for distortion.
7 Carefully reassemble the carburettor using the new gaskets and parts supplied with the overhaul kit and making the adjustments as described in the following paragraphs.
8 Where an idle cut-off solenoid is fitted, it may be tested after removal as follows. Connect a 12-volt battery to it (positive terminal to the solenoid terminal, negative terminal to the solenoid body), and check that the plunger is retracted fully into the body. Disconnect the battery, and check that the plunger is pushed out by spring pressure. If the valve does not perform as expected, and cleaning does not improve the situation, the solenoid valve must be renewed.
9 To test the slow-cut solenoid and feedback solenoid valves (SCSV and FBSV), apply 12 volts to the valve wiring and check that it is heard to click. Using an ohmmeter check that there is no continuity between the two wires and the valve body, then connect an ohmmeter to the two wires and check that the internal resistance of the valve is as given in the *Specifications*.

Adjustments

Float height setting

10 Invert the carburettor body, so the float is at the top resting on the needle valve. With the gasket removed, use a steel rule or vernier calipers to check the distance between the joint face of the body and the mid-point of the nearest rib on the float. If adjustment is necessary, alter the clearance by carefully bending the float stopper tang until the clearance is as specified.

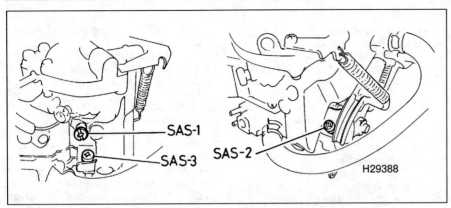

13.19 Speed adjustment screw (SAS) locations on the carburettor

Throttle position sensor (TPS)

11 This adjustment must be made with the carburettor refitted on the inlet manifold and all connections in place. First disconnect the accelerator cable from the carburettor.

12 Back off the two adjustment screws (throttle stop and fast idle) so that the throttle valve is completely closed but note the number of turns on each screw so that the adjustment can be reset again.

13 Connect a digital voltmeter between terminals 2 and 3 on the sensor.

14 Switch on the ignition (but do not start the engine) and check that 250 mV is measured on the voltmeter. If not, loosen the sensor mounting screws and turn it as required - turning it clockwise increases the voltage. Tighten the screws on completion.

15 Disconnect the voltmeter and reset the adjustment screws to their original setting. Reconnect the accelerator cable with reference to Section 7.

Dashpot

16 Start the engine and run it to normal operating temperature. Turn off all electrical components and carry out the adjustment with the cooling fan stopped. If power steering is fitted, make sure that the steering is pointing straight ahead.

17 With the engine idling, open the throttle valve the full stroke of the dashpot rod until the free lever contacts the SAS-3 screw.

18 Close the throttle valve until the SAS-2 contacts the free lever and note the specified engine idle speed at that moment.

19 If the idle speed is not as specified, adjust the dashpot setting by turning the SAS-3 adjustment screw **(see illustration)**.

20 Release the free lever and verify that the engine returns to its idle speed slowly.

Electric choke system

21 Check that the alignment marks on the electric choke and bimetal assembly are lined up correctly.

22 Make sure the engine coolant temperature is below 10°C.

23 Start the engine and place your hand on the electric choke body to check the operation of the choke valve and fast idle cam. The choke valve should open as the choke body temperature rises. The fast idle cam should release as the engine coolant temperature rises and the choke opener operates.

24 If the electric choke body remains cool even after the engine is warmed up, check the choke heater as follows.

25 Unplug the electric choke heater connector and check the heater with an ohmmeter. It should indicate about 6 ohms. If the resistance is not as specified, replace the bimetal assembly (electric choke body).

Fast idle setting

26 To ensure accuracy, the carburettor must be at room temperature (20°C) or colder. Set the fast idle lever on the scribed line of the fast idle cam.

27 Use the shank of a twist drill to measure the clearance between the wall of the throttle bore and the primary throttle valve. Refer to the *Specifications* for the required drill size **(see illustration)**.

28 If necessary, adjust the clearance by turning the fast idle adjustment screw in the appropriate direction. Once the clearance is correctly set, remove the twist drill.

Choke pull-down setting

29 To ensure accuracy, the carburettor must be at room temperature (20°C) or colder.

30 Close the choke valve by lightly pressing the upper edge of the valve by finger. Now fully open the throttle valve and check that the gap between the upper edge of the choke valve and the choke bore is as given in the *Specifications*. Use the shank of a twist drill to make the check **(see illustration)**.

31 If adjustment is necessary, bend the tang on the throttle lever as required.

Choke opener setting

32 Close the choke valve by lightly pressing the upper edge of the valve by finger. Now push the opener rod towards the diaphragm and check that the gap between the upper edge of the choke valve and the choke bore is as given in the Specifications.

33 If adjustment is necessary, bend the hooked tang on the throttle lever as required.

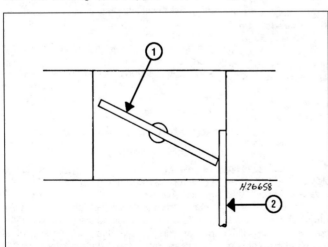

13.27 Measuring the primary throttle valve (1) to throttle bore clearance using a twist drill (2)

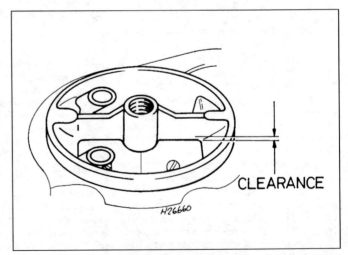

13.30 Check the choke pull-down setting as described in the text by measuring the gap between the choke flap and inlet as shown

Idle-up setting

34 Make sure that the idle speed is adjusted as described in Chapter 1.
35 Unbolt the solenoid mounting bracket from the transmission end of the cylinder head. Remove the electrical connector from the bottom f the idle-up control solenoid. Using a bridging wire, connect one of the solenoid terminals to the positive terminal of the battery and the other solenoid terminal to the negative terminal of the battery. This applies intake manifold vacuum to the idle-up actuator, which activates the actuator.
36 Open the throttle slightly - until the engine speed reaches about 2000 rpm - then slowly close it.
37 Note the indicated engine speed. Adjust it, if necessary, to the specified rpm with the throttle opener adjustment screw.
38 Repeat the procedure in paragraph 36 and check the engine speed again.
39 Remove the bridging wire and reattach the wiring.

Air conditioning idle-up setting

40 Connect a tachometer to the engine in accordance with the manufacturer's instructions.
41 Start the engine then switch on the air conditioner. This opens the solenoid valve, which allows intake manifold vacuum to move the actuator to its full open position. Note the indicated engine speed and compare the reading to the specified rpm.
42 If the engine speed is incorrect, adjust it with the throttle adjusting screw.

Idle speed and mixture

43 Refer to Chapter 1.

14 Inlet manifold - removal and refitting

Note: *Refer to the warning note in Section 1 before proceeding.*

Removal

1 Remove the carburettor as described in Section 12.
2 Drain the cooling system as described in Chapter 1. If necessary, remove the thermostat as described in Chapter 3.
3 Noting the correct fitted location of each hose, release the retaining clips and disconnect the vacuum servo unit hose, the coolant hoses and the vacuum/breather hoses from the manifold.
4 Unscrew the retaining bolts and remove the support bracket from underneath the manifold.
5 Make a final check that all the necessary vacuum/breather hoses have been disconnected from the manifold.
6 Slacken and remove the manifold retaining nuts and bolts, noting the correct fitted location of the engine lifting bracket, then manoeuvre the manifold away from the head and out of the

engine compartment. Recover the gaskets from the manifold studs and discard.

Refitting

7 Refitting is the reverse of the removal procedure, noting the following points:
  a) *Prior to refitting, examine all the manifold studs for signs of damage and corrosion; remove all traces of corrosion, and repair or renew any damaged studs.*
  b) *Ensure that the manifold and cylinder head mating surfaces are clean and dry, and fit the new gaskets. Install the manifold, ensuring that the lifting bracket is correctly positioned, and tighten its retaining nuts and bolts to the specified torque setting.*
  c) *Ensure that the support bracket is fitted the correct way up with the "UP" marking at the top. Tighten the bracket bolts by hand to settle the bracket in position then tighten them to the specified torque setting.*
  d) *Ensure that all relevant hoses are reconnected to their original positions, and are securely held (where necessary) by their retaining clips.*
  e) *Refit the carburettor as described in Section 12.*
  f) *On completion, refill the cooling system as described in Chapter 1.*

15 Exhaust manifold - removal and refitting

Removal

1 Disconnect the battery negative lead.
Caution: If the radio/cassette in your vehicle is equipped with an anti-theft system, make sure you have the correct activation code before disconnecting the battery.
2 Apply the handbrake then jack up the front of the vehicle and support on axle stands (see *"Jacking and Vehicle Support"*).
3 Working beneath the vehicle, remove the nuts that secure the exhaust downpipe to the exhaust manifold. Apply penetrating oil to the threads to make removal easier. Recover the gasket.
4 Remove the air cleaner assembly as described in Section 2, then disconnect the hot-air hose from the exhaust manifold.
5 Where applicable, disconnect the wiring from the oxygen sensor.
6 Where applicable, unscrew the nuts and remove the air injection tube from the manifold.
7 Unbolt and remove the outer hot-air shroud.
8 Unscrew and remove the exhaust manifold mounting nuts noting the location of the engine lifting eye. Withdraw the manifold from the studs on the cylinder head, and recover the gasket.
9 Unbolt the inner hot-air shroud from the manifold, and unscrew the oxygen sensor where fitted.

Refitting

10 Refitting is the reverse of the removal procedure, noting the following points:
  a) *Examine the exhaust manifold studs for damage and corrosion; remove all traces of corrosion, and repair or renew any damaged studs.*
  b) *Ensure that the manifold and cylinder head sealing faces are clean and flat, and fit the new manifold gasket. Refit the manifold retaining nuts, ensuring that the lifting bracket is correctly positioned, and tighten them to the specified torque.*
  c) *Reconnect the front pipe to the manifold using the information given in Section 16, and refit the oxygen sensor (where fitted) with reference to Chapter 4C.*

16 Exhaust system - general information, removal and refitting

General information

1 The exhaust system consists of two sections on non-catalytic converter engines; the front pipe section, incorporating the front silencer box, and the tailpipe section which incorporates the main silencer box. On catalytic converter engines a three-section exhaust system is fitted; the front pipe (incorporating a braided flexible joint), the catalytic converter, and the tailpipe section which incorporates the main silencer box. The sections are joined by flanged joints which are secured by nuts or bolts.
2 The system is suspended throughout its entire length by rubber mountings.

Removal

3 The exhaust sections can be removed individually, or alternatively, the complete system can be removed as a unit.
4 To remove the system or part of the system, first jack up the front and/or rear of the car, and support it on axle stands (see *"Jacking and Vehicle Support"*). Alternatively, position the car over an inspection pit, or on car ramps.

Front pipe

5 Where applicable, disconnect the oxygen sensor wiring.
6 Undo the nuts securing the front pipe flange joint to the manifold, and the single bolt securing the front pipe to its mounting bracket. Separate the flange joint, and collect the gasket.
7 Support the front pipe then slacken and remove the bolts securing the front pipe flange joint to the tailpipe or catalytic converter. On catalytic converter engines recover the gasket.
8 Release the front pipe from the rubber mounting and remove it from underneath the vehicle.

Catalytic converter

9 Support the catalytic converter, then slacken and remove the bolts and nuts securing the front and tail pipe flange joints to the catalytic converter. Withdraw the catalytic converter from under the vehicle and recover the front gasket.

Tailpipe

10 Slacken and remove the bolts/nuts securing the tailpipe flange joint to the front pipe/catalytic converter and separate the joint.

11 Support the tailpipe then slacken and remove the bolts and nuts securing the tailpipe to its mounting brackets and rubbers. Remove the tailpipe from underneath the vehicle and recover the spacer from the mounting rubber.

Complete system

12 Undo the nuts securing the front pipe flange joint to the manifold, and the single bolt securing the front pipe to its mounting bracket. Separate the flange joint, and collect the gasket.

13 Support the exhaust system then slacken and remove the nuts and bolts securing the tailpipe to the mounting bracket and rubbers. Release the front pipe from the mounting rubber, then remove the complete exhaust system from underneath the vehicle and recover the spacers from the rubber mountings.

Refitting

14 Each section is refitted by reversing the removal sequence, noting the following points:

a) Ensure that all traces of corrosion have been removed from the flanges, and renew all necessary gaskets.

b) Inspect the rubber mountings for signs of damage or deterioration, and renew as necessary.

c) Prior to tightening the exhaust system fasteners, ensure that all rubber mountings are correctly located, and that there is adequate clearance between the exhaust system and vehicle underbody. Ensure that all fasteners are tightened to their specified torque settings.

Chapter 4 Part B:
Fuel and exhaust systems - multi-point fuel injection engines

Contents

Accelerator cable - removal, refitting and adjustment 3
Accelerator pedal - removal and refitting 4
Air cleaner assembly - removal and refitting 2
Air cleaner filter element renewal . . . . .See Chapter 1
Exhaust manifold - removal and refitting 15
Exhaust system - general information, removal and refitting 16
Exhaust system check . . . . .See Chapter 1
Fuel filter - renewal . . . . .See Chapter 1
Fuel gauge sender unit - removal and refitting 9
Fuel injection system - depressurisation 7
Fuel injection system - general information 6
Fuel injection system - testing and adjustment 11
Fuel injection system components - removal and refitting 13
Fuel pump - removal and refitting 8
Fuel tank - removal and refitting 10
General fuel system checks . . . . .See Chapter 1
General information and precautions 1
Inlet manifold - removal and refitting 14
Throttle housing - removal and refitting 12
Unleaded petrol - general information and usage 5

Degrees of difficulty

Easy, suitable for novice with little experience	Fairly easy, suitable for beginner with some experience	Fairly difficult, suitable for competent DIY mechanic 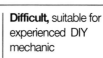	Difficult, suitable for experienced DIY mechanic	Very difficult, suitable for expert DIY or professional

Specifications

Fuel system data

Fuel pump type	Electric, immersed in tank
Fuel system pressure (at specified idle speed):	
With pressure regulator vacuum hose connected	2.75 bar
With pressure regulator vacuum hose disconnected	3.26 to 3.47 bar

MFI types 1 and 2

Throttle position sensor resistances:	
At idle	480 to 520 mV
At full throttle	3.5 to 6.5 kΩ
Idle speed control motor resistance	5.0 to 35.0 Ω
Motor position sensor resistance	3.5 to 6.5 kΩ
Inlet air temperature sensor resistance	2.33 to 2.97 kΩ at 20°C
Engine coolant temperature sensor resistance:	
At 20°C	2.5 kΩ
At 80°C	0.3 kΩ
Injector coil resistance	13.0 to 16.0 Ω
Specified idle speed	700 ± 100 rpm
Idle mixture CO content	Less than 1.0 % (not adjustable - controlled by ECU)

MFI type 3

Throttle position sensor resistances:	
At idle	480 to 520 mV
At full throttle	3.5 to 6.5 kΩ
Idle speed control actuator frequency	100 Hz
MAP sensor output voltage:	
At ignition switch on	4.5 to 5.0 volts
At idle speed	1.0
Inlet air temperature sensor resistance:	
At 20°C	2.5 kΩ
At 80°C	0.3 kΩ
Engine coolant temperature sensor resistance:	
At 20°C	2.5 kΩ
At 80°C	0.3 kΩ
Injector coil resistance	13.0 to 16.0 Ω
Specified idle speed	825 ± 100 rpm
Idle mixture CO content	Less than 1.0 % (not adjustable- controlled by ECU)

Recommended fuel

Minimum octane rating . . . . 95 RON unleaded (UK unleaded premium).
Leaded fuel must **not** be used

Torque wrench settings

	Nm	lbf ft
Air cleaner mounting	9	7
Air cleaner mounting bracket	19	14
Inlet manifold	18	13
Inlet manifold stay bracket	22	16
Throttle housing	19	14
Exhaust manifold	18	13
Exhaust manifold shroud	30	22
Oxygen sensor	45	33
Front pipe to manifold	35	26
Front pipe mounting bolt	35	26
Front pipe to catalytic converter	45	33
Fuel rail	12	9
Fuel pressure regulator	9	7
Temperature sensor	25	19
Throttle position sensor	1.5 to 2.5	1.1 to 1.9
Fuel pressure regulator bolts	9	7
High pressure hose to fuel filter	30	22
High pressure hose to fuel tank	35	26
Fuel tank drain plug	18	13
Fuel filter mounting bolts	12	9
Accelerator arm bracket bolts	12	9

1 General information and precautions

The fuel supply system consists of a fuel tank (which is mounted under the rear of the car, with an electric fuel pump immersed in it), a fuel filter, fuel feed and return lines. The fuel

1.1 Accumulator in the fuel line from the tank to the engine compartment

pump supplies fuel to the fuel rail, which acts as a reservoir for the four fuel injectors which inject fuel into the inlet tracts. The fuel filter incorporated in the feed line from the pump to the fuel rail ensures that the fuel supplied to the injectors is clean. An accumulator is incorporated in the fuel line from the tank to the engine compartment **(see illustration)**.

Refer to Section 6 for further information on the operation of the fuel injection system, and to Section 16 for information on the exhaust system.

⚠️ *Warning: Many of the procedures in this Chapter require the removal of fuel lines and connections, which may result in some fuel spillage. Before carrying out any operation on the fuel system, refer to the precautions given in "Safety first!" at the beginning of this manual, and follow them implicitly. Petrol is a highly-dangerous and volatile liquid, and the precautions necessary when handling it cannot be overstressed.*

Note: Residual pressure will remain in the fuel lines long after the vehicle was last used. When disconnecting any fuel line, first depressurise the fuel system as described in Section 7.

2 Air cleaner assembly - removal and refitting

Removal

Early models (MFI types 1 and 2)

1 Release the retaining clips and remove the duct connecting the air cleaner cover to the throttle housing. Disconnect the vacuum hose and cable tie **(see illustrations)**.

2 Disconnect the airflow meter wiring from the air cleaner cover. If necessary remove the cover and the air filter element with reference to Chapter 1.

3 Unbolt and remove the resonator from the side of the air cleaner **(see illustrations)**.

2.1a Disconnect the inlet air duct from the throttle housing . . .

2.1b . . . and from the air cleaner cover . . .

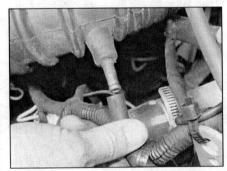

2.1c . . . then disconnect the vacuum hose . . .

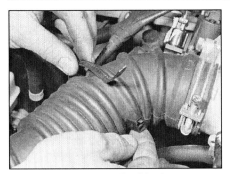

2.1d . . . and cable tie

2.3a Unscrew the mounting bolts . . .

2.3b . . . and remove the resonator from the air cleaner

4 Unscrew the mounting bolts from the right-hand inner wing panel, then withdraw the air cleaner assembly from the engine compartment.

Later models (MFI type 3)

5 Release the retaining clip securing the throttle housing air duct to the air cleaner cover. Loosen the clip and disconnect the air duct from the resonator. Unscrew the mounting bolts and remove the resonator.
6 If necessary remove the air cleaner cover and the air filter element with reference to Chapter 1.
7 Loosen the clip securing the air inlet duct to the air cleaner body.
8 Unscrew and remove the mounting bolts and withdraw the air cleaner body from the inlet duct. If necessary, unbolt the inlet duct from the inner body then unscrew the nut and separate the duct from the bracket. The mounting bracket may also be unbolted from the body.

Refitting

9 Refitting is a reversal of the removal procedure.

---

3 Accelerator cable - removal, refitting and adjustment

Removal

1 Working in the engine compartment, unhook the accelerator inner cable from the throttle cam.
2 Unscrew and remove the outer cable bracket retaining bolts and free the outer cable from the inlet manifold surge tank (upper section of the inlet manifold).
3 Working back along the length of the cable, free it from the mounting supports, retaining clips and ties, noting its correct routing **(see illustration)**.
4 From inside the vehicle, reach up behind the facia and unhook the inner cable from the top of the accelerator pedal. Tie a length of string to the end of the inner cable to help the refitting procedure.
5 Working in the engine compartment, unbolt the cable guide from the bulkhead and remove the cable from the vehicle **(see illustration)**.

When the end of the cable appears, untie the string and leave it in position - it can then be used to draw the cable back into position on refitting.

Refitting

6 Tie the string to the end of the cable, then use the string to draw the cable into position through the bulkhead. Once the cable end is visible, untie the string, and connect the inner cable to the upper end of the accelerator pedal.
7 From within the engine compartment, insert and tighten the cable guide bolts on the bulkhead.
8 Work along the cable, ensuring it is correctly routed, securing it in position with the retaining clips and ties.
9 Connect the inner cable to the throttle cam then refit the outer cable bolts tightening them lightly. Adjust the cable as described below then securely tighten both bolts.

Adjustment

10 Ensure that all electrical items are switched off then start the engine and warm it up to normal operating temperature.
11 Ensure that the idle speed is correctly set (see Chapter 1) then switch the engine off.
12 Ensure that the cable is correctly routed then check that there is a small amount of freeplay (approximately 1 to 2 mm of slack) in the cable.
13 If adjustment is necessary, turn on the ignition switch (without starting the engine) and leave it switched on for approximately 15 seconds; this will initialise the idle speed

3.3 One of the accelerator cable mounting supports

control servo. Slacken the bolts securing the accelerator cable to the inlet manifold surge tank and adjust the cable so that there is 1.0 to 2.0 mm freeplay in the inner cable before securely retightening the cable retaining bolts.
14 Ensure that the throttle cam is fully against its stop then have an assistant depress the accelerator pedal, and check that the throttle cam opens fully and returns smoothly to its stop then recheck the cable adjustment. On models with automatic transmission, once the accelerator cable is correctly adjusted, check the kickdown cable adjustment as described in Chapter 7B.

---

4 Accelerator pedal - removal and refitting

Refer to Chapter 4A, Section 8.

---

5 Unleaded petrol - general information and usage

Note: *The information given in this Chapter is correct at the time of writing. If updated information is thought to be required, check with a Hyundai dealer. If travelling abroad, consult one of the motoring organisations (or a similar authority) for advice on the fuel available.*

The fuel recommended is given in the *Specifications* of this Chapter, followed by the equivalent petrol currently on sale in the UK.

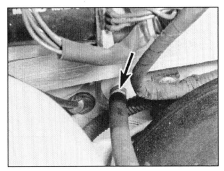

3.5 Accelerator cable mounting on the bulkhead

All Hyundai multi-point injection (MPI) models are designed to run on fuel with a minimum octane rating of 95 (RON). All models have a catalytic converter, and so must be run on unleaded fuel only. Under no circumstances should leaded fuel (UK "4-star") be used, as this may damage the converter.

Super unleaded petrol (98 octane) can also be used in all models if wished, though there is no advantage in doing so.

6 Fuel injection system - general information

The engine management (fuel injection/ ignition) system as fitted to all fuel-injected models incorporates a closed-loop catalytic converter and various emission control components. The system is referred to as both MFI and MPI by the manufacturers. Refer to Chapter 4C for information on the emission control system and to Chapter 5 for information on the ignition side of the system; the fuel side of the system operates as follows.

The fuel pump (which is immersed in the fuel tank) supplies fuel from the tank to the fuel rail, via a filter located in the engine compartment. Fuel supply pressure is controlled by the pressure regulator on the end of the fuel rail. When the optimum operating pressure of the fuel system is exceeded, the regulator allows excess fuel to return to the tank.

The electrical control system consists of the ECU, along with the following sensors:

a) *Airflow sensor - fitted to MFI type 1 and 2 systems. Informs the ECU of volume of air entering the engine. MFI type 3 system does not have an airflow sensor as it uses information from other sensors to determine the volume of air.*

b) *Throttle position sensor (also contains the idle position switch) - informs the ECU of the throttle position, and the rate of throttle opening/closing.*

c) *Coolant temperature sensor - informs the ECU of engine temperature.*

d) *Inlet air temperature sensor - informs the ECU of the temperature of the air passing through the inlet manifold.*

e) *Lambda/oxygen sensor - informs the ECU of the oxygen content of the exhaust gases (explained in greater detail in Part C of this Chapter).*

f) *Barometric pressure sensor - this sensor is only fitted to the MFI type 1 and 2 systems. It is located on the airflow meter in the air cleaner, and determines the altitude that the vehicle is at so that adjustments can be made to the air-fuel ratio.*

g) *Manifold Absolute Pressure (MAP) sensor - this sensor is only fitted to the MFI type 3 system. It informs the ECU of the load on the engine (expressed in terms of inlet manifold vacuum). The sensor is located in the engine compartment on the bulkhead.*

h) *Crank angle sensor and TDC sensor (contained in the distributor assembly) - informs the ECU of the crankshaft position and engine speed.*

i) *Vehicle speed sensor (contained in the speedometer assembly) - informs the ECU of the vehicle speed.*

j) *Power steering pressure switch (contained in the power steering pump) - informs the ECU when the power steering pump is under load.*

All the above signals are analysed by the ECU, and it selects the fuelling response appropriate to those values. The ECU controls the fuel injectors (varying the pulse width - the length of time the injectors are held open - to provide a richer or weaker mixture, as appropriate). The mixture is constantly varied by the ECU, to provide the best setting for cranking, starting (with either a hot or cold engine), warm-up, idle, cruising, and acceleration.

The ECU also has full control over the engine idle speed, via the idle speed control servo which bypasses the throttle valve. When the throttle valve is closed, the ECU controls the opening of the servo, which in turn regulates the amount of air entering the manifold, and so controls the idle speed.

The ECU also controls the exhaust and evaporative emission control systems, which are described in detail in Part C of this Chapter.

If there is an abnormality in any of the readings obtained from either the coolant temperature sensor, the inlet air temperature sensor or the lambda/oxygen sensor, the ECU enters its back-up mode. In this event, it ignores the abnormal sensor signal, and assumes a pre-programmed value which will allow the engine to continue running (albeit at reduced efficiency). If the ECU enters this back-up mode, the warning light on the instrument panel will come on, and the relevant fault code will be stored in the ECU memory.

If the warning light comes on, the vehicle should be taken to a Hyundai dealer at the earliest opportunity where a complete test of the engine management system can then be carried out.

7 Fuel injection system - depressurisation

Note: *Refer to the warning note in Section 1 before proceeding.*

> **Warning: The following procedure will merely relieve the pressure in the fuel system - remember that fuel will still be present in the system components and take precautions accordingly before disconnecting any of them.**

1 The fuel system referred to in this Section is defined as the tank-mounted fuel pump, the fuel filter, the fuel injectors, the fuel rail and the pressure regulator, and the metal pipes and flexible hoses of the fuel lines between these components. All these contain fuel which will be under pressure while the engine is running or while the ignition is switched on. The pressure will remain for some time after the ignition has been switched off, and it must be relieved in a controlled fashion when any of the system components are disturbed for servicing work.

2 Remove the rear seat cushion (early models) or spare wheel (later models), then remove the cover and disconnect the fuel pump wiring. This will disable the fuel pump.

3 Start the engine and allow it to run until it stalls, indicating that the fuel pressure present in the fuel lines/rail assembly has been released, then switch off the engine.

4 Reconnect the fuel pump wiring and refit the seat cushion.

8 Fuel pump - removal and refitting

Note: *Refer to the warning note in Section 1 before proceeding.*

Removal

1 Remove the fuel tank (see Section 10).

2 Mark the hoses for identification purposes, then slacken the retaining clips and disconnect the fuel hoses from the top of the pump, and plug the hose ends. To disconnect the high pressure hose, hold the union with one spanner then unscrew and remove the union nut with another spanner.

3 Make alignment marks between the fuel pump and tank then slacken and remove the pump retaining bolts.

4 Carefully unclip the fuel pump assembly and lift it out of the fuel tank, taking great care not to damage the filter, or to spill fuel onto the interior of the vehicle. Recover the pump gasket and discard it - a new one must be used on refitting.

5 Loosen the clips and remove the fuel pump from the bracket. Recover the pick-up filter and insulator.

6 Check all components for wear and damage and renew them as necessary. The fuel pick-up filter should be renewed if it shows signs of damage or clogging.

Refitting

7 Reassemble the fuel pump using a reversal of the dismantling procedure. Ensure that the fuel pump pick-up filter is clean and free of debris and that the tank and pump mating surfaces are clean and dry.

8 Fit the new gasket to the top of the fuel tank and carefully manoeuvre the pump assembly into the fuel tank, and clip it into position in the base of the tank.

9 Refit the pump retaining bolts and tighten them securely.

10 Reconnect the hoses to the top of the fuel pump, using the marks made on removal to ensure that they are correctly reconnected, and securely tighten their retaining clips. The high pressure hose union must be tightened to the specified torque.

11 Refit the fuel tank to the vehicle (see Section 10).

9 Fuel gauge sender unit - removal and refitting

Refer to Chapter 4A, Section 5.

10 Fuel tank - removal and refitting

1 Refer to Chapter 4A, Section 6, bearing in mind the following.

a) *Depressurise the fuel system as described in Section 7 of this Chapter before disconnecting the battery negative terminal. Once the fuel system has been depressurised, free the fuel pump wiring grommet from the floor so the wiring connector is free to move as the fuel tank is lowered out of position.*

b) *The high pressure fuel supply line hose union on the left-hand side of the tank is disconnected by unscrewing the union nut.*

c) *On refitting, ensure that the pump wiring is routed up through the floor as the tank is raised into position. Start the engine and check carefully for fuel leaks before taking the vehicle on the road.*

11 Fuel injection system - testing and adjustment

Testing

1 If a fault appears in the fuel injection system, first ensure that all the system wiring connectors are securely connected and free of corrosion. Ensure that the fault is not due to poor maintenance; ie, check that the air cleaner filter element is clean, the spark plugs are in good condition and correctly gapped, the cylinder compression pressures are correct, the ignition timing is correct, and that the engine breather hoses are clear and undamaged, referring to Chapters 1, 2 and 5 for further information.

2 If these checks fail to reveal the cause of the problem, the vehicle should be taken to a suitably-equipped Hyundai dealer for testing. A connector is incorporated in the engine management circuit in the fusebox, into which a special electronic diagnostic tester can be plugged. The tester will locate the fault quickly and simply, alleviating the need to test all the system components individually, which is a time-consuming operation that also carries a risk of damaging the ECU.

Adjustment

Idle speed and CO mixture (general)

3 Experienced home mechanics with a considerable amount of skill and equipment (including a good-quality tachometer and a good-quality, carefully-calibrated exhaust gas analyser) may be able to check the exhaust CO level and the idle speed. However, if these are found to be in need of adjustment, it is highly recommended that the car is taken to a suitably-equipped Hyundai dealer for diagnostic testing. It is not possible to adjust the CO level as this function is taken care of by the engine management ECU. On engines with the MFI type 1 and 2 fuel injection system, it is possible to check and adjust the idle speed as follows provided an accurate tachometer is available,

Idle speed adjustment (MFI type 1 and 2 fuel injection system)

4 Run the engine to normal operating temperature, and check that all electrical components have been switched off. The check and adjustment must be made with the electric cooling fan stopped. On models with power steering make sure that the steering is pointing straight ahead. Manual transmissions must be in neutral and automatic transmissions in "P" or "N".

5 Stop the engine and connect a tachometer to it, then restart it and allow it to idle.

6 Increase the engine speed to between 2000 and 3000 rpm for at least 5 seconds, then allow the engine to idle for 2 minutes.

7 Check that the idle speed is as given in the *Specifications*. If not, first check and if necessary adjust the ignition timing with reference to Chapter 5.

8 After re-checking the idle speed, if it is still incorrect disconnect the air duct from the throttle housing and clean the throttle valve and housing bore of any carbon deposits. Turn the throttle valve as necessary to do this, and re-connect the air duct on completion.

9 If the idle speed is still incorrect, loosen the bolts securing the accelerator cable adjustment bracket to the inlet manifold so that the bracket is loose.

10 Switch on the ignition (but do not start the engine) and leave it on for at least 15 seconds. The idle speed control (ISC) plunger will extend to the fast idle position then retract to the closed position after 15 seconds. Switch off the ignition and disconnect the wiring from the ISC motor.

11 Quickly open and release the throttle valve several times to ensure it is not sticking, then back off the Fixed SAS (speed adjustment screw) so that it is clear of the lever.

12 Start the engine and let it idle. Check that the idle speed is as given in the *Specifications*. If necessary, adjust the idle speed by turning the ISC (idle speed control) screw located below the fixed SAS adjustment screw. Note that if the engine has been overhauled and has covered less than 300 miles, the idle speed should be between 20 and 100 rpm lower than the specified speed; when the engine is fully run-in the idle speed will increase.

13 With the engine idling, screw in the SAS adjustment screw until the engine speed just starts to increase, then back it off until the speed ceases to drop. From this point back off the screw half a turn.

14 Switch off the ignition and disconnect the tachometer.

12 Throttle housing - removal and refitting

Removal

1 Disconnect the battery negative lead.
Caution: If the radio/cassette in your vehicle is equipped with an anti-theft system, make sure you have the correct activation code before disconnecting the battery.

2 Slacken the retaining clip then disconnect the air inlet duct from the throttle housing.

3 On models with the MFI type 1 and 2 system, clamp the coolant hoses then loosen the clips and disconnect the hoses from bottom of the throttle housing.

4 Disconnect the accelerator inner cable from the throttle cam. On automatic transmission models, also disconnect the kickdown cable.

5 Disconnect the wiring from the throttle position sensor and the idle speed control motor assembly.

6 Disconnect the vacuum hose(s), noting their location where necessary **(see illustration)**.

7 Unscrew and remove the retaining screws and remove the throttle housing from the inlet manifold. Recover the housing gasket and discard it; a new one must be used on refitting **(see illustration)**.

12.6 Vacuum hose connection on the throttle housing

Refitting

8 Ensure that the mating surfaces are clean and dry then offer up the new gasket and refit the throttle housing, tightening its retaining bolts to the specified torque.

9 Reconnect the vacuum hose(s) and wiring and connect the accelerator cable to the throttle cam. On automatic transmission models reconnect the kickdown cable.

10 Reconnect the air inlet duct and tighten the clip, then reconnect the battery.

11 Reconnect the coolant hoses where necessary and tighten the clips.

12 On completion, adjust the accelerator cable as described in Section 3 and, where necessary, the kickdown cable as described in Chapter 7B. Check and if necessary top up the cooling system.

13 Fuel injection system components - removal and refitting

Fuel rail and injectors

Note: *Refer to the warning note in Section 1 before proceeding.*

HAYNES HINT *If a faulty injector is suspected, before condemning the injector, it is worth trying the effect of one of the proprietary injector-cleaning treatments.*

13.2 Fuel feed hose/union on the right-hand end of the fuel rail

13.5 Recover the injector seals and O-rings from the inlet manifold

12.7 Throttle housing mounted on the right-hand side of the inlet manifold

Removal

1 Depressurise the fuel system as described in Section 7 then disconnect the battery negative lead.

Caution: If the radio/cassette in your vehicle is equipped with an anti-theft system, make sure you have the correct activation code before disconnecting the battery.

2 Position cloth rags beneath the right-hand end of the fuel rail, then unbolt the fuel feed hose/union from the end of the fuel rail. Recover the O-ring seal from the union and discard it; a new one must be used on refitting **(see illustration)**.

3 Loosen the retaining clip and disconnect the fuel return hose and the vacuum pipe from the fuel pressure regulator.

4 Release the retaining clips and disconnect the wiring connectors from the four injectors **(see illustration)**.

13.4 Wiring connectors on the fuel injectors

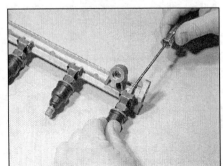

13.6a Slide out the retaining clip . . .

5 Unscrew and remove the fuel rail retaining bolts then carefully ease the fuel rail and injector assembly out from the inlet manifold and remove it from the vehicle. Recover the spacers which are fitted between the fuel rail and inlet manifold. Recover the injector seals from the inlet manifold and discard them; they must be renewed whenever they are disturbed **(see illustration)**.

6 Slide out the retaining clip(s) and remove the relevant injector(s) from the fuel rail. Remove the upper O-ring and rubber seal from each injector and discard; all removed O-rings and seals must be renewed **(see illustrations)**.

Refitting

7 Refitting is a reversal of the removal procedure, noting the following points.

   a) *Fit new O-rings and seals to all injector unions.*
   b) *Apply a smear of engine oil to the O-ring and seal to aid installation then ease the injectors and fuel rail into position ensuring that the O-ring is not displaced.*
   c) *Ensure that the spacers are correctly positioned between the fuel rail and manifold before tightening the retaining bolts to the specified torque.*
   d) *Fit a new O-ring seal to the feed hose union groove and tighten the union retaining bolts securely.*
   e) *On completion start the engine and check for fuel leaks.*

Fuel pressure regulator

Note: *Refer to the warning note in Section 1 before proceeding.*

Removal

8 Depressurise the fuel system as described in Section 7 then disconnect the battery negative lead.

Caution: If the radio/cassette in your vehicle is equipped with an anti-theft system, make sure you have the correct activation code before disconnecting the battery.

9 Loosen the retaining clip and disconnect the fuel return hose and the vacuum pipe from the fuel pressure regulator **(see illustrations)**.

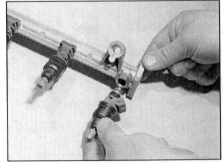

13.6b . . . then ease the injector out from the fuel rail and recover its upper O-ring and seal

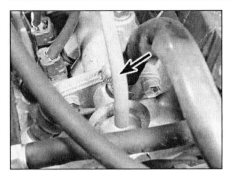

13.9a Disconnect the vacuum pipe . . .

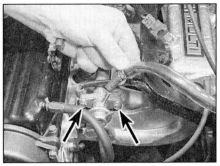

13.9b . . . and the return hose from the fuel pressure regulator (mounting bolts arrowed)

13.10 Remove the fuel pressure regulator from the end of the fuel rail (sealing ring arrowed)

10 Unscrew the retaining bolts and remove the pressure regulator from the end of the fuel rail. Recover the O-ring seal from the regulator and discard it; a new one must be used on refitting **(see illustration)**.

Refitting

11 Refitting is the reverse of removal, noting the following.
a) *Fit the new O-ring seal to the regulator groove and smear it with engine oil to ease installation.*
b) *Tighten the regulator bolts to the specified torque and reconnect the fuel return hose and vacuum hose.*

Throttle position sensor

Removal

12 Disconnect the battery negative lead.
Caution: If the radio/cassette in your vehicle is equipped with an anti-theft system, make sure you have the correct activation code before disconnecting the battery.
13 Disconnect the wiring from the throttle position sensor **(see illustration)**.
14 Slacken and remove the two retaining screws then disengage the sensor from the throttle valve spindle and remove it from the vehicle.

Refitting

15 Engage the sensor with the throttle valve spindle and lightly tighten its retaining screws.
16 Connect a multimeter, set to the resistance (ohmmeter) function, to the terminals of the sensor as shown **(see illustration)**.

17 Switch on the ignition (but do not start the engine) and leave it on for at least 15 seconds. The idle speed control (ISC) plunger will extend to the fast idle position then retract to the closed position after 15 seconds. Switch off the ignition and disconnect the wiring from the ISC motor.
18 Check the resistance of the sensor with the throttle at the idle position is as given in the *Specifications*. Slowly open the throttle and check that the resistance value increases progressively. Check that the resistance with the throttle fully open is as given in the *Specifications*.
19 If necessary, loosen the retaining screws and re-position the sensor as required, then tighten the screws to the specified torque. Disconnect the multimeter.
20 Reconnect the wiring to the sensor, then reconnect the battery.

Electronic Control Unit (ECU)

Removal

21 The ECU is located under the left-hand side of the facia. First disconnect the battery negative lead.
Caution: If the radio/cassette in your vehicle is equipped with an anti-theft system, make sure you have the correct activation code before disconnecting the battery.
22 Remove the glovebox (RHD) or lower facia panel (LHD) as described in Chapter 11.
23 Undo the retaining screws and remove the protective covers.

24 Disconnect the wiring then undo the retaining screws and remove the ECU from the vehicle.

Refitting

25 Refitting is a reversal of the removal procedure ensuring that the wiring connector is securely fitted.

Idle speed control motor assembly (MFI types 1 and 2)

Removal

26 Remove the throttle housing as described in Section 12.
27 Undo the retaining screws and remove the idle speed control motor assembly and seal from the base of the throttle housing. Discard the seal; a new one should be used on refitting **(see illustration)**.

Refitting

28 Ensure that the new seal is correctly located in its groove then fit the motor assembly to the base of the throttle housing and securely tighten its retaining screws.
29 Refit the throttle housing as described in Section 12.

Idle speed control (ISC) actuator (MFI type 3)

Removal

30 It is located at the rear of the engine compartment on the bulkhead.
31 Loosen the clips and disconnect the air hoses from the actuator.

13.13 The throttle position sensor and wiring connector

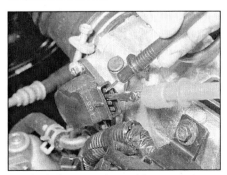

13.16 Connect the multimeter to the throttle position sensor as shown

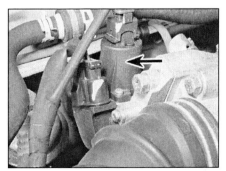

13.27 Idle speed control motor assembly

13.48 Air cleaner cover showing the airflow sensor mounting screws

32 Disconnect the wiring.
33 Unscrew the mounting bolts and withdraw the actuator from the bulkhead.

Refitting

34 Refitting is a reversal of removal.

Manifold absolute pressure (MAP) sensor (MFI type 3)

Removal

35 It is situated in the rear, left-hand corner of the engine compartment where it is mounted onto the bulkhead.
36 Disconnect the wiring connector and vacuum hose from the MAP sensor.
37 Free the MAP sensor from the bracket and remove it from the engine compartment.

Refitting

38 Refitting is the reverse of the removal procedure.

Coolant temperature sensor

39 It is screwed into the right-hand end of the thermostat housing. Refer to Chapter 3 for removal and refitting details.

Inlet air temperature sensor

Removal

40 On the MFI type 1 and 2 systems, the inlet air temperature sensor is integral with the airflow meter located in the air cleaner and cannot be removed separately. On the MFI type 3 system, the inlet air temperature sensor is screwed into the inlet air duct between the air cleaner and the throttle housing.

41 Disconnect the wiring then unscrew the sensor and remove it from the air inlet duct.

Refitting

42 Refitting is a reversal of removal.

Crank angle sensor and TDC sensor

43 The crank angle sensor is incorporated in the distributor body and cannot be removed separately. If faulty the complete distributor body will have to be renewed (see Chapter 5).

Engine management system relay unit

Removal

44 The relay unit is located beneath the left-hand side of the facia. To remove it, first disconnect the battery negative lead.
Caution: If the radio/cassette in your vehicle is equipped with an anti-theft system, make sure you have the correct activation code before disconnecting the battery.
45 Reach up behind the facia and disconnect the wiring then undo the retaining screw and withdraw the relay unit.

Refitting

46 Refitting is the reverse of removal.

Airflow sensor (MFI types 1 and 2)

Removal

47 Remove the air cleaner cover as described in Chapter 1.
48 Unscrew and remove the screws and withdraw the airflow sensor from the air cleaner cover. Recover the grommet and cap from the top of the cover, and the gasket and noise filter from the bottom of the cover **(see illustration)**.

Refitting

49 Refitting is a reversal of removal.

Vehicle speed sensor

50 It is incorporated in the speedometer unit inside the instrument panel. Removal and refitting procedures for the instrument panel are given in Chapter 12.

---

14 Inlet manifold - removal and refitting

Note: *Refer to the warning note in Section 1 before proceeding.*

Removal

MFI type 1 and 2 systems

1 Depressurise the fuel system as described in Section 7.
2 Disconnect the battery negative lead.
Caution: If the radio/cassette in your vehicle is equipped with an anti-theft system, make sure you have the correct activation code before disconnecting the battery.
3 Drain the cooling system as described in Chapter 1.
4 Loosen the clips and disconnect the air duct from the air cleaner and throttle housing. Withdraw the duct from the engine compartment.
5 Remove the throttle housing from the inlet manifold as described in Section 12.
6 Unscrew the bolts and remove the accelerator outer cable bracket from the surge tank. Position the accelerator cable to one side.
7 Loosen the clips and disconnect the crankcase ventilation hose and brake servo vacuum hose **(see illustration)**.
8 Disconnect the vacuum hoses and unbolt the wiring loom supports **(see illustrations)**.
9 Remove the fuel rail and injectors as described in Section 13. Tape over or plug all fuel hoses to prevent entry of dust and dirt.
10 Unbolt and remove the surge tank (the upper section) from the top of the inlet manifold. Recover the gasket.
11 Loosen the clip and disconnect the heater hose from the inlet manifold.
12 Disconnect the wiring from the two engine temperature sensors on the right-hand end of the inlet manifold.
13 Remove the thermostat as described in Chapter 3.
14 Remove the distributor and ignition coil as described in Chapter 5. Also remove the power transistor with reference to Chapter 5.

14.7 Brake servo vacuum hose connection to the inlet manifold

14.8a Wiring loom support at the left-hand end of the inlet manifold . . .

14.8b . . . and at the right-hand end of the inlet manifold

15 Unbolt and remove the stay from under the inlet manifold.
16 Unscrew the mounting nuts and bolts and withdraw the inlet manifold from the engine. Recover the gasket.

MFI type 3 system

17 Depressurise the fuel system as described in Section 7.
18 Disconnect the battery negative lead.
Caution: If the radio/cassette in your vehicle is equipped with an anti-theft system, make sure you have the correct activation code before disconnecting the battery.
19 Drain the cooling system as described in Chapter 1.
20 Remove the idle speed control actuator as described in Section 13. Loosen the clips and disconnect the air hoses from the surge tank (upper inlet manifold) and inlet air duct.
21 Disconnect the air temperature sensor wiring and hoses from the air inlet duct, then loosen the clips and disconnect the air duct from the air cleaner and throttle housing. Withdraw the duct from the engine compartment.
22 Remove the throttle housing from the inlet manifold as described in Section 12.
23 Unscrew the bolts and remove the accelerator outer cable bracket from the surge tank. Position the accelerator cable to one side.
24 Loosen the clip and disconnect the MAP sensor vacuum hose from the surge tank (upper section of the inlet manifold).
25 Loosen the clips and disconnect the crankcase ventilation hose and brake servo vacuum hose.
26 Disconnect the vacuum hoses.
27 Remove the fuel rail and injectors as described in Section 13. Tape over or plug all fuel hoses to prevent entry of dust and dirt.
28 Unbolt and remove the surge tank (manifold upper section) from the top of the inlet manifold. Recover the gasket.
29 Loosen the clip and disconnect the heater hose from the inlet manifold.
30 Disconnect the wiring from the two engine temperature sensors on the right-hand end of the inlet manifold.
31 Remove the thermostat as described in Chapter 3.
32 Remove the distributor and ignition coil as described in Chapter 5. Also remove the power transistor with reference to Chapter 5.
33 Unbolt and remove the stay from under the inlet manifold.
34 Unscrew the mounting nuts and bolts and withdraw the inlet manifold from the engine. Recover the gasket.

Refitting

35 Refitting is the reverse of the removal procedure with reference to the relevant Chapters and Sections, noting the following points:

a) *Prior to refitting, examine the manifold studs for signs of damage and corrosion; remove all traces of corrosion, and repair or renew any damaged studs.*
b) *Ensure that the manifold and cylinder head mating surfaces are clean and dry, and fit the new gasket. Install the manifold, and tighten its retaining nuts and bolts to the specified torque setting.*
c) *Fit the stay bracket and tighten all the bracket bolts by hand to settle the bracket in position then tighten them to the specified torque setting.*
d) *Ensure that all relevant hoses are reconnected to their original positions, and are securely held (where necessary) by their retaining clips.*
e) *Refer to Chapter 1 when refilling the cooling system.*
f) *Reconnect and adjust the accelerator cable as described in Section 3 then, where necessary, adjust the kickdown cable as described in Chapter 7B.*

15 Exhaust manifold - removal and refitting

Removal

1 Firmly apply the handbrake, then jack up the front of the vehicle and support it on axle stands (see *"Jacking and Vehicle Support"*). Where fitted unbolt and remove the splash guards.
2 Working beneath the vehicle, unscrew and remove the nuts securing the exhaust downpipe to the exhaust manifold. Also unscrew the support bracket bolts. Lower the downpipe from the manifold and support on an axle stand, then recover the gasket.
3 Working in the engine compartment, remove the air cleaner assembly as described in Section 2. Remove the hot-air hose from the exhaust manifold shroud.
4 Where the oxygen sensor is located on the exhaust manifold, remove it as described in Chapter 4C.
5 On models with an air injection system, unscrew the flare nuts on the air injection tube. Remove the tube from the exhaust manifold.
6 Unbolt and remove the hot-air shrouds from the manifold.
7 Slacken and remove the retaining nuts securing the manifold to the head, noting the fitted location of the engine lifting bracket **(see illustration)**. Withdraw the manifold from the cylinder head and remove it from the engine compartment. Remove and discard the manifold gasket.

Refitting

8 Refitting is the reverse of the removal procedure, noting the following points:
a) *Examine all the exhaust manifold studs for signs of damage and corrosion; remove*

all traces of corrosion, and repair or renew any damaged studs.
b) *Ensure that the manifold and cylinder head sealing faces are clean and flat, and fit the new manifold gasket. Refit the lifting bracket and tighten the manifold retaining nuts to the specified torque.*
c) *Reconnect the front pipe to the manifold, using a new gasket and retaining nuts using the information given in Section 16.*

16 Exhaust system - general information, removal and refitting

General information

1 The exhaust system consists of two sections on non-catalytic converter engines; the front pipe section, incorporating the front silencer box, and the tailpipe section which incorporates the main silencer box. On catalytic converter engines a three-section exhaust system is fitted; the front pipe (incorporating a braided flexible joint), the catalytic converter, and the tailpipe section which incorporates the main silencer box. The sections are joined by flanged joints which are secured by nuts or bolts.
2 The system is suspended throughout its entire length by rubber mountings.

Removal

3 The exhaust sections can be removed individually, or alternatively, the complete system can be removed as a unit.
4 To remove the system or part of the system, first jack up the front and/or rear of the car, and support it on axle stands (see *"Jacking and Vehicle Support"*). Alternatively, position the car over an inspection pit, or on car ramps.

Front pipe

5 Where applicable, disconnect the oxygen sensor wiring.
6 Undo the nuts securing the front pipe flange joint to the manifold, and the single bolt securing the front pipe to its mounting bracket. Separate the flange joint, and collect the gasket **(see illustration)**.

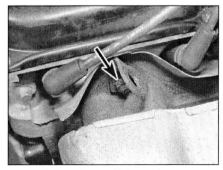

15.7 Exhaust manifold retaining nut with lifting bracket

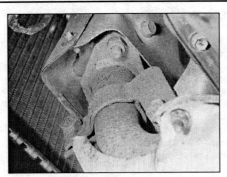

16.6 Exhaust front pipe connection to the exhaust manifold

16.9 Exhaust system tailpipe mounting and flange joint to the catalytic converter

7 Support the front pipe then slacken and remove the bolts securing the front pipe flange joint to the tailpipe or catalytic converter. On catalytic converter engines recover the gasket.

8 Release the front pipe from the rubber mounting and remove it from underneath the vehicle.

Catalytic converter

9 Support the catalytic converter, then slacken and remove the bolts and nuts securing the front and tailpipe flange joints to the catalytic converter. Withdraw the catalytic converter from under the vehicle and recover the front gasket **(see illustration)**.

Tailpipe

10 Where applicable, disconnect the wiring from the oxygen sensor at the front of the tailpipe.

11 Slacken and remove the bolts/nuts securing the tailpipe flange joint to the front pipe/catalytic converter and separate the joint.

12 Support the tailpipe then slacken and remove the bolts and nuts securing the tailpipe to its mounting brackets and rubbers. Remove the tailpipe from underneath the vehicle and recover the spacer from the mounting rubber **(see illustrations)**.

Complete system

13 Where applicable, disconnect the wiring from the oxygen sensor either on the front pipe or tailpipe.

14 Undo the nuts securing the front pipe flange joint to the manifold, and the bolts from the mounting bracket. Separate the flange joint, and collect the gasket.

15 Support the exhaust system then slacken and remove the nuts and bolts securing the tailpipe to the mounting bracket and rubbers. Release the front pipe from the mounting rubber, then remove the complete exhaust system from underneath the vehicle and recover the spacers from the rubber mountings.

Refitting

16 Each section is refitted by reversing the removal sequence, noting the following points:

a) *Ensure that all traces of corrosion have been removed from the flanges, and renew all necessary gaskets.*

b) *Inspect the rubber mountings for signs of damage or deterioration, and renew as necessary.*

c) *Prior to tightening the exhaust system fasteners, ensure that all rubber mountings are correctly located, and that there is adequate clearance between the exhaust system and vehicle underbody. Ensure that all fasteners are tightened to their specified torque settings.*

d) *Ensure that the oxygen sensor wiring is correctly routed and in no danger of touching the hot exhaust/engine.*

16.12a Exhaust tailpipe centre mounting . . .

16.12b . . . right-hand rear mounting . . .

16.12b . . . and left-hand rear mounting

Chapter 4 Part C:
Emissions control systems

Contents

Catalytic converter - general information and precautions 3
Emissions control systems - testing and component renewal 2
General information 1

Degrees of difficulty

Easy, suitable for novice with little experience	Fairly easy, suitable for beginner with some experience	Fairly difficult, suitable for competent DIY mechanic	Difficult, suitable for experienced DIY mechanic	Very difficult, suitable for expert DIY or professional

Specifications

Adjustment data

Purge control solenoid valve coil resistance	36 to 44Ω
Thermal valve temperature:	
Opening temperature	50°C minimum
Closing temperature	61 to 69°C
EGR control solenoid valve coil resistance	36 to 44Ω

Torque wrench settings

	Nm	lbf ft
Exhaust gas recirculation (EGR) valve	23	17
EGR thermo valve	30	22
PCV valve	10	7
Oxygen sensor	44	32

1 General information

The models covered by this manual have various features built into the fuel system to help minimise harmful emissions as follows. The systems fitted will depend on country and local emission laws.
a) Positive crankcase ventilation (PCV) system
b) Jet air system
c) Exhaust gas recirculation (EGR) system
d) Evaporative emission control
e) Secondary air supply system
f) Dashpot/idle-up actuator (carburettor models only)
g) Catalytic converter

Positive crankcase ventilation system

To reduce the emission of unburned hydrocarbons from the crankcase into the atmosphere, the engine is sealed, and the blow-by gases and oil vapour are drawn from inside the crankcase, through the PCV valve (screwed into the valve cover), into the inlet manifold, to be burned by the engine during normal combustion.

Under conditions of high manifold vacuum, the gases will be sucked positively out of the crankcase. Under conditions of low manifold vacuum, the gases are forced out of the crankcase by the (relatively) higher crankcase pressure; if the engine is worn, the raised crankcase pressure (due to increased blow-by) will cause some of the flow to return under all manifold conditions.

Jet air system

In addition to inlet and exhaust valves, each combustion chamber is equipped with a smaller jet valve which allows a super lean mixture to be admitted into the combustion chamber during the inlet stroke. The jet air is channelled from the atmospheric side of the throttle valve and effectively operates only at idle or at light load when the pressure difference between each side of the throttle valve is greatest. This super lean mixture swirls as it enters the combustion chamber, and the swirl continues throughout the compression stroke to improve flame propagation after ignition. When the throttle valve is open more that the light load position, there is no pressure difference and the jet air system does not function.

Exhaust gas recirculation (EGR) system

This system is designed to reduce oxides of nitrogen in the exhaust gases. This is achieved by taking some of the exhaust gases from the cylinder head exhaust ports and recirculating them back into the inlet manifold, where they are burned again during normal combustion. The exhaust gas recirculation (EGR) valve is fitted to the right-hand side of the inlet manifold.

On early models the system is controlled by an EGR valve, a sub-EGR valve and a thermo valve. On later models there is no sub-EGR valve, and a vacuum regulator valve is used to modulate the vacuum signal to the EGR valve.

Evaporative emissions control system

To minimise the escape of unburned hydrocarbons into the atmosphere, an evaporative emissions control system is fitted to models with a catalytic converter. The fuel tank filler cap is sealed, and a carbon canister collects the petrol vapours generated in the tank (and carburettor float chamber on FBC models) when the car is parked. It stores them until the vapours can be cleared into the inlet manifold when the engine is running.

The system consists of a canister, a bowl vent valve (FBC models), a purge control valve, an overfill limiter (to control fuel tank pressure), a thermal valve (carburettor models), a fuel check valve (to prevent leakage if the vehicle rolls over) and a specially designed fuel filler cap (to prevent escape of fuel vapours).

Secondary air supply system

The secondary air supply system delivers air to the exhaust manifold through a reed valve to promote further oxidation of exhaust gases during engine warm-up, deceleration and heavy engine loads. The reed valve is actuated by vacuum generated by exhaust pulsation. The secondary air supply valve is actuated by inlet manifold vacuum when the solenoid valve is energised by the ECU.

Dashpot/idle-up actuator

The dashpot/idle-up actuator has two functions - the first to reduce the amount of unburnt hydrocarbons in the exhaust gases on the overrun, and the second to increase the idle speed when the engine is under increased load. On the overrun, the actuator prevents the throttle valve from closing completely when the driver releases the accelerator pedal suddenly at high engine speeds. When the power steering pump, electric cooling fan, or stop light switch is operated with the engine idling, the actuator slightly opens the throttle valve to compensate for the additional load on the engine. The actuator is controlled by a solenoid valve which allows vacuum from the inlet manifold to move the actuator rod which in turn opens the throttle valve.

Catalytic converter and oxygen sensor

To minimise the amount of pollutants which escape into the atmosphere, all models are fitted with a catalytic converter in the exhaust system. The system is of the "closed-loop" type, in which an exhaust gas sensor provides the engine management control unit constant feedback, enabling the unit to adjust the mixture to provide the best possible conditions for the converter to operate.

The sensor's tip is sensitive to oxygen, and sends the control unit a varying voltage depending on the amount of oxygen in the exhaust gases; if the inlet air/fuel mixture is too rich, the sensor sends a high-voltage signal. The voltage falls as the mixture weakens. Peak conversion efficiency of all major pollutants occurs if the inlet air/fuel mixture is maintained at the chemically-correct ratio for the complete combustion of

2.3 Removing the PCV valve from the cylinder head cover

petrol - 14.7 parts (by weight) of air to 1 part of fuel (the "stoichiometric" ratio). The sensor output voltage alters in a large step at this point, the control unit using the signal change as a reference point, and correcting the inlet air/fuel mixture accordingly by altering the fuel injector pulse width (injector opening time). The sensor has a built-in heating element (controlled by the control unit), to quickly bring the sensor's tip to an efficient operating temperature.

2 Emissions control systems - testing and component renewal

Positive crankcase ventilation system

Testing

1 Inspect the breather hose for signs of damage or deterioration and renew if necessary.
2 If the hose is in good condition, unscrew the PCV valve from the cylinder head cover (see below) and reconnect it to the breather hose. Start the engine, allowing it to idle, and place a finger over the end of the PCV valve; if the valve is functioning correctly vacuum should be present in the hose. If not, disconnect the hose from the valve and check that the internal plunger move by inserting a thin screwdriver or similar tool into the engine side of the valve. If the PCV valve is faulty it must be renewed. **Note:** *Prior to renewing the valve, try cleaning the valve in solvent and see if this frees the valve internals.*

PCV valve - removal and refitting

3 Disconnect the breather hose from the PCV valve then unscrew the valve from the cylinder head cover (see illustration).
4 Refit the new valve to the cylinder head cover, tightening it to the specified torque, and reconnect the breather hose.

Jet air system

Testing

5 To adjust the jet air valve clearances, refer to Chapter 1.

Jet air valve renewal

6 To overhaul or replace the jet air valves, refer to Chapter 2B.

Exhaust gas recirculation (EGR) system

Testing

7 If the system is thought to be faulty, first check that the hoses linking the thermo valve and the exhaust gas recirculation (EGR) valve are in good condition and unblocked.
8 To check the thermo valve, which is screwed into the right-hand end of the inlet manifold, with the engine cold, disconnect the EGR valve hose from the valve. Start the

engine and allow it to idle then slowly increase the engine speed to 2500 rpm; with the engine cold no vacuum should be present at the valve union. Warm the engine up to normal operating temperature (coolant temperature at least 80°C) and check that vacuum is now present at the valve union. If the valve does not perform as expected, it is faulty and must be renewed.
9 To check the operation of the EGR valve, disconnect the vacuum hose from the top of the valve, and fit a length of hose to the valve union. Suck on the hose end; check that the valve diaphragm is pulled up, and returns quickly when the vacuum is released. If the valve operation is sticky or does not move at all, the EGR valve must be renewed.

Exhaust gas recirculation (EGR) valve - removal and refitting

10 Disconnect the vacuum hose from the EGR valve, which is mounted on the left-hand end of the inlet manifold.
11 Unscrew the two retaining bolts and remove the valve from the manifold. Remove the gasket and discard it.
12 Refitting is the reverse of removal, using a new gasket and tightening the mounting bolts to the specified torque.

EGR thermo valve - removal and refitting

13 The thermo valve is screwed into the right-hand side of the inlet manifold. The engine should be cold before removing the valve.
14 Have ready a suitable plug which can be used to plug the valve aperture in the manifold whilst it is removed. Ensure that the plug used, will not damage the manifold, and do not use anything which will allow foreign matter to enter the cooling system.
15 Disconnect both vacuum hoses from the valve then carefully unscrew the valve from the manifold. Plug the valve aperture.
16 Refitting is the reverse of removal, applying a smear of sealing compound to the valve threads prior to refitting and tightening the valve to the specified torque.

Evaporative emissions control system

Testing

17 If the system is thought to be faulty, disconnect the hoses from the carbon canister and purge control/bowl vent/solenoid control valves (as applicable), and check that they are clear by blowing through them. On carburettor models the canister and purge control valve are located on the bulkhead at the rear of the engine compartment and the bowl vent valve (FBC models) is located on the carburettor. On MPI fuel injection models the canister is located beneath the front right-hand wheelarch, and the solenoid valve is located on the bulkhead at the rear of the engine compartment.
18 Detailed checking of the system should

be entrusted to a Hyundai dealer who will have the necessary equipment.

Carbon canister - removal and refitting

19 On fuel injection models jack up the front of the vehicle and support on axle stands (see "*Jacking and Vehicle Support*"). Remove the roadwheel and wheelarch liner for access to the carbon canister.
20 Make a note of the correct fitted location of each hose on the canister. To avoid the possibility of connecting the hoses incorrectly on refitting, make identification marks between each hose and its canister union (the canister unions are marked for identification).
21 Release the retaining clips and free the canister from its mounting bracket.
22 Disconnect the hoses and remove the canister.
23 Refitting is a reverse of the removal procedure, ensuring that the hoses are correctly reconnected.

Purge control valve - removal and refitting

24 The valve is located at the rear of the inlet manifold where it is mounted onto the engine compartment bulkhead.
25 To renew the valve, depress the retaining clip and disconnect the wiring.
26 Release the retaining clips (where fitted) then disconnect the hoses from the valve, and free the valve from its mounting bracket.
27 Refitting is a reverse of the removal procedure, ensuring that the hoses are correctly reconnected.

Secondary air supply system

Testing

28 Remove the secondary air control valve as described later, then blow air into the air cleaner hose aperture and check that the valve is shut. Connect a vacuum pump to the vacuum diaphragm stub and apply a vacuum of 5.9 in-Hg, and check that it is possible to blow through the air cleaner aperture but not through the exhaust manifold aperture. If the valve does not function correctly, it must be renewed.

Secondary air control valve - removal and refitting

29 Identify all hoses for position, then disconnect them. Note that the metal tube to the exhaust is connected with a union nut.
30 Unscrew and remove the mounting bolts and withdraw the valve from the right-hand end of the cylinder head.
31 Refitting is a reversal of removal.

Dashpot/idle-up actuator

Testing

32 Push the dashpot rod into the dashpot, making sure that the rod enters the dashpot slowly, then release the rod and check that it returns quickly. If not, the dashpot must be renewed. Refer to Chapter 4A for details of checking and adjustment.

Dashpot - renewal

33 Unscrew the retaining nut and washer and remove the dashpot from the side of the carburettor. If necessary, remove the air cleaner housing to improve access to the dashpot (see Chapter 4A).
34 Refitting is the reverse of removal, but on completion carry out the adjustment described in Chapter 4A.

Oxygen (Lambda) sensor

Testing

35 If the CO at the exhaust tailpipe is too high, then a fault is present in the carburettor FBC system or MPI fuel injection system (as applicable). Detailed testing of the oxygen sensor and catalytic converter must be left to a Hyundai dealer who has access to the necessary test equipment.

Oxygen sensor - renewal

Note: *The Lambda sensor is delicate, and it will not work if it is dropped or knocked, if its power supply is disrupted, or if any cleaning materials are used on it.*
36 The oxygen sensor is screwed either into the exhaust manifold or front pipe **(see illustration)**. Where it is located in the front pipe, apply the handbrake then jack up the front of the vehicle and support it on axle stands (see "*Jacking and Vehicle Support*").
37 Trace the wiring back from the sensor, freeing it from any relevant retaining clips. Disconnect the wiring at the connector **(see illustration)**.
38 Unscrew the sensor, and withdraw it from the vehicle.
39 Refitting is a reverse of the removal procedure. Prior to installing the sensor, apply a smear of high-temperature grease to the sensor threads. Tighten the sensor to the specified torque and ensure that the wiring is correctly routed, and in no danger of contacting either the exhaust system or the engine.

3 Catalytic converter - general information and precautions

The catalytic converter is a reliable and simple device which needs no maintenance in itself, but there are some facts of which an owner should be aware if the converter is to function properly for its full service life.
  a) *DO NOT use leaded petrol in a car with a catalytic converter - the lead will coat the precious metals, reducing their converting efficiency, and will eventually destroy the converter.*
  b) *Always keep the ignition and fuel systems well-maintained in accordance with the manufacturer's schedule.*
  c) *If the engine develops a misfire, do not drive the car at all (or at least as little as possible) until the fault is cured.*
  d) *DO NOT push- or tow-start the car - this will soak the catalytic converter in unburned fuel, causing it to overheat when the engine does start.*
  e) *DO NOT switch off the ignition at high engine speeds.*
  f) *DO NOT use fuel or engine oil additives - these may contain substances harmful to the catalytic converter.*
  g) *DO NOT continue to use the car if the engine burns oil to the extent of leaving a visible trail of blue smoke.*
  h) *Remember that the catalytic converter operates at very high temperatures. DO NOT, therefore, park the car in dry undergrowth, over long grass, or over piles of dead leaves, after a long run.*
  i) *Remember that the catalytic converter is FRAGILE - do not strike it with tools during servicing work.*
  j) *The catalytic converter, used on a well-maintained and well-driven car, should last for between 50 000 and 100 000 miles, but if the converter is no longer effective, it must be renewed.*

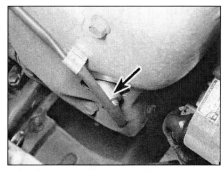

2.36 Oxygen sensor located in the exhaust manifold

2.37 Oxygen sensor wiring connector

Notes

Chapter 5
Engine electrical systems

Contents

Alternator - removal and refitting 11
Alternator - testing and overhaul 12
Battery - removal and refitting 4
Battery - testing and charging 3
Battery check . . . . .See "Weekly checks"
Charging system - testing 10
Distributor - removal and refitting 8
Electrical fault-finding - general information 2
General information and precautions 1
Ignition HT coil - removal, testing and refitting 7

Ignition switch - removal and refitting 16
Ignition system - general information 5
Ignition system - testing 6
Ignition system check . . . . .See Chapter 1
Ignition timing - checking and adjustment 9
Oil pressure warning light switch - removal and refitting 17
Spark plug renewal . . . . .See Chapter 1
Starter motor - removal and refitting 14
Starter motor - testing and overhaul 15
Starting system - testing 13

Degrees of difficulty

Easy, suitable for novice with little experience		Fairly easy, suitable for beginner with some experience		Fairly difficult, suitable for competent DIY mechanic		Difficult, suitable for experienced DIY mechanic		Very difficult, suitable for expert DIY or professional	

Specifications

System type . . . . 12-volt, negative earth

Battery
Type . . . . Low-maintenance or maintenance-free
Charge condition:
  Poor . . . . 12.5 volts
  Normal . . . . 12.6 volts
  Good . . . . 12.7 volts

Ignition system
System type:*
  Carburettor models . . . . Breakerless electronic ignition
  Fuel-injected models . . . . Breakerless electronic ignition controlled by fuel injection ECU
*Refer to text for further information on each relevant system
Firing order . . . . 1-3-4-2 (No 1 cylinder at timing belt end)
Ignition timing (at specified idle speed):
  Conventional (CONV) carburettor models (except 1.5 automatic) . . . $4° \pm 2°$ BTDC at 800 ± 30 rpm
  Conventional (CONV) carburettor models (1.5 automatic) . . . . $4° \pm 2°$ BTDC at 850 ± 30 rpm
  FBC carburettor models . . . . $5° \pm 2°$ BTDC at 700 ± 50 rpm
  Fuel-injected models* . . . . $5° \pm 2°$ BTDC at 700 ± 100 rpm
Ignition HT coil resistances:*
  Carburettor models:
    Primary windings . . . . 1.2 ± 0.12 ohms
    Secondary windings . . . . 13.7 ± 2.1 k ohms
  Fuel injection models:
    Primary windings . . . . 0.8 ± 0.08 ohms
    Secondary windings . . . . 12.1 ± 1.8 k ohms
*The above results are approximate values, and are accurate only when the coil is at 20°C. See text for further information.
Ballast resistor resistance . . . . 1.15 to 1.55 ohms

Torque wrench settings

	Nm	lbf ft
Distributor mounting nut	12	9
Alternator mounting bolts:		
Lower bolt	23	17
Upper (adjustment) bolt	14	10
Starter motor mounting bolts	30	22
Oil pressure switch	19	14

1 General information and precautions

General information

The "engine" electrical system includes all charging, starting and ignition system components. Because of their engine-related functions, these components are covered separately from the "body" electrical devices such as the lights, instruments, etc (which are covered in Chapter 12).

The electrical system is of the 12-volt negative earth type.

The battery is of the low-maintenance or "maintenance-free" (sealed for life) type, and is charged by the alternator, which is belt-driven from the crankshaft pulley.

The starter motor is of the pre-engaged type, incorporating an integral solenoid. On starting, the solenoid moves the drive pinion into engagement with the flywheel ring gear before the starter motor is energised. Once the engine has started, a one-way clutch prevents the motor armature being driven by the engine until the pinion disengages from the flywheel.

Refer to Section 5 for further information on the ignition system.

Precautions

Further details of the various systems are given in the relevant Sections of this Chapter. While some repair procedures are given, the usual course of action is to renew the component concerned. The owner whose interest extends beyond mere component renewal should obtain a copy of the "Automobile Electrical & Electronic Systems Manual", available from the publishers of this manual.

It is necessary to take extra care when working on the electrical system, to avoid damage to semi-conductor devices (diodes and transistors), and to avoid the risk of personal injury. In addition to the precautions given in "Safety first!" at the beginning of this manual, observe the following when working on the system:

Always remove rings, watches, etc before working on the electrical system. Even with the battery disconnected, capacitive discharge could occur if a component's live terminal is earthed through a metal object. This could cause a shock or nasty burn.

Do not reverse the battery connections. Components such as the alternator, or any other components having semi-conductor circuitry, could be irreparably damaged.

If the engine is being started using jump leads and a slave battery, connect the batteries positive-to-positive and negative-to-negative (see "Jump starting"). This also applies when connecting a battery charger.

Never disconnect the battery terminals, the alternator, any electrical wiring, or any test instruments, when the engine is running.

Do not allow the engine to turn the alternator when the alternator is not connected.

Never "test" for alternator output by "flashing" the output lead to earth.

Never use an ohmmeter of the type incorporating a hand-cranked generator for circuit or continuity testing.

Always ensure that the battery negative lead is disconnected when working on the electrical system.

Before using electric-arc welding equipment on the car, disconnect the battery, alternator and components such as electronic control units, to protect them from the risk of damage.

The radio/cassette unit fitted may have a built-in security code, to deter thieves. If the power source to the unit is cut, the anti-theft system will activate. Even if the power source is immediately reconnected, the radio/cassette unit will not function until the correct security code has been entered. Therefore, if you do not know the correct security code for the radio/cassette unit, **do not** disconnect the battery negative terminal, or remove the radio/cassette unit from the vehicle. Refer to "Radio/ cassette unit anti-theft system - precaution" in the Reference Section of this manual.

2 Electrical fault-finding - general information

Refer to Chapter 12.

3 Battery - testing and charging

Standard and low-maintenance battery - testing

1 If the vehicle covers a small annual mileage, it is worthwhile checking the specific gravity of the electrolyte every three months, to determine the state of charge of the battery. Use a hydrometer to make the check, and compare the results with the following table. Note that the specific gravity readings assume an electrolyte temperature of 15°C (60°F); for every 10°C (18°F) below 15°C (60°F), subtract 0.007. For every 10°C (18°F) above 15°C (60°F), add 0.007. However, for convenience, the temperatures quoted in the following table are ambient (outdoor air) temperatures, above or below 25°C (77°F):

	Above 25°C (77°F)	Below 25°C (77°F)
Fully-charged	1.210 to 1.230	1.270 to 1.290
70% charged	1.170 to 1.190	1.230 to 1.250
discharged	1.050 to 1.070	1.110 to 1.130

2 If the battery condition is suspect, first check the specific gravity of electrolyte in each cell. A variation of 0.040 or more between any cells indicates loss of electrolyte, or deterioration of the internal plates.

3 If the specific gravity variation is 0.040 or more, a new battery should be fitted. If the cell variation is satisfactory but the battery is discharged, it should be charged as described later in this Section.

Maintenance-free battery - testing

4 In cases where a "sealed for life" maintenance-free battery is fitted, topping-up and testing of the electrolyte in each cell is not possible. The condition of the battery can therefore only be tested using a battery condition indicator or a voltmeter.

5 One type of maintenance-free battery which may be fitted is the "Delco" type maintenance-free battery, with a built-in charge condition indicator. The indicator is located in the top of the battery casing, and indicates the condition of the battery from its colour. If the indicator shows green, then the battery is in a good state of charge. If the indicator turns darker, eventually to black, then the battery requires charging, as described later in this Section. If the indicator shows clear/yellow, then the electrolyte level in the battery is too low to allow further use, and the battery should be renewed. **Do not** attempt to charge, load or jump start a battery when the indicator shows clear/yellow.

6 If testing the battery using a voltmeter, connect the voltmeter across the battery, and compare the result with those given in the Specifications under "charge condition". The test is only accurate if the battery has not been subjected to any kind of charge for the previous six hours. If this is not the case, switch on the headlights for 30 seconds, then wait four to five minutes before testing the battery after switching off the headlights. All other electrical circuits must be switched off, so check that the doors and tailgate are fully shut when making the test.

7 If the voltage reading is less than 12.2 volts, then the battery is discharged, whilst a reading of 12.2 to 12.4 volts indicates a partially-discharged condition.

8 If the battery is to be charged, remove it from the vehicle (Section 4) and charge it as described later in this Section.

Standard and low-maintenance battery - charging

Note: The following is intended as a guide only. Always refer to the manufacturer's recommendations (often printed on a label attached to the battery) before charging a battery.

9 Charge the battery at a rate of 3.5 to 4 amps, and continue to charge the battery at this rate until no further rise in specific gravity is noted over a four-hour period.

10 Alternatively, a trickle charger charging at the rate of 1.5 amps can safely be used overnight.

11 Specially rapid "boost" charges which are claimed to restore the power of the battery in 1 to 2 hours are not recommended, as they can cause serious damage to the battery plates through overheating.

12 While charging the battery, note that the temperature of the electrolyte should never exceed 37.8°C (100°F).

Maintenance-free battery - charging

Note: *The following is intended as a guide only. Always refer to the manufacturer's recommendations (often printed on a label attached to the battery) before charging a battery.*

13 This battery type takes considerably longer to fully recharge than the standard type, the time taken being dependent on the extent of discharge, but it can take anything up to three days.

14 A constant-voltage type charger is required, to be set, when connected, to 13.9 to 14.9 volts, with a charger current below 25 amps. Using this method, the battery should be usable within three hours, giving a voltage reading of 12.5 volts, but this is for a partially-discharged battery and, as mentioned, full charging can take considerably longer.

15 If the battery is to be charged from a fully-discharged state (condition reading less than 12.2 volts), have it recharged by your Hyundai dealer or local automotive electrician, as the charge rate is higher, and constant supervision during charging is necessary.

4 Battery - removal and refitting

Removal

1 The battery is located on the front right-hand side of the engine compartment.
2 Loosen the nut, and disconnect the clamp from the battery negative terminal.
3 Remove the insulation cover (where fitted) and disconnect the positive clamp in the same way.
4 Unscrew the nuts and washers and remove the battery retaining clamp. Recover the support rods **(see illustration)**.
5 Lift the battery out of the engine compartment. Where fitted remove the battery tray.

4.4 Battery retaining clamp and support rod

Refitting

6 Refitting is a reversal of removal, but smear petroleum jelly on the terminals when reconnecting the leads, and always reconnect the positive lead first, and the negative lead last.

5 Ignition system - general information

Carburettor models

A breakerless electronic ignition system is fitted on carburettor models. The system comprises solely of the HT ignition coil and the distributor, the distributor being driven off the camshaft.

The distributor contains a toothed rotor (or reluctor) mounted onto its shaft, and the igniter unit which is fixed to its body. The system operates as follows.

When the ignition is switched on but the engine is stationary, the igniter unit is inoperative and no current flows through the ignition system primary (LT) circuit.

As the crankshaft rotates, the rotor moves through the magnetic field created by the igniter unit. When the rotor teeth are correctly positioned, a small AC voltage is created. The igniter unit uses this voltage to switch on the ignition system primary (LT) circuit.

As the rotor teeth move out of alignment, the AC voltage changes, and the igniter unit switches off the primary (LT) circuit. This causes a high voltage to be induced in the coil secondary (HT) windings, which then travels down the HT lead to the distributor and onto the relevant spark plug.

The system incorporates a ballast resistor mounted on the side of the ignition coil.

Fuel-injected models

On fuel injection models, the ignition system is integrated with the fuel system, to form a combined fuel/ignition system which is controlled by the fuel injection ECU (see Chapter 4 for further information on the fuel side of the system).

The distributor contains a crank angle sensor, which informs the ECU of engine speed and crankshaft position, and a TDC sensor which informs the ECU of the position of No 1 cylinder piston. Based on this information, and the information received from its other sensors, the ECU then calculates the correct ignition timing setting, and switches the power transistor unit on and off accordingly. This causes a high voltage to be induced in the coil secondary (HT) windings, which then travels onto the relevant spark plug. The ignition HT coil and power transistor are both located on the inlet manifold.

6 Ignition system - testing

> **Warning:** *Voltages produced by the electronic ignition system are extremely high, and care must be taken when working on the system with the ignition switched on. Persons with surgically-implanted cardiac pacemaker devices should keep well clear of the ignition circuits, components and test equipment*

Note: *Refer to the warning given in Section 1 before starting work. Always switch off the ignition before disconnecting or connecting any component, and when using a multi-meter to check resistances.*

1 The components of electronic ignition systems are normally very reliable; most faults are far more likely to be due to loose or dirty connections, or to "tracking" of HT voltage due to dirt, dampness or damaged insulation, than to the failure of any of the system's components. Always check the wiring thoroughly before condemning an electrical component, and work methodically to eliminate all other possibilities before deciding that a particular component is faulty.

2 The old practice of checking for a spark by holding the live end of an HT lead a short distance away from the engine is not recommended; not only is there a high risk of a powerful electric shock, but the HT coil or power transistor unit will very likely be damaged. Similarly, never try to "diagnose" misfires by pulling off one HT lead at a time.

Engine will not start

3 If the engine either will not turn over at all, or only turns very slowly, check the battery and starter motor. Connect a voltmeter across the battery terminals (meter positive probe to battery positive terminal), then disconnect the ignition coil HT lead from the distributor cap and earth it to a suitable point on the engine. Note the voltage reading obtained while turning over the engine on the starter for (no more than) ten seconds. If the reading obtained is less than approximately 9.5 volts, first check the battery, starter motor and charging system as described in the relevant Sections of this Chapter.

4 If the engine turns over at normal speed but will not start, check the HT circuit by connecting a timing light (following the equipment manufacturer's instructions) and turning the engine over on the starter motor; if the light flashes, voltage is reaching the spark plugs, so these should be checked first. If the light does not flash, check the HT leads themselves, followed by the distributor cap, carbon brush and rotor arm using the information given in Chapter 1.

5 If there is a spark, check the carburettor /fuel injection system (as applicable) referring to Chapter 4 for further information.

7.1 Location of the ignition coil on early carburettor models

7.3 Ignition coil clamp bolts on an early carburettor model

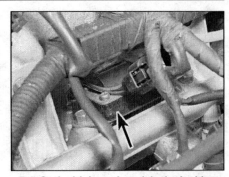

7.4 On fuel-injected models the ignition coil is located on the inlet manifold

6 If there is still no spark, check the voltage at the ignition HT coil "+" terminal; it should be the same as the battery voltage (ie, at least 11.7 volts). If the voltage at the coil is more than 1 volt less than that at the battery, check the feed back through the fusebox and ignition switch to the battery and its earth until the fault is found.

7 If the feed to the HT coil is sound, check the coil's primary and secondary winding resistance as described later in this Section; renew the coil if faulty, but be careful to check carefully the condition of the wiring (LT) connections themselves before doing so, to ensure that the fault is not due to dirty or poorly-fastened connectors.

8 If the HT coil is in good condition, the fault is probably within the distributor assembly (ie. the igniter unit and/or pick-up coil/crank angle sensor/No 1 cylinder TDC sensor - as applicable). Testing of the distributor assembly should be entrusted to a Hyundai dealer.

Engine misfires

9 An irregular misfire suggests either a loose connection or intermittent fault on the primary circuit, or an HT fault on the coil side of the rotor arm.

10 With the ignition switched off, check carefully through the system, ensuring that all connections are clean and securely fastened. If the equipment is available, check the LT circuit as described above.

11 Check that the HT coil, the distributor cap and the HT leads are clean and dry. Check the leads themselves and the spark plugs (by substitution, if necessary), then check the distributor cap, carbon brush and rotor arm as described in Chapter 1.

12 Regular misfiring is almost certainly due to a fault in the distributor cap, HT leads or spark plugs. Use a timing light (paragraph 4 above) to check whether HT voltage is present at all leads.

13 If HT voltage is not present on any particular lead, the fault will be in that lead, or in the distributor cap. If HT is present on all leads, the fault will be in the spark plugs; check and renew them if there is any doubt about their condition.

14 If no HT is present, check the HT coil; its secondary windings may be breaking down under load.

---

7 Ignition HT coil -
removal, testing
and refitting

Removal

Carburettor models

1 On early models the ignition coil is located in the front left-hand corner of the engine compartment **(see illustration)**. On later models it is located on the left-hand side of the bulkhead in the left-hand rear corner of the engine compartment. Prior to removal, make sure that the ignition is switched off.

2 Note the location of the coil LT wiring then disconnect it from the coil. Also disconnect the HT lead from the coil.

3 Unscrew the coil clamp bolts then withdraw the coil from the engine compartment **(see**

illustration). On early models it is necessary to unscrew the ballast resistor clamp screw and move the resistor to one side.

Fuel injection models

4 The ignition coil is located on the inlet manifold **(see illustration)**. Remove the surge tank (upper manifold) from the inlet manifold with reference to Chapter 4B.

5 Disconnect the wiring from the ignition coil then unscrew the mounting bolts and remove the unit from the inlet manifold.

Testing

6 Testing of the coil consists of using a multimeter set to its resistance function, to check the primary (LT "+" to "-" terminals) and secondary (LT "+" to HT lead terminal) windings for continuity. Compare the results obtained to those given in the *Specifications* at the start of this Chapter. Note that the resistance of the coil windings will vary slightly according to the coil temperature - the results in the *Specifications* are approximate values with the coil at 20°C.

7 Check that there is no continuity between the HT lead terminal and the coil body.

8 If the coil is faulty, renew it.

Refitting

9 Refitting is a reversal of the removal procedure, ensuring that the wiring connector and HT lead are securely reconnected.

---

8 Distributor -
removal and refitting

Removal

1 Disconnect the battery negative lead.
Caution: If the radio/cassette in your vehicle is equipped with an anti-theft system, make sure you have the correct activation code before disconnecting the battery.

2 Position No 1 cylinder at TDC on its compression stroke as described in Chapter 2A.

3 Release the retaining clips then remove the distributor cap, positioning it clear of the distributor body. Recover the cap seal from the distributor and mark the position of the rotor arm end on the distributor body rim using a scriber or a marker pen **(see illustrations)**.

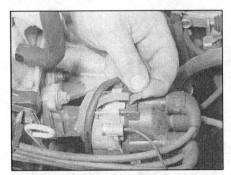

8.3a Releasing the distributor cap retaining clips

8.3b Mark the position of the rotor arm end on the distributor body rim using a scriber or a marker pen

8.6 Mark the distributor flange in relation to the cylinder head before loosening the mounting nut

8.7a Unplug the two leads from the igniter . . .

8.7b . . . and remove the wiring clip screw to release the wiring

4 Trace the distributor low tension wiring back to the connector then disconnect it. Alternatively the wiring may be disconnected later (see paragraph 7).

5 On carburettor models, disconnect the hose(s) from the vacuum diaphragm unit.

6 Check the distributor flange and cylinder head for alignment marks. If no marks are visible, using a scriber or suitable marker pen, mark the relationship of the distributor body to the cylinder head. Unscrew and remove the mounting nut and washer, and withdraw the distributor from the cylinder head. Remove the O-ring from the end of the distributor body and discard it; a new one must be used on refitting **(see illustration)**.

7 Where the wiring is still connected (see paragraph 4) unplug the two leads from the igniter then unscrew the clip screw and

release the wiring from the side of the distributor **(see illustrations)**.

8 If necessary pull off the rotor arm. On carburettor models remove the vacuum diaphragm unit by unscrewing its retaining screws and detaching it from the base unit. Also on carburettor models the igniter unit may be removed by unscrewing the mounting screws - note that one of the screws retains the earth wire **(see illustrations)**.

Refitting

9 Where removed on carburettor models, refit the vacuum diaphragm unit making sure its pushrod is correctly engaged with the base pin, and securely tighten its retaining screws. Refit the igniter unit, ensuring its wiring is correctly reconnected, and lightly tighten its retaining screws. Align one of the rotor teeth with the igniter pick-up lug and set the air gap

between two components to approximately 0.8 mm before securely tightening the igniter retaining screws **(see illustration)**.

10 Press the rotor arm firmly onto the distributor shaft.

11 Lubricate the new O-ring with a smear of engine oil, and fit it to the groove in the distributor body. Examine the distributor cap seal for wear or damage, and renew if necessary.

12 Position the rotor arm slightly to the side of the mark made on the distributor prior to removal; in this position the punch mark on the side of the distributor drive gear will align with the cut-out on the base of the distributor housing **(see illustration)**.

13 Align the previously made marks on the distributor body and cylinder head then insert the distributor, whilst rotating the rotor arm slightly to ensure that the camshaft and drive gear engage correctly.

14 Align the mark cast onto the distributor flange with the centre of the mounting stud or alternately align the marks made prior to removal. Refit the washer and mounting nut, and tighten lightly at this stage.

15 Ensure that the seal is correctly located in its groove, then refit the cap assembly to the distributor and secure it in position with the retaining clips.

16 Reconnect the distributor wiring, and on carburettor models reconnect the vacuum hose(s) to the diaphragm unit.

17 Check and, if necessary, adjust the ignition timing as described in Section 9, then securely tighten the distributor mounting nut.

8.8a Unscrew the retaining screws . . .

8.8b . . . then tilt the vacuum diaphragm unit and detach it from the pin on the base

8.8c To remove the igniter unit, unscrew the mounting screws

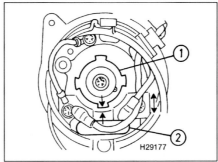

8.9 Ensure that the air gap between the rotor (1) and igniter pick-up (2) is correctly set

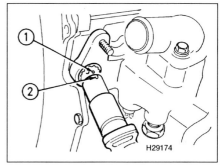

8.12 Align the punch mark on the drive gear (1) with the cut-out (2) on the distributor base

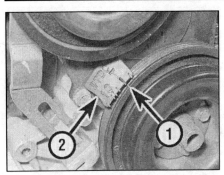

9.2 Crankshaft pulley notch (1) and timing belt cover timing marks (2)

9 Ignition timing - checking and adjustment

1 To check the ignition timing, a stroboscopic timing light will be required.
2 The timing marks are in the form of marks on the timing belt cover, which align with a notch on the crankshaft pulley rim (see illustration). The marks on the timing belt cover are spaced at intervals of 5°, with TDC being marked with a "T". The marks to the left of the "T" are before top dead centre (BTDC) and the marks to the right are after top dead centre (ATDC). The ignition timing is checked as follows.
3 Start the engine, warm it up to normal operating temperature, and then switch off. The timing check and adjustment must be made with all electrical accessories, including the electric cooling fan and air conditioning compressor, switched off.
4 Connect the timing light to No 1 cylinder (nearest the timing belt) plug lead as described in the timing light manufacturer's instructions. Make sure that the timing light wires are positioned clear of the moving and/or hot parts of the engine.
5 On MFI fuel injection models, connect a jumper lead between the battery negative (earth) terminal and the wiring loom ignition timing adjustment connector terminal. On early models this connector is located near the bulkhead on the left-hand side of the inlet manifold, but on later models it is located near the battery on the right-hand side of the cylinder head.
6 Start the engine, allowing it to idle at the specified speed, and point the timing light at the crankshaft pulley. The pulley notch should be aligned with the relevant point on the timing belt cover scale (see Specifications for the correct timing setting).
7 If adjustment is necessary, slacken the distributor mounting nut, then slowly rotate the distributor body as required until the crankshaft pulley notch is correctly positioned. Turning the distributor anticlockwise will advance the ignition timing and turning it clockwise will retard the ignition timing.

Warning: At all times, avoid touching the HT leads, and keep loose clothing, long hair, etc, well away from the moving parts of the engine. Once the marks are correctly aligned, hold the distributor stationary, and tighten its mounting nut securely. Recheck that the timing marks are still correctly aligned and, if necessary, repeat the adjustment procedure.

8 When the timing is correctly set, increase the engine speed, and check that the pulley mark advances to beyond the beginning of the timing reference marks, returning to the specified mark when the engine is allowed to idle; this shows that the distributor advance mechanism is functioning.
9 With the ignition timing correct, stop the engine and disconnect the timing light.

10 Charging system - testing

Note: Refer to the warnings given in "Safety first!" and in Section 1 of this Chapter before starting work.

1 If the ignition/no-charge warning light fails to come on when the ignition is switched on, first check the alternator wiring connections for security. If satisfactory, check that the warning light bulb has not blown, and that the bulbholder is secure in its location in the instrument panel. If the light still fails to come on, check the continuity of the warning light feed wire from the alternator to the bulbholder. If all is satisfactory, the alternator is at fault, and should be taken to an auto-electrician for testing and repair.
2 If the ignition warning light comes on when the engine is running, stop the engine as soon as possible. Check that the drivebelt is correctly tensioned (see Chapter 1), that the drivebelt is not contaminated (with oil or water, for example), and that the alternator connections are secure. If all is so far satisfactory, the alternator should be taken to an auto-electrician for testing and repair.
3 If the alternator output is suspect, even though the warning light functions correctly, the regulated voltage may be checked as follows.

4 Connect a voltmeter across the battery terminals, and start the engine.
5 Increase the engine speed until the voltmeter reading remains steady; the reading should be approximately 12 to 13 volts, and no more than 14 volts.
6 Switch on as many electrical accessories (eg, the headlights, heated rear window and heater blower) as possible, and check that the alternator maintains the regulated voltage at around 13 to 15 volts.
7 If the regulated voltage is not as stated, the fault may be due to worn brushes, weak brush springs, a faulty voltage regulator, a faulty diode, a severed phase winding, or worn or damaged slip-rings. If this is the case then the alternator should be taken to an auto-electrician for testing and repair.

11 Alternator - removal and refitting

Removal

1 Disconnect the battery negative lead.
Caution: If the radio/cassette in your vehicle is equipped with an anti-theft system, make sure you have the correct activation code before disconnecting the battery.
2 To improve access, firmly apply the handbrake then jack up the front of the vehicle and support it on axle stands (see "Jacking and Vehicle Support"). Remove the left-hand front roadwheel, then unbolt and remove the wheelarch liner from under the left-hand wheelarch.
3 Loosen the alternator lower mounting pivot bolt, then loosen the upper adjustment lockbolt and back off the adjustment bolt until the alternator can be swivelled towards the engine sufficiently to release the auxiliary drivebelt from the alternator pulley (see illustrations).
4 Remove the rubber covers (where fitted) from the alternator terminals, then unscrew the retaining nut and disconnect the wiring from the rear of the alternator.
5 Unscrew the alternator upper and lower mounting bolts and washers, then manoeuvre the alternator away from its mounting brackets and out of position.

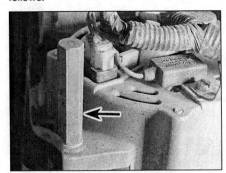

11.3a Alternator lower mounting bolt (early model)

11.3b Alternator upper adjustment bolt (later models)

Refitting

6 Refitting is a reversal of removal, but tension the auxiliary drivebelt as described in Chapter 1 and tighten the alternator mounting bolts to the specified torque settings.

12 Alternator - testing and overhaul

If the alternator is thought to be suspect, it should be removed from the vehicle and taken to an auto-electrician for testing. Most auto-electricians will be able to supply and fit brushes at a reasonable cost. However, check on the cost of repairs before proceeding as it may prove more economical to obtain a new or exchange alternator.

13 Starting system - testing

Note: Refer to the precautions given in "Safety first!" and in Section 1 of this Chapter before starting work.

1 If the starter motor fails to operate when the ignition key is turned to the "start" position, the following may be the cause:
 a) The battery is faulty.
 b) The electrical connections between the switch, solenoid, battery and starter motor are somewhere failing to pass the necessary current from the battery through the starter to earth.
 c) The solenoid is faulty.
 d) The starter motor is mechanically or electrically defective.

2 To check the battery, switch on the headlights. If they dim after a few seconds, this indicates that the battery is discharged - recharge (see Section 3) or renew the battery. If the headlights glow brightly, operate the ignition switch and observe the lights. If they dim, then this indicates that current is reaching the starter motor, therefore the fault must lie in the starter motor. If the lights continue to glow brightly (and no clicking sound can be heard from the starter motor solenoid), this indicates that there is a fault in the circuit or solenoid - see following paragraphs. If the starter motor turns slowly when operated, but the battery is in good condition, then this indicates that either the starter motor is faulty, or there is considerable resistance somewhere in the circuit.

3 If a fault in the circuit is suspected, disconnect the battery leads (including the earth connection to the body), the starter/solenoid wiring and the engine/transmission earth strap. Thoroughly clean the connections, reconnect the leads and wiring, then use a voltmeter or test light to check that full battery voltage is available at the battery positive lead connection to the solenoid, and that the earth is sound. Smear petroleum jelly around the battery terminals to prevent corrosion - corroded connections are amongst the most frequent causes of electrical system faults.

4 If the battery and all connections are in good condition, check the circuit by disconnecting the wire from the solenoid blade terminal. Connect a voltmeter or test light between the wire end and a good earth (such as the battery negative terminal), and check that the wire is live when the ignition switch is turned to the "start" position. If it is, then the circuit is sound - if not, the circuit wiring can be checked as described in Chapter 12.

5 The solenoid contacts can be checked by connecting a voltmeter or test light between the battery positive feed connection on the starter side of the solenoid, and earth. When the ignition switch is turned to the "start" position, there should be a reading or lighted bulb, as applicable. If there is no reading or lighted bulb, the solenoid is faulty and should be renewed.

6 If the circuit and solenoid are proved sound, the fault must lie in the starter motor. In this event, it may be possible to have the starter motor overhauled by a specialist, but check on the availability and cost of spares before proceeding, as it may prove more economical to obtain a new or exchange motor.

14 Starter motor - removal and refitting

Removal

1 Disconnect the battery negative lead.
Caution: If the radio/cassette in your vehicle is equipped with an anti-theft system, make sure you have the correct activation code before disconnecting the battery.
2 On fuel-injected models remove the air cleaner assembly as described in Chapter 4.
3 So that access to the motor can be gained both from above and below, firmly apply the handbrake, then jack up the front of the vehicle and support it on axle stands (see "Jacking and Vehicle Support").
4 Where applicable on later models, remove the EGR valve as described in Chapter 4C.
5 Disconnect the speedometer cable from the transmission with reference to Chapter 12.
6 Unscrew the nut and disconnect the main battery cable from the starter motor. Also disconnect the wiring from the solenoid **(see illustration)**.
7 Unscrew the starter motor mounting bolts, supporting the motor as the bolts are withdrawn, and withdraw the starter motor from the engine **(see illustration)**.

Refitting

8 Refitting is a reversal of removal, but tighten the mounting bolts to the specified torque setting.

15 Starter motor - testing and overhaul

If the starter motor is thought to be suspect, it should be removed from the vehicle and taken to an auto-electrician for testing. Most auto-electricians will be able to supply and fit brushes at a reasonable cost. However, check on the cost of repairs before proceeding as it may prove more economical to obtain a new or exchange motor.

16 Ignition switch - removal and refitting

Removal

1 Disconnect the battery negative lead.
Caution: If the radio/cassette in your vehicle is equipped with an anti-theft system, make sure you have the correct activation code before disconnecting the battery.
2 Remove the steering wheel as described in Chapter 10.
3 Remove the facia lower trim panel and the steering column shrouds as described in Chapters 10 and 11.

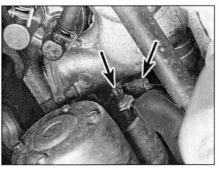

14.6 Disconnecting the wires (arrowed) from the rear of the solenoid

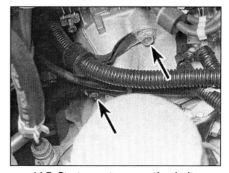

14.7 Starter motor mounting bolts

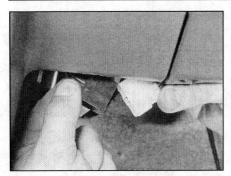

16.4a Disconnect the ignition switch wiring . . .

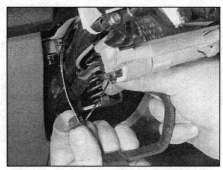

16.4b . . . and release the plastic cable-tie

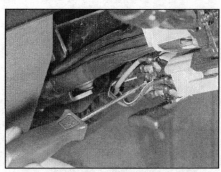

16.7a Unscrew the retaining screw . . .

4 Disconnect the ignition switch wiring below the facia and where necessary release the plastic cable-tie **(see illustrations)**.

Early models

5 The shear-head bolts must now be removed. To do this either cut slots in them with a hacksaw and use a screwdriver to unscrew them, or alternatively drill off the heads and unscrew the shanks after removing the switch.
6 Separate the ignition switch from the clamp. It may be necessary to use a punch and hammer to drive the screws out. Remove the ignition switch assembly from inside the vehicle.

Later models

7 Unscrew the retaining screw and withdraw the ignition switch from the lock housing **(see illustrations)**.
8 Withdraw the ignition switch from inside the vehicle.

Refitting

9 Refitting is a reversal of removal, but use new shear-head bolts on early models and tighten them until their heads break off.

17 Oil pressure warning light switch - removal and refitting

Removal

1 The switch is located on the front left-hand side of the cylinder block, below the exhaust manifold.
2 Disconnect the wiring then unscrew the switch from the cylinder block. Be prepared for some oil spillage. If the switch is to be left removed from the engine for any length of time, plug the hole to prevent oil loss and entry of dust and dirt.

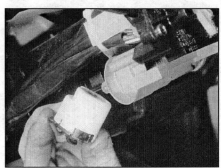

16.7b . . . and withdraw the ignition switch from the lock housing

Refitting

3 Clean the switch threads and apply a smear of sealant to them.
4 Refit the switch and tighten it to the specified torque. Reconnect the wiring.

Chapter 6
Clutch

Contents

Clutch - check and adjustment 2
Clutch and brake pedal free play check . . . . .See Chapter 1
Clutch assembly - removal, inspection and refitting 9
Clutch cable - removal and refitting 3
Clutch hydraulic hose and lines - removal and refitting 6
Clutch hydraulic system - bleeding 7
Clutch master cylinder - removal, overhaul and refitting 4
Clutch pedal - removal and refitting 8
Clutch release mechanism - removal, inspection and refitting 10
Clutch slave cylinder - removal, overhaul and refitting 5
General information 1

Degrees of difficulty

Easy, suitable for novice with little experience	Fairly easy, suitable for beginner with some experience	Fairly difficult, suitable for competent DIY mechanic	Difficult, suitable for experienced DIY mechanic	Very difficult, suitable for expert DIY or professional

Specifications

Type . . . .   Single dry plate with diaphragm spring, cable operated on carburettor models and hydraulically operated on fuel-injected models

Clutch adjustment data
Carburettor models (cable operated clutch):
  Clutch pedal height (released):
    Early (pre-1991) models . . . .   182 to 187 mm
    RHD later (1991-on) models . . . .   178 mm
    LHD later (1991-on) models . . . .   172 mm
  Clutch pedal height (clutch disengaged):
    Early models . . . .   33 mm
    Later models . . . .   65 mm
  Clutch pedal free play . . . .   20 to 30 mm
  Clutch pedal stroke . . . .   145 mm
  Clutch cable free play (between adjusting nut and cable holder) . . . .   5.0 to 6.0 mm
Fuel-injected models (hydraulically operated clutch):
  Clutch pedal height (released):
    RHD models . . . .   178 mm
    LHD models . . . .   172 mm
  Clutch pedal height (clutch disengaged):
    Early models . . . .   40 mm
    Later models . . . .   70 mm
  Clutch pedal free play . . . .   20 to 30 mm
  Clutch pedal stroke:
    RHD models . . . .   145 mm
    LHD models . . . .   150 mm
  Clutch cable free play . . . .   5 to 6 mm
  Clevis pin free play (measured at the pedal) . . . .   1 to 3 mm

Friction disc
Diameter:
  Carburettor models . . . .   184 mm
  Fuel-injected models . . . .   200 mm
Minimum friction material-to-rivet head depth:
  Early models . . . .   1.2 mm
  Later models . . . .   0.3 mm

Torque wrench settings

	Nm	lbf ft
Pressure plate retaining bolts	18	13
Pedal pivot bolt nut:		
Carburettor models	19	14
Fuel-injected models	24	18
Pedal bracket to floor	10	7
Master cylinder mounting nuts	12	9
Slave cylinder mounting bolts	19	14
Starter inhibitor switch to pedal bracket	9	7
Hydraulic line union nut	15	11
Reservoir retaining clamp	6	4
Hydraulic pipe union bolt to slave cylinder	23	17

1 General information

The clutch consists of a friction disc, a pressure plate assembly, a release bearing and the release mechanism; all of these components are contained in the bellhousing, sandwiched between the engine and the transmission.

The friction disc is fitted between the engine flywheel and the clutch pressure plate, and is allowed to slide on the transmission input shaft splines.

The pressure plate assembly is bolted to the engine flywheel. When the engine is running, drive is transmitted from the crankshaft, via the flywheel, to the friction disc (these components being clamped securely together by the pressure plate assembly) and from the friction disc to the transmission input shaft.

To disconnect the drive, the spring pressure must be relaxed. On the models covered in this manual, two different types of clutch release mechanism are used.

On carburettor models a cable-operated release mechanism is used. Depressing the clutch pedal pulls the inner cable, and this turns the release fork. The release fork then presses the release bearing against the pressure plate spring fingers. This causes the springs to deform and releases the clamping force on the pressure plate. To ensure correct operation, the clutch must be regularly adjusted.

On fuel-injected models the clutch release mechanism is operated hydraulically. Depressing the pedal pushes on the master cylinder pushrod. This hydraulically forces the slave cylinder piston which is connected to the end of the clutch release fork lever. The release fork acts on its pivot and presses the release bearing against the pressure plate spring fingers. This causes the springs to deform and releases the clamping force on the pressure plate. The hydraulic clutch is self-adjusting and requires no manual adjustment.

On later models a starter motor inhibitor switch is fitted to the clutch pedal mounting bracket. With this system the clutch pedal must be depressed before it is possible to operate the starter motor.

2 Clutch - check and adjustment

Carburettor models (cable operated)

1 The clutch adjustment is made by first setting the clutch pedal height, and then adjusting the pedal free play.

2 Pull back the carpet from underneath the clutch pedal, and ensure that there are no obstructions between the pedal and floor panel. Measure the distance from the centre of the clutch pedal pad to the floor **(see illustration)**. **Note:** *This measurement can be taken with the carpet in position, so long as the thickness of the carpet is added onto the pedal height measurement.* The pedal height should be as given in the *Specifications* at the start of this Chapter.

3 If the pedal height is not within the specified range, it may be adjusted on pre-1991 models by loosening the lock nut and turning the adjustment bolt as necessary - tighten the locknut on completion. On 1991-on models no adjustment of the height is possible and if it is not as specified damage may have occurred to one or more of the components.

4 With the pedal height as specified, check the pedal free play as follows.

5 Slowly depress the clutch pedal, and measure the distance that the clutch pedal pad travels from the at-rest position to the point where resistance is felt. This is the pedal free play, and should be within the range given in the *Specifications*.

6 If freeplay adjustment is necessary, working within the engine compartment, locate the clutch cable adjuster nut, which is situated at the bulkhead end of the clutch cable. Remove all freeplay from the cable by gently pulling the outer cable out from the bulkhead, then rotate the knurled adjusting ring until the clearance between the ring and cable sealing grommet is approximately 5 to 6 mm **(see illustration)**. Recheck the clutch pedal free play as described in paragraph 5, and readjust if necessary.

7 With the pedal height and free play within the specified limits, fully depress the clutch pedal and check that the distance from the centre of the clutch pedal pad to floor is as given in the *Specifications* with the clutch fully disengaged.

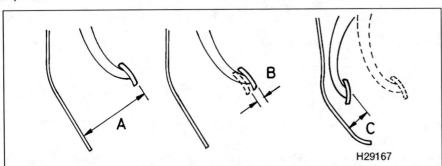

2.2 Clutch pedal adjustment

A *Pedal height (released) measurement*

B *Pedal freeplay measurement*

C *Pedal height (depressed) measurement*

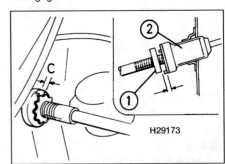

2.6 Turn the knurled adjusting ring (1) so that the clearance (C) between the ring and the sealing grommet (2) is as given in the text

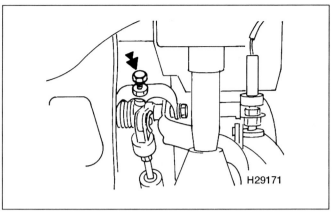

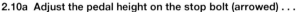

2.10a Adjust the pedal height on the stop bolt (arrowed) . . .

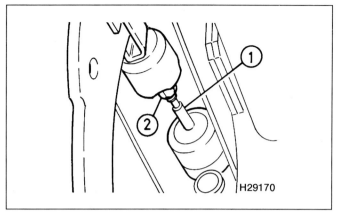

2.10b . . . and the clevis pin/pushrod free play by loosening the locknut (2) and turning the pushrod (1)

Fuel-injected models (hydraulically operated)

8 The clutch hydraulic system is self-adjusting and therefore requires no checking or manual adjustment other than ensuring the fluid level remains correct. The following check should only be necessary if the pedal or master cylinder is disturbed.

9 Measure the clutch pedal height as described in paragraph 2. With the clutch pedal in the at-rest position check the freeplay in the pedal clevis pin by measuring the distance that the clutch pedal pad travels. **Note:** *This check is measuring the clevis pin slack and pushrod freeplay only and should not be confused with the pedal freeplay check (paragraph 11).*

10 If the pedal height and/or clevis pin/pushrod freeplay are not within the specified limits, first adjust the pedal height by slackening the locknut and adjusting the pedal stop bolt on the mounting bracket as necessary; tighten the locknut on completion. Now adjust the clevis pin/pushrod free play by slackening the pushrod linkage locknut and rotating the pushrod with a pair of pliers as necessary; tighten the locknut on completion **(see illustrations)**.

11 Depress the clutch pedal a few times to settle it in position then fully depress it and check that the distance from the centre of the clutch pedal pad to floor is as given in the *Specifications* (pedal height with clutch disengaged). Release the pedal and check the pedal freeplay as described in paragraph 5, measuring the pedal travel from the at-rest position to the point where resistance in the hydraulic circuit is felt. If the pedal clearance or freeplay are not within the specified limits, then it is likely that there is air in the hydraulic system and the system should be bled as described in Section 7. If this fails to solve the problem then it is likely that the clutch or master/slave cylinder are faulty.

3 Clutch cable - removal and refitting

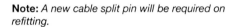

Note: *A new cable split pin will be required on refitting.*

Removal

1 If necessary, to improve access to the transmission end of the cable, firmly apply the handbrake then jack up the front of the vehicle and support it on axle stands (see "*Jacking and Vehicle Support*"). Unbolt and remove the splash guard from under the engine compartment.

2 Working in the engine compartment, locate the clutch cable adjuster nut, which is situated at the bulkhead end of the clutch cable, and fully slacken the adjuster knurled ring to obtain maximum freeplay in the cable.

3 Remove the split pin securing the inner cable to the clutch release lever. Detach the inner cable from the lever then free the outer cable from the transmission bracket.

4 From inside the vehicle, reach up behind the facia and unhook the cable from the upper end of the clutch pedal.

5 Return to the engine compartment and release the cable grommet from the bulkhead and withdraw the cable, releasing it from any relevant retaining clips and guides. Note its correct routing, and remove it from the vehicle.

6 Examine the cable, looking for worn end fittings or a damaged outer casing, and for signs of fraying of the inner cable. Check the cable's operation; the inner cable should move smoothly and easily through the outer casing. Remember that a cable that appears serviceable when tested off the car may well be much heavier in operation when in its working position. Renew the cable if it shows signs of excessive wear or any damage.

Refitting

7 Apply a thin smear of multi-purpose grease to the cable end fittings, then pass the cable through the engine compartment bulkhead and locate the cable grommet securely in its guide.

8 From inside the vehicle, hook the inner cable onto the clutch pedal, and check that it is correctly located.

9 Ensuring that the cable is correctly routed and retained by all the relevant retaining clips and guides, pass the lower end of the cable through the mounting bracket. Engage the inner cable with the release lever and secure it in position with a new split pin.

10 Adjust the clutch as described in Section 2 then refit any components removed for access and lower the vehicle to the ground.

4 Clutch master cylinder - removal, overhaul and refitting

Note: *A new clevis pin split pin will be required on refitting.*

Removal

1 Remove the master cylinder reservoir cap, and syphon the hydraulic fluid from the reservoir. Alternatively, open the slave cylinder bleed screw, and gently pump the clutch pedal to expel the fluid through a plastic tube connected to the screw; tighten the screw when all the fluid has been removed.

 Warning: Do not syphon the fluid by mouth, as it is poisonous; use a syringe or an old poultry baster

2 Remove all traces of dirt from the master cylinder. Slacken and remove the union nut and disconnect the hydraulic line from the master cylinder. Catch any fluid in a suitable container and plug the line and master cylinder port to minimise fluid loss and prevent the entry of dirt into the system.

3 From inside the vehicle, reach up behind the facia and withdraw the split pin from the clutch pedal pushrod clevis pin. Remove the washer and withdraw the clevis pin from the pushrod end.

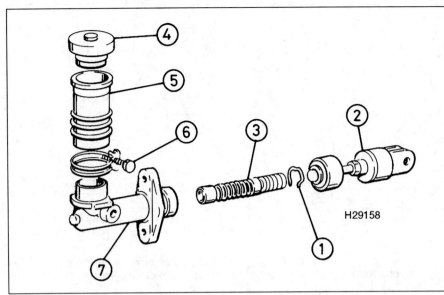

4.6 Clutch master cylinder components - fuel injected models

1 *Retaining clip*	3 *Piston*	6 *Retaining clip*
2 *Pushrod and dust*	4 *Reservoir cap*	7 *Body*
cover	5 *Reservoir*	

4 Return to the engine compartment then unscrew and remove the retaining nuts and remove the master cylinder from the studs on the bulkhead, along with its gasket. Take care not to spill any hydraulic fluid on the vehicle's paintwork.

Overhaul

5 Clean thoroughly the outside of the cylinder and carefully clamp the cylinder in a vice equipped with soft jaws.
6 Loosen the retaining clip and remove the fluid reservoir from the master cylinder body **(see illustration)**.
7 Release the dust cover from the rear of the master cylinder to gain access to the piston retaining clip.
8 Compress the retaining clip then remove it from the end of the cylinder and withdraw the pushrod, piston assembly and spring.
9 Examine the surfaces of the piston and cylinder. If they are scored or corroded, renew the master cylinder complete.
10 If the cylinder is in good condition, obtain a piston repair kit which will contain all the necessary renewable items.
11 Ensure all components are clean and dry and lubricate the piston assembly with fresh hydraulic fluid.
12 Fit the spring to the piston then carefully enter the assembly into the cylinder. Ease the piston into position with a twisting motion, taking great care not to trap the seal lips.
13 Fit the pushrod to the end of the piston and install the circlip, making sure it is correctly located in the cylinder groove. Check the operation of the piston and pushrod assembly then seat the pushrod dust cover on the master cylinder body.

14 Refit the fluid reservoir to the master cylinder and tighten its retaining clamp.

Refitting

15 Ensure the cylinder and bulkhead mating surfaces are clean and dry, then locate the new gasket on the bulkhead studs.
16 Manoeuvre the master cylinder into position on the studs whilst ensuring that the pushrod clevis engages correctly with the pedal. Refit and tighten the master cylinder retaining nuts to the specified torque.
17 Apply a smear of multi-purpose grease to the clevis pin then fit the pin and washer and secure it in position with a new split pin.
18 Reconnect the hydraulic fluid line to the master cylinder, and tighten the union nut to the specified torque. **Note:** *Do not overtighten the union nut.*
19 Refill the master cylinder reservoir with the correct type of fluid and bleed the hydraulic system as described in Section 7.
20 On completion check and adjust the clutch pedal settings as described in Section 2.

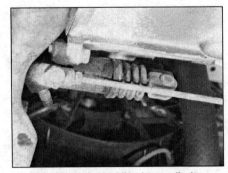

5.3 Clutch hydraulic slave cylinder

5 Clutch slave cylinder - removal, overhaul and refitting

Removal

1 Firmly apply the handbrake then jack up the front of the vehicle and support it on axle stands (see "*Jacking and Vehicle Support*").
2 Minimise fluid loss by first removing the master cylinder reservoir cap, and then tightening it down onto a piece of polythene, to obtain an airtight seal. Alternatively, syphon all the hydraulic fluid from the reservoir then open the slave cylinder bleed screw, and gently pump the clutch pedal to expel the fluid through a plastic tube connected to the screw; tighten the screw when all the fluid has been removed.
3 Wipe away all traces of dirt around the hydraulic pipe union on the slave cylinder and unscrew the union nut **(see illustration)**. Carefully ease the pipe out of the cylinder, and plug or tape over its end to prevent dirt entry. Wipe off any spilt fluid immediately.
4 Unscrew the two cylinder retaining bolts and carefully draw the cylinder off the pushrod which will remain attached to the clutch release lever. Alternatively, disconnect the pushrod from the release lever by extracting the "C" clip and removing the clevis pin.

Overhaul

5 Clean the outside of the cylinder.
6 Remove the dust cover (and retaining ring where fitted) from the cylinder and withdraw the piston assembly and spring, noting which way around the spring is fitted **(see illustration)**.
7 If necessary, unscrew and remove the union bolt and washers securing the fluid union adaptor to the side of the cylinder and withdraw the restrictor valve and spring from the cylinder body. New sealing washers will be needed on reassembly.
8 Examine the surfaces of the piston and cylinder. If they are scored or corroded, renew the slave cylinder complete.
9 If the cylinder is in good condition, obtain a piston repair kit which will contain all the necessary renewable items.
10 Ensure all components are clean and dry and lubricate the piston assembly with fresh hydraulic fluid.
11 Fit the spring to the piston, with its smaller (tapered) end facing the piston, then carefully enter the assembly into the cylinder. Ease the piston into position with a twisting motion, taking great care not to trap the seal lips.
12 Depress the piston and fit the dust cover (and retaining ring where fitted), making sure it is correctly located on the cylinder body.
13 Where removed, refit the spring and restrictor valve to the slave cylinder. Position a new sealing washer on each side of the fluid union then fit the union bolt and tighten it to the specified torque.

Refitting

14 Apply a smear of grease to the release fork pushrod and ease the slave cylinder onto the rod. Fit the cylinder retaining bolts and tighten them securely. If the pushrod was removed reconnect it to the release lever by refitting the clevis pin and retaining with the "C" clip, before refitting the slave cylinder.

15 Reconnect the hydraulic pipe to the slave cylinder and tighten its union nut to the specified torque. **Note:** *Do not overtighten the union nut.* Where applicable, remove the polythene from the master cylinder.

16 Bleed the hydraulic system as described in Section 7.

17 On completion check the clutch pedal settings as described in Section 2.

6 Clutch hydraulic hose and lines - removal and refitting

Removal

1 Remove the master cylinder reservoir cap, and syphon the hydraulic fluid from the reservoir. Alternatively, open the slave cylinder bleed screw, and gently pump the clutch pedal to expel the fluid through a plastic tube connected to the screw; tighten the screw when all the fluid has been removed.

2 To remove one of the two rigid hydraulic lines, first unscrew the union nut from the master or slave cylinder (as applicable) then, using a further spanner to hold the flexible hose, unscrew the union nut and disconnect the line from the hose. Withdraw the line from the engine compartment **(see illustration)**.

3 To remove the flexible hose, first unscrew the rigid line union nuts while holding the flats on the hose with a further spanner, then pull out the retaining clips and disconnect the hose from the mounting bracket. Withdraw the hose from the engine compartment.

Refitting

4 Refitting is a reversal of removal; tighten the union nuts to the specified torque and bleed the hydraulic system as described in Section 7. **Note:** *Do not overtighten the union nuts.*

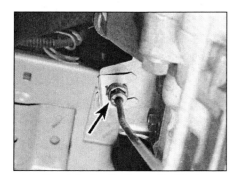

6.2 Clutch hydraulic line to flexible hose union nut

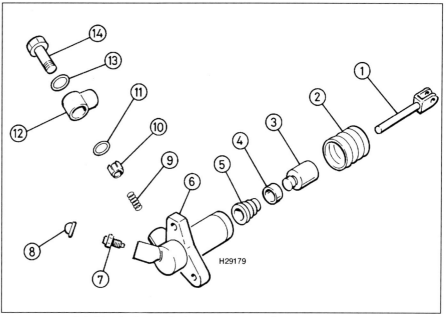

5.6 Clutch slave cylinder components - fuel injected models

1 Pushrod	*6 Body*	*11 Sealing washer*
2 Dust cover	*7 Bleed screw*	*12 Fluid union adapter*
3 Piston	*8 Dust cap*	*13 Sealing washer*
4 Seal	*9 Spring*	*14 Union bolt*
5 Spring	*10 Restrictor valve*	

7 Clutch hydraulic system - bleeding

⚠ *Warning: Hydraulic fluid is poisonous; wash off immediately and thoroughly in the case of skin contact, and seek immediate medical advice if any fluid is swallowed or gets into the eyes. Certain types of hydraulic fluid are flammable, and may ignite when allowed into contact with hot components; when servicing any hydraulic system, it is safest to assume that the fluid is flammable, and to take precautions against the risk of fire as though it is petrol that is being handled. Hydraulic fluid is also an effective paint stripper, and will attack plastics; if any is spilt, it should be washed off immediately, using copious quantities of fresh water. Finally, it is hygroscopic (it absorbs moisture from the air) - old fluid may be contaminated and unfit for further use. When topping-up or renewing the fluid, always use the recommended type, and ensure that it comes from a freshly opened sealed container.*

1 The correct operation of any hydraulic system is only possible after removing all air from the components and circuit; this is achieved by bleeding the system.

2 During the bleeding procedure, add only clean, unused hydraulic fluid of the recommended type; never re-use fluid that has already been bled from the system. Ensure that sufficient fluid is available before starting work.

3 If there is any possibility of incorrect fluid being already in the system, the hydraulic circuit must be flushed completely with uncontaminated, correct fluid.

4 If hydraulic fluid has been lost from the system, or air has entered because of a leak, ensure that the fault is cured before continuing further.

5 The bleed screw is screwed directly into the top of the slave cylinder body; to gain access firmly apply the handbrake then jack up the front of the vehicle and support it on axle stands (see "*Jacking and Vehicle Support*").

6 Check that all pipes and hoses are secure, unions tight and the bleed screw is closed. Clean any dirt from around the bleed screw.

7 Unscrew the master cylinder fluid reservoir cap, and top up the fluid level to the upper (MAX) level line; refit the cap loosely, and remember to maintain the fluid level at least above the lower (MIN) level line throughout the procedure, or there is a risk of further air entering the system.

8 There are a number of one-man, do-it-yourself bleeding kits currently available from motor accessory shops. It is recommended that one of these kits is used whenever possible, as they greatly simplify the bleeding operation, and reduce the risk of expelled air and fluid being drawn back into the system. If such a kit is not available, the basic (two-man) method must be used, which is described in detail below.

9 If a kit is to be used, prepare the vehicle as described previously, and follow the kit manufacturer's instructions, as the procedure may vary slightly according to the type being used; generally, they are as outlined below in the relevant sub-section.

Bleeding - basic (two-man) method

10 Collect a clean glass jar, a suitable length of plastic or rubber tubing which is a tight fit over the bleed screw, and a ring spanner to fit the screw. The help of an assistant will also be required.

11 Remove the dust cap from the slave cylinder bleed screw. Fit the spanner and tube to the screw, place the other end of the tube in the jar, and pour in sufficient fluid to cover the end of the tube.

12 Ensure that the fluid level is maintained at least above the lower level line in the reservoir throughout the procedure.

13 Have the assistant fully depress the clutch pedal several times to build up pressure, then maintain it on the final downstroke.

14 While pedal pressure is maintained, unscrew the bleed screw (approximately one turn) and allow the compressed fluid and air to flow into the jar. The assistant should maintain pedal pressure and should not release it until instructed to do so. When the flow stops, tighten the bleed screw again, have the assistant fully release the pedal slowly, and recheck the reservoir fluid level.

15 Repeat the steps given in paragraphs 13 and 14 until the fluid emerging from the bleed screw is free from air bubbles. If the master cylinder has been drained and refilled allow approximately five seconds between cycles for the master cylinder passages to refill.

16 When no more air bubbles appear, tighten the bleed screw securely, remove the tube and spanner, and refit the dust cap. Do not overtighten the bleed screw.

Bleeding - using a one-way valve kit

17 As their name implies, these kits consist of a length of tubing with a one-way valve fitted, to prevent expelled air and fluid being drawn back into the system; some kits include a translucent container, which can be positioned so that the air bubbles can be more easily seen flowing from the end of the tube.

18 The kit is connected to the bleed screw, which is then opened. The user returns to the driver's seat, depresses the clutch pedal with a smooth, steady stroke, and slowly releases it; this is repeated until the expelled fluid is clear of air bubbles.

19 Note that these kits simplify work so much that it is easy to forget the clutch fluid reservoir level; ensure that this is maintained at least above the lower level line at all times.

Bleeding - using a pressure-bleeding kit

20 These kits are usually operated by the reservoir of pressurised air contained in the spare tyre. However, note that it will probably be necessary to reduce the pressure to a lower level than normal; refer to the instructions supplied with the kit.

21 By connecting a pressurised, fluid-filled container to the clutch fluid reservoir, bleeding can be carried out simply by opening the bleed screw and allowing the fluid to flow out until no more air bubbles can be seen in the expelled fluid.

22 This method has the advantage that the large reservoir of fluid provides an additional safeguard against air being drawn into the system during bleeding.

All methods

23 When bleeding is complete, and correct pedal feel is restored, tighten the bleed screw securely and wash off any spilt fluid. Refit the dust cap to the bleed screw then lower the vehicle to the ground.

24 Check the hydraulic fluid level in the master cylinder reservoir, and top-up if necessary (see "Weekly Checks" and Chapter 1).

25 Discard any hydraulic fluid that has been bled from the system; it will not be fit for re-use.

26 Check the operation of the clutch pedal as described in Section 2. If the clutch is still not operating correctly, air must still be present in the system, and further bleeding is required. Failure to bleed satisfactorily after a reasonable repetition of the bleeding procedure may be due to worn master cylinder/slave cylinder seals.

8   Clutch pedal -
removal and refitting

Removal

Carburettor models

1 Working in the engine compartment, locate the clutch cable adjuster nut, which is situated at the bulkhead end of the clutch cable, and fully slacken the adjuster knurled ring to obtain maximum freeplay in the cable.

2 From inside the vehicle, reach up behind the facia and unhook the inner cable from the upper end of the clutch pedal.

3 On early RHD models (pre-1991) unscrew the nut from the pedal pivot bolt and recover the washers, then pull out the pivot bolt until it is possible to withdraw the pedal from the bracket. On LHD models unscrew the nut and recover the washers, then slide the pedal from the pivot on the bracket. If necessary the two half-bushes may be removed from the pedal.

4 On later models use circlip pliers to extract the circlip from the end of the pedal pivot shaft (part of the pedal) and slide off the washer. Slide the pedal from the bracket and recover the wave washer from the pedal pivot shaft. Remove the pedal pivot bushes from the mounting bracket and if necessary remove the pedal rubber pad.

5 Examine all components for signs of wear or damage and renew as necessary.

Fuel-injected models

6 Remove the split pin and washer and withdraw the clevis pin securing the clutch pedal to the master cylinder pushrod.

7 Unscrew and remove the pivot nut, washer and bolt then remove the pedal and spring assembly from the bracket, noting which way around the spring is fitted. Remove the bushes and spring from the pedal and if necessary remove the pedal rubber pad.

8 Inspect the pivot bushes and springs for signs of wear or damage and renew as necessary.

Refitting

Carburettor models

9 Refitting is a reversal of removal, but apply multi-purpose grease to the pedal pivot and bushes and tighten the pivot nut to the specified torque. On completion adjust the pedal and cable as described in Section 2.

Fuel-injected models

10 Refitting is a reversal of removal, but apply multi-purpose grease to the pedal pivot and bushes and tighten the pivot nut to the specified torque. On completion check and adjust the pedal as described in Section 2.

9   Clutch assembly -
removal, inspection
and refitting

⚠ **Warning: Dust created by clutch wear and deposited on the clutch components may contain asbestos, which is a health hazard. DO NOT blow it out with compressed air, or inhale any of it. DO NOT use petrol or petroleum-based solvents to clean off the dust. Brake system cleaner or methylated spirit should be used to flush the dust into a suitable receptacle. After the clutch components are wiped clean with rags, dispose of the contaminated rags and cleaner in a sealed, marked container.**
Note: Although some friction materials may no longer contain asbestos, it is safest to assume that they do, and to take precautions accordingly.

Removal

1 Unless the complete engine/transmission unit is to be removed from the car and separated for major overhaul (see Chapter 2), the clutch can be reached by removing the transmission as described in Chapter 7A.

2 Before disturbing the clutch, use chalk or a marker pen to mark the relationship of the pressure plate assembly to the flywheel.

3 Working in a diagonal sequence, slacken the pressure plate bolts by half a turn at a time, until spring pressure is released and the bolts can be unscrewed by hand.

9.6 Measuring the depth of the rivet heads below the friction material surface

9.13 Fit the friction disc so that its spring hub assembly faces away from the flywheel

9.14 Refitting the pressure plate

4 Prise the pressure plate assembly off its locating dowels, and collect the friction disc, noting which way round the disc is fitted.

Inspection

Note: *Due to the amount of work necessary to remove and refit clutch components, it is usually considered good practice to renew the clutch friction disc, pressure plate assembly and release bearing as a matched set, even if only one of these is actually worn enough to require renewal. It is also worth considering the renewal of the clutch components on a preventive basis if the engine and/or transmission have been removed for some other reason.*

5 When cleaning clutch components, read first the warning at the beginning of this Section; remove dust using a clean, dry cloth, and working in a well-ventilated atmosphere.

6 Check the friction disc linings for signs of wear, damage or oil contamination. If the friction material is cracked, burnt, scored or damaged, or if it is contaminated with oil or grease (shown by shiny black patches), the friction disc must be renewed. Measure the depth of the rivets below the friction material surface. If the depth of any rivet is equal to, or less than, the service limit given in the *Specifications*, then the friction disc must be renewed **(see illustration)**.

7 If the friction material is still serviceable, check that the centre boss splines are unworn, that the torsion springs are in good condition and securely fastened, and that all the rivets are tight. If any wear or damage is found, the friction disc must be renewed.

8 If the friction material is fouled with oil, this must be due to an oil leak from the crankshaft oil seal, from the sump-to-cylinder block joint, or from the transmission input shaft. Renew the seal or repair the joint, as appropriate, as described in Chapter 2 or 7A, before installing the new friction disc.

9 Check the pressure plate assembly for obvious signs of wear or damage; shake it to check for loose rivets or worn or damaged fulcrum rings, and check that the drive straps securing the pressure plate to the cover do not show signs (such as a deep yellow or blue discoloration) of overheating. If the diaphragm

spring is worn or damaged, or if its pressure is in any way suspect, the pressure plate assembly should be renewed.

10 Examine the machined bearing surfaces of the pressure plate and of the flywheel; they should be clean, completely flat, and free from scratches or scoring. If either is discoloured from excessive heat, or shows signs of cracks, it should be renewed - although minor damage of this nature can sometimes be polished away using emery paper.

11 Check that the release bearing contact surface rotates smoothly and easily, with no sign of noise or roughness. Also check that the surface itself is smooth and unworn, with no signs of cracks, pitting or scoring. If there is any doubt about its condition, the bearing must be renewed.

Refitting

12 On reassembly, ensure that the disc contact surfaces of the flywheel and pressure plate are completely clean, smooth, and free from oil or grease. Use solvent to remove any protective grease from new components.

13 Fit the friction disc so that its spring hub assembly faces away from the flywheel; there may also be a marking showing which way round the plate is to be refitted. On the Hyundai friction disc the side with the manufacturer's stamp mark must face away from the flywheel **(see illustration)**.

14 Refit the pressure plate assembly, aligning the marks made on dismantling (if the original pressure plate is re-used), and locating the pressure plate on its three locating dowels **(see illustration)**. Fit the pressure plate bolts, but tighten them only finger-tight, so that the friction disc can still be moved.

15 The friction disc must now be centralised, so that when the transmission is refitted, its input shaft will pass through the splines at the centre of the friction disc.

16 Centralisation can be achieved by passing a screwdriver or other long bar through the friction disc and into the hole in the crankshaft; the friction disc can then be moved around until it is centred on the crankshaft hole. Alternatively, a clutch-aligning -tool can be used to eliminate the guesswork; these can be obtained from most

accessory shops **(see illustration)**. A home-made aligning tool can be fabricated from a length of metal rod or wooden dowel which fits closely inside the crankshaft hole, and has insulating tape wound around it to match the diameter of the friction disc splined hole.

17 When the friction disc is centralised, tighten the pressure plate bolts evenly and in a diagonal sequence to the specified torque setting.

18 Apply a thin smear of molybdenum disulphide grease to the splines of the friction disc and the transmission input shaft, and also to the release fork shaft.

Caution: Do not apply too much grease as there is a risk that it will contaminate the friction disc material.

19 Refit the transmission (see Chapter 7A).

10 Clutch release mechanism - removal, inspection and refitting

Note: *Refer to the warning concerning the dangers of asbestos dust at the beginning of Section 9.*

Removal

1 Unless the complete engine/transmission unit is to be removed from the car and separated for major overhaul (see Chapter 2B), the clutch release mechanism can be reached by removing the transmission only, as described in Chapter 7A.

9.16 Centralise the friction disc with an alignment tool (arrowed) then tighten the pressure plate bolts

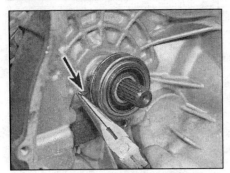

10.2 Unhooking the release bearing retaining clip

10.3 Roll pins (arrowed) securing the release lever and fork to the shaft

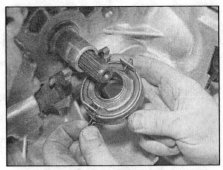

10.9 Locate the retaining clip in the bearing groove then engage the spring ends in the release fork holes

2 Using pliers, unhook the bearing retaining clip from the release fork and slide the bearing and clip off from the guide tube **(see illustration)**.

3 To remove the release lever and fork, drill out or extract the roll pins securing the fork to the shaft **(see illustration)** - Hyundai technicians use a special extractor tool which consists of a threaded rod which is inserted through the roll pin with a small nut screwed onto its inner end. Noting the correct fitted location of the lever return spring (carburettor models only), withdraw the release lever from the transmission housing then remove the release fork, spring (if fitted) and foam seals from the bellhousing. Renew the foam seals if they show signs of damage or deterioration.

Inspection

4 Check the release mechanism, renewing any component which is worn or damaged.

Carefully check all bearing surfaces and points of contact.

5 When checking the release bearing itself, note that it is often considered worthwhile to renew it as a matter of course. Check that the contact surface rotates smoothly and easily, with no sign of noise or roughness, and that the surface itself is smooth and unworn, with no signs of cracks, pitting or scoring. If there is any doubt about its condition, the bearing must be renewed.

Refitting

6 Apply a smear of molybdenum disulphide grease to the release lever shaft pivot bushes and the contact surfaces of the release fork and bearing.

7 Engage the return spring (where fitted) with the release fork and fit the assembly to the bellhousing.

8 Position the foam seals on either side of the fork and spring assembly ensuring the return spring is correctly located in the transmission housing. Slide the release lever into the housing, engaging it with the seals, spring and fork. Align the shaft holes with those of the release fork and secure the fork to the shaft by tapping in the new roll pins.

9 Ensure that the retaining clip is correctly engaged in the release bearing groove then slide the release bearing and spring clip into position **(see illustration)**. Engage the bearing with the release fork and secure it in position by locating the ends of the retaining clip in the fork holes.

10 Check the operation of the release mechanism then refit the transmission as described in Chapter 7A.

Chapter 7 Part A:
Manual transmission

Contents

Gearchange cables - removal, checking and refitting 4
Gearchange lever assembly - removal, overhaul and refitting 5
Gearchange mechanism - checking and adjustment 2
Gearchange rod assembly - removal, overhaul and refitting 3
General information 1
Oil seals - renewal 6
Reversing light switch - testing, removal and refitting 7
Speedometer drive - removal and refitting 8
Transmission - removal and refitting 9
Transmission oil level check . . . . .See Chapter 1
Transmission overhaul - general information 10

Degrees of difficulty

 Easy, suitable for novice with little experience
 Fairly easy, suitable for beginner with some experience
 Fairly difficult, suitable for competent DIY mechanic
 Difficult, suitable for experienced DIY mechanic
Very difficult, suitable for expert DIY or professional

Specifications

General
Type . . . . Manual, four or five forward speeds and reverse. Synchromesh on all forward speeds

Torque wrench settings

	Nm	lbf ft
Gearchange cable support bracket bolts	14	10
Gearchange lever assembly mounting bolts	14	10
Gearchange rod to transmission bolt	32	23
Support rod to transmission bolt	49	36
Transmission filler and drain plugs	33	24
Engine/transmission right-hand mounting:		
Mounting to body bolts	47	35
Mounting through bolt	100	74
Mounting bracket to transmission nut/bolt	70	52
Flywheel lower cover plate bolts	19	14
Reversing light switch	33	24
Speedometer drive mounting bolt	4	3
Engine to transmission unit bolts	47	35

2.3 Remove the split pins (1) and detach the gearchange cables from the lever. The cable lengths are adjusted by turning the adjusters (2)

1 General information

The transmission is contained in a cast-aluminium alloy casing bolted to the engine's right-hand end, and consists of the gearbox and final drive differential - often called a transaxle. A four- or five-speed transmission is fitted according to model.

Drive is transmitted from the crankshaft via the clutch to the input shaft, which has a splined extension to accept the clutch friction plate, and rotates in ball-bearings. From the input shaft, drive is transmitted to the intermediate shaft, which rotates in taper roller bearings (early models) or ball bearings (later models). Drive is then transmitted to the output shaft, which rotates in taper roller bearings. From the output shaft, the drive is transmitted to the differential crownwheel, which rotates with the differential case and planetary gears and drives the sun gears and driveshafts. The rotation of the planetary gears on their shaft allows the inner roadwheel to rotate at a slower speed than the outer roadwheel when the car is cornering.

The input, intermediate and output shafts are arranged side by side, parallel to the crankshaft and driveshafts, so that their gear pinion teeth are in constant mesh. In the neutral position, the output shaft gear pinions rotate freely, so that drive cannot be transmitted to the crownwheel.

Gear selection is via a floor-mounted lever and selector rods (early models) or selector cables (later models). The selector rods/cables cause the appropriate selector fork to move its respective synchro-sleeve along the shaft, to lock the gear pinion to the synchro-hub. Since the synchro-hubs are splined to the input and intermediate shafts, this locks the pinion to the shaft, so that drive can be transmitted. To ensure that gear-changing can be made quickly and quietly, a synchro-mesh system is fitted to all forward gears, consisting of baulk rings and spring-loaded keys. The synchro-mesh cones are formed on the mating faces of the baulk rings and gear pinions.

2 Gearchange mechanism - checking and adjustment

Checking

1 If a stiff, sloppy or imprecise gearchange leads you to suspect that a fault exists within the linkage, check it as follows. On the rod linkage, apply the handbrake then jack up the front of the vehicle and support on axle stands (see "*Jacking and Vehicle Support*"). Check the bushes of the support rod and gearchange rod for seizure or excessive play and if necessary renew them with reference to Section 3. On the cable linkage check the routing of the cables. On both types, check the gear lever bushes with reference to Section 4.

Adjustment (cable linkage)

Note: *There is no adjustment for the rod-type linkage.*

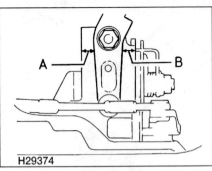

2.7 The clearance between the front (A) and rear (B) of the gearchange lever base must be equal

2 Remove the centre console as described in Chapter 11.
3 Set the gearchange lever and transmission levers (in the engine compartment) to the neutral position then remove the split pins and detach both the gearchange cables from the base of the gearchange lever **(see illustration)**.
4 Position the select inner cable end fitting over the rearmost lever on the gearchange lever assembly, and if necessary loosen the locknuts and adjust the length of the cable so that the fitting locates easily on the lever stub. Tighten the locknuts and refit the split pin.
5 Position the shift inner cable end fitting over the gearchange lever base, and if necessary loosen the locknuts and adjust the length of the cable so that the fitting locates easily on the lever stub. Tighten the locknuts and refit the split pin.
6 Note that the cable adjusters must be engaged with equal threads on the inner cable; to check this the select cable resin bushing end surface must align with the lever side surface, and the shift cable resin bushing end surface must align with the split pin hole.
7 Check that the clearance between the front and rear of the gearchange lever base is equal (ie the base is vertical) **(see illustration)**.
8 Check the operation of the gearchange linkage then refit the centre console as described in Chapter 11.

3 Gearchange rod assembly - removal, overhaul and refitting

Note: *The gearchange rod assembly is fitted to early models (approx pre-1991).*

Removal

1 Apply the handbrake, then jack up the front of the vehicle and support on axle stands (see "*Jacking and Vehicle Support*").
2 Unscrew and remove the gearchange lever knob, then unscrew the mounting screws and remove the centre console (refer to Chapter 11 if necessary).
3 Unscrew and remove the mounting nuts securing the gearchange lever assembly to the floor **(see illustration)**.

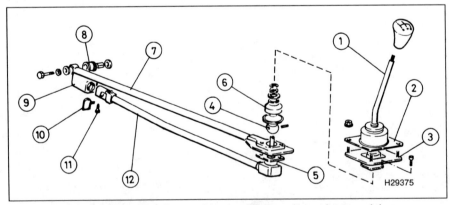

3.3 Gearchange rod assembly - modified version on later models

1 Gear lever	4 Fulcrum ball	7 Extension rod	10 Locking wire
2 Gaiter	5 Dust boot	8 Bushing	11 Set screw
3 Insulator	6 Rubber insulator	9 Dust cover	12 Gearchange rod

4.4 Slide out the retaining clips and free the cables from their brackets

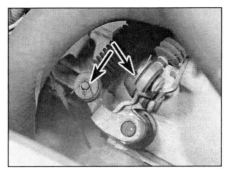

4.6a Remove the split pins . . .

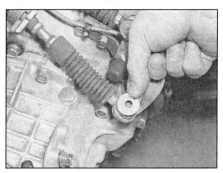

4.6b . . . and washers and disconnect the cables from the transmission levers

4 Unscrew and remove the bolt securing the support rod to the rear of the transmission and recover the washers.

5 Unscrew and remove the bolt securing the gearchange rod to the transmission, and withdraw the assembly from under the vehicle. Where necessary cut free the locking wire before unscrewing the bolt.

Overhaul

6 To dismantle the assembly, extract the E-ring from the base of the gear lever then unscrew the bolts and separate the support and gearchange rods.

7 Support the gear lever in a vice, then drive out the pin from the fulcrum ball using a suitable drift. Slide the fulcrum ball from the lever.

8 Examine the components for wear and damage and renew as necessary.

9 Reassemble the assembly using a reversal of the dismantling procedure, but apply multi-purpose grease to the fulcrum ball and inside surface of the dust cover.

Refitting

10 Refitting is a reversal of removal, but tighten the mounting bolts to the specified torque and where necessary fit locking wire to the bolt securing the gearchange rod to the rear of the transmission. Check the operation of the gearchange before lowering the vehicle to the ground.

4 Gearchange cables - removal, checking and refitting

Removal

1 Remove the centre console assembly as described in Chapter 11. On fuel-injected models, remove the air cleaner housing as described in Chapter 4B to gain access to the transmission end of the cables.

2 Prior to removal make identification marks on the cables and gearchange/transmission levers to avoid confusion on refitting.

3 Position the gearchange lever in the neutral position then remove the split pins and detach the cables from the base of the lever. Take care not to disturb the position of the

transmission shift and select levers whilst the cables are disconnected.

4 Slide out the retaining clips and free the cables from their brackets **(see illustration)**.

5 Work back along the cables, freeing them from any relevant retaining clips and clamps. Unscrew the two bolts securing the cable grommet bracket to the bulkhead.

6 From inside the engine compartment, remove the split pins and washers and free the cables from the transmission levers **(see illustrations)**.

7 Slide out the retaining clips securing the cables to the transmission bracket then, noting the cable assembly correct routing, free the cable grommet from the bulkhead and remove the assembly from the vehicle **(see illustrations)**.

Checking

8 Examine each cable, looking for worn end fittings or a damaged outer casing, and for signs of fraying of the inner cable. Check the cable's operation; the inner cable should move smoothly and easily through the outer casing. Remember that a cable that appears serviceable when tested off the car may well be much heavier in operation when in its working position. Renew the cable if it shows signs of excessive wear or any damage.

Refitting

9 Apply a smear of multi-purpose grease to the cable end fittings and the lever pivots. If new cables are being fitted, transfer the marks made prior to removal to aid refitting.

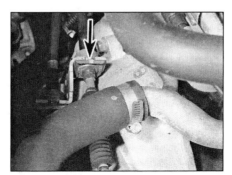

4.7a Slide out the left-hand retaining clip . . .

10 Manoeuvre the cables into position, ensuring they are correctly routed, and locate the cable grommet in the bulkhead. Tighten the bolts.

11 Engage the lower end of each outer cable with its relevant transmission bracket and secure the cables in position with the retaining clips. Connect the inner cables to the transmission levers then refit the washers and secure them in position with new split pins.

12 From inside the vehicle, refit and tighten the select cable clamp retaining nuts.

13 Ensure the cables are correctly routed then engage the cables with their respective locations in the lever base and secure them in position with the retaining clips and split pins.

14 Ensure both the transmission shift and select levers are still in the neutral position then check and adjust the cables as described in Section 2.

5 Gearchange lever assembly - removal, overhaul and refitting

Note: *On the rod-type gearchange, the lever is removed together with the rod assembly as described in Section 3.*

Removal

1 Apply the handbrake then jack up the front of the vehicle and support on axle stands (see *"Jacking and Vehicle Support"*).

2 Remove the centre console as described in Chapter 11.

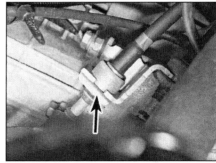

4.7b . . . and right-hand retaining clip and free the outer cables from the mounting bracket on the transmission

5.4 Gearchange lever assembly

3 Set the gearchange lever to the neutral position then remove the split pins and detach both the gearchange cables from the base of the gearchange lever. Slide out the retaining clips and disconnect the cables from their supports on the gearchange lever assembly. Position the cables to one side.
4 Working beneath the vehicle, unscrew the nuts/ securing the gearchange lever assembly to the floor. If the bolts turn with the nuts, have an assistant hold the bolt heads inside the vehicle (see illustration).
5 Withdraw the gearchange lever assembly from inside the vehicle. Recover the spacers and bushes.

Overhaul

6 Unscrew and remove the bolt securing the gear lever to the control lever and withdraw the gear lever. Note the location of the bushes and spacers.
7 Unscrew and remove the bolt securing the control lever to the mounting bracket, and withdraw noting the location of the return spring, bushes and spacers.
8 Examine the components for wear and damage and renew as necessary.
9 Reassemble the components using a reversal of the dismantling procedure, but apply multi-purpose grease to the bushes and bearing surfaces.

Refitting

10 Refitting is a reversal of removal, but tighten the mounting bolts to the specified torque and check and if necessary adjust the cables as described in Section 2.

6 Oil seals - renewal

Driveshaft oil seals

1 Chock the rear wheels, apply the handbrake, then jack up the front of the car and support it on axle stands (see "Jacking and Vehicle Support"). Remove the appropriate front roadwheel.
2 Drain the transmission oil as described in Chapter 1.

7.4 Disconnecting the reversing light switch wiring

3 Working as described in Chapter 8, free the inner end of the driveshaft from the transmission, and place it clear of the seal, noting that there is no need to unscrew the driveshaft retaining nut; the driveshaft can be left secured to the hub. Support the driveshaft, to avoid placing any strain on the driveshaft joints or gaiters.
4 Carefully prise the oil seal out of the transmission using a large flat-bladed screwdriver.
5 Remove all traces of dirt from the area around the oil seal aperture, then apply a smear of grease to the outer lip of the new oil seal. Ensure the seal is correctly positioned, with its sealing lip facing inwards, and drive it squarely into position, using a tubular drift (such as a large socket) which bears only on the hard outer edge of the seal.
6 Refit the driveshaft with reference to Chapter 8.
7 Refill the transmission with the specified type and amount of oil, as described in Chapter 1.

Input shaft and gearchange lever shaft oil seals

8 To renew these oil seals, the transmission must be dismantled. This task should therefore be entrusted to a Hyundai dealer or transmission specialist.

7 Reversing light switch - testing, removal and refitting

Testing

1 The reversing light circuit is controlled by a plunger-type switch that is screwed into the top of the transmission casing. If a fault develops in the circuit, first ensure that the circuit fuse has not blown.
2 To test the switch, disconnect the wiring connector, and use a multimeter (set to the resistance function) or a battery-and-bulb test circuit to check that there is continuity between the switch terminals only when reverse gear is selected. If this is not the case, and there are no obvious breaks or other damage to the wires, the switch is faulty, and must be renewed.

Removal

3 To improve access to the switch on fuel-injected models, remove the air intake duct as described in Chapter 4B.
4 Disconnect the wiring connector, then unscrew the switch from the transmission casing along with its sealing washer (see illustration). Note: The switch plunger contacts a ball on the 5th/reverse selector shaft - if the transmission is in the vehicle, the ball will remain in position, however if the transmission is removed, take care not to allow the ball to drop out.

Refitting

5 Fit a new sealing washer to the switch, then screw it back into position in the top of the transmission housing and tighten it to the specified torque. Reconnect the wiring connector, and test the operation of the circuit. Refit any components removed for access.

8 Speedometer drive - removal and refitting

Removal

1 The speedometer drive is situated on the rear of the transmission housing, next to the inner end of the left-hand driveshaft. Access to the drive can be gained from above noting that it will be necessary to remove the air cleaner housing on fuel-injected models. If necessary to further improve access, chock the rear wheels, firmly apply the handbrake, then jack up the front of the car and support it on axle stands (see "Jacking and Vehicle Support").
2 Unscrew the knurled retaining ring and disconnect the speedometer cable from the drive (see illustration).
3 Unscrew and remove the retaining bolt and withdraw the speedometer drive and driven pinion assembly from the transmission housing, along with its sealing ring.
4 If necessary, carefully tap out the roll pin and slide the driven pinion out of the housing. The oil seal can then be levered out from the top housing.

8.2 Unscrew the knurled retaining ring and disconnect the speedometer cable from the drive

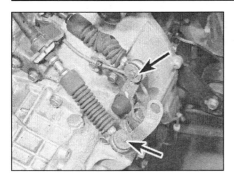

9.7a Remove the split pins and washers . . .

9.7b . . . then unbolt the cable bracket

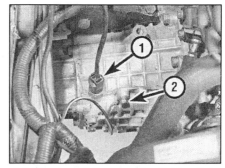

9.8 Disconnect the reversing light switch wiring (1) then unbolt the earth strap (2)

Refitting

5 Where necessary, press the new seal into position in the top of the housing making sure its sealing lip is facing inwards. Lubricate the pinion shaft with a smear of oil and slide the pinion into position. Align the pinion groove with the housing hole and secure the pinion in position with the roll pin.

6 Fit a new sealing ring to the speedometer housing and lubricate it with a smear of oil to ease installation.

7 Ease the speedometer drive into position in the transmission, ensuring that the drive and driven pinions are correctly engaged, and securely tighten the retaining bolt.

8 Reconnect the cable to the drive and securely tighten its retaining ring. Lower the vehicle to the ground.

9 Transmission - removal and refitting

Removal

1 Chock the rear wheels, then firmly apply the handbrake. Jack up the front of the vehicle, and securely support it on axle stands (see "*Jacking and Vehicle Support*").

2 Remove both front roadwheels then undo the retaining screws and remove the splash guard from under the engine compartment and the liner from under the right-hand wheel arch.

3 Disconnect the battery negative lead.
Caution: If the radio/cassette in your vehicle is equipped with an anti-theft system, make sure you have the correct activation code before disconnecting the battery.

4 Drain the transmission oil as described in Chapter 1, then refit the drain and filler plugs, and tighten them to their specified torque settings.

5 On fuel-injected models, remove the air cleaner assembly and air duct as described in Chapter 4B.

6 Detach the clutch slave cylinder and line (hydraulically-operated clutch) or clutch cable (cable-operated clutch) with reference to Chapter 6. If care is taken, it is not necessary to drain the fluid from the hydraulic lines, and the slave cylinder and lines can be positioned to one side in the engine compartment; secure the cylinder pushrod in position with a stout elastic band or cable tie (to prevent the piston being accidentally expelled). Do not depress the clutch pedal while the slave cylinder is disconnected.

7 Disconnect the gearchange rods or cables (as applicable) with reference to Sections 3 or 4 - if preferred, unbolt the cable bracket from the transmission **(see illustrations)**.

8 Disconnect the wiring from the reversing light switch, then undo the bolt and disconnect the earth strap from the transmission housing **(see illustration)**.

9 Where necessary disconnect the vacuum hose on the 5-speed transmission

10 Unscrew the knurled ring and disconnect the speedometer cable from the rear of the transmission.

11 Remove the starter motor as described in Chapter 5.

12 Unscrew and remove the upper bolts securing the transmission to the engine.

13 Unscrew the retaining bolts and remove the flywheel lower cover plate from the transmission bellhousing **(see illustration)**.

14 Referring to Chapter 8, remove the right-hand driveshaft and disconnect the left-hand driveshaft from the transmission. Note that it is not necessary to remove the left-hand driveshaft completely; it can be left attached to the hub assembly and released from the transmission as the hub is pulled outwards. **Note:** *Do not allow the shaft to hang down under its own weight as this could damage the constant velocity joints/gaiters.*

15 Place a jack and block of wood beneath the transmission, and raise the jack to take the weight of the transmission. Support the weight of the engine with a further jack or hoist.

16 Unscrew and remove the bolt and washers securing the engine/transmission stabilising rod to the rear of the transmission then slacken the nut and bolt securing the rod to the body and pivot the rod clear of the transmission unit **(see illustration)**.

17 Unscrew and remove the through-bolt and nut from the right-hand engine/transmission mounting then unbolt and remove the mounting bracket **(see illustration)**.

9.13 Removing the flywheel lower cover plate

9.16 Unscrew the bolt securing the stabilising rod to the rear of the transmission and pivot the rod clear

9.17 Right-hand engine/transmission mounting through-bolt (1) and mounting bracket bolts (2)

18 With the jack positioned beneath the transmission taking the weight, unscrew and remove the remaining bolts securing the transmission to the engine. Note the correct fitted positions of each bolt, and the necessary brackets, as they are removed, to use as a reference on refitting. Make a final check that all components have been disconnected, and are positioned clear of the transmission so that they will not hinder the removal procedure.

19 With the bolts removed, move the trolley jack and transmission to the right, to free it from its locating dowels. Once the transmission is free, lower the jack and manoeuvre the unit out from under the vehicle. Remove the locating dowels from the transmission or engine if they are loose, and keep them in a safe place.

Refitting

20 The transmission is refitted by a reversal of the removal procedure, bearing in mind the following points:

a) Apply a little high-melting-point grease to the splines of the transmission input shaft. Do not apply too much, otherwise there is a possibility of the grease contaminating the clutch friction disc.

b) Ensure the locating dowels are correctly positioned prior to installation.

c) Tighten all nuts and bolts to the specified torque (where given).

d) Renew the driveshaft oil seals (see Section 6) then refit the driveshafts with reference to Chapter 8.

e) Reconnect the gearchange rods/cables to the transmission and, where necessary adjust the cables as described in Section 2.

f) Refit the clutch cable or slave cylinder and lines with reference to Chapter 6.

g) On completion, refill the transmission with the specified type and quantity of lubricant, as described in Chapter 1.

10 Transmission overhaul - general information

Overhauling a manual transmission unit is a difficult and involved job for the DIY home mechanic. In addition to dismantling and reassembling many small parts, clearances must be precisely measured and, if necessary, changed by selecting shims and spacers. Internal transmission components are also often difficult to obtain, and in many instances, extremely expensive. Because of this, if the transmission develops a fault or becomes noisy, the best course of action is to have the unit overhauled by a specialist repairer, or to obtain an exchange reconditioned unit.

Nevertheless, it is not impossible for the more experienced mechanic to overhaul the transmission, provided the special tools are available, and the job is done in a deliberate step-by-step manner, so that nothing is overlooked.

The tools necessary for an overhaul include internal and external circlip pliers, bearing pullers, a slide hammer, a set of pin punches, a dial test indicator, and possibly a hydraulic press. In addition, a large, sturdy workbench and a vice will be required.

During dismantling of the transmission, make careful notes of how each component is fitted, to make reassembly easier and more accurate.

Before dismantling the transmission, it will help if you have some idea what area is malfunctioning. Certain problems can be closely related to specific areas in the transmission, which can make component examination and replacement easier. Refer to the Fault diagnosis Section of this manual for more information.

Chapter 7 Part B:
Automatic transmission

Contents

Automatic transmission - removal and refitting 11
Automatic transmission fluid level check . . . . .See Chapter 1
Automatic transmission fluid renewal . . . . .See Chapter 1
Automatic transmission overhaul - general information 12
Fluid cooler - general information 9
General information 1
Kickdown cable - adjustment 5
Kickdown cable - removal and refitting 6
Oil seals - renewal 8
Selector cable - adjustment 2
Selector cable - removal and refitting 3
Selector lever assembly - removal and refitting 4
Speedometer drive - removal and refitting 7
Starter inhibitor/reversing light switch - general information,
    removal, refitting and adjustment 10

Degrees of difficulty

Easy, suitable for novice with little experience		Fairly easy, suitable for beginner with some experience		Fairly difficult, suitable for competent DIY mechanic		Difficult, suitable for experienced DIY mechanic		Very difficult, suitable for expert DIY or professional	

Specifications

General
Type . . . . Automatic three- or four-speed, and reverse
Designation:
    Three-speed KM171-5-APX2
    Four-speed KM176

Torque wrench settings

	Nm	lbf ft
Transmission mounting to transmission:		
3-speed	50	37
4-speed	70	52
Transmission-to-engine mounting bolt:		
10 mm	48	35
8 mm	33	24
Starter motor	31	23
Bellhousing cover:		
20 mm	19	14
14 mm	11	8
Torque converter to driveplate:		
3-speed	50	37
4-speed	75	55
Drain plug	33	24
Starter inhibitor/reversing light switch	11	8
Speedometer drive	4	3
Transmission selector lever to transmission	19	14
Filter gauze	7	5
Sump	11	8

1 General information

Either a three- or four-speed automatic transmission is fitted, consisting of a torque converter, an epicyclic geartrain, and hydraulically-operated gear change. The three-speed version is fitted with a kick-down cable linked to the accelerator cable. The four-speed version is controlled by an ECU and is fully electronic incorporating an accelerator pedal switch, fluid temperature sensor and vehicle speed sensor.

The torque converter provides a fluid coupling between engine and transmission, which acts as an automatic clutch, and also provides a degree of torque multiplication when accelerating.

The epicyclic geartrain provides the forward or reverse gear ratios, according to which of its component parts are held stationary or allowed to turn. The components of the geartrain are held or released by brakes and clutches which are activated by a hydraulic control unit. A fluid pump within the transmission provides the necessary hydraulic pressure to operate the brakes and clutches.

Driver control of the transmission is by a six-position selector lever. The transmission has a "drive" position, and a "hold" facility on the first two gear ratios. The "drive" position "D" provides automatic changing throughout the range of gear ratios, and is the one to

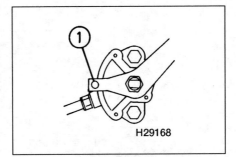

2.3 Ensure that the selector lever is in neutral by aligning the selector lever hole (1) with the transmission housing hole

select for normal driving. An automatic kickdown facility shifts the transmission down a gear if the accelerator pedal is fully depressed. The "hold" facility is very similar, but limits the number of gear ratios available - ie when the selector lever is in the "2" position, only the first two ratios can be selected; in the "L" (Low) position, only the first ratio can be selected. The lower ratio "hold" is useful for providing engine braking when travelling down steep gradients, or for preventing unwanted selection of top gear on twisty roads. Note, however, that the transmission should never be shifted down a position at high engine speeds.

Due to the complexity of the automatic transmission, any repair or overhaul work must be left to a dealer or transmission specialist with the necessary special equipment for fault diagnosis and repair. The contents of the following Sections are therefore confined to supplying general information, and any service information and instructions that can be used by the owner.

2 Selector cable - adjustment

1 Position the selector lever firmly against its detent in the "N" position.
2 To improve access to the transmission end of the selector cable on fuel-injected models, remove the air cleaner assembly and air duct (see Chapter 4B).
3 Ensure that the transmission selector lever hole is correctly aligned with the hole in the housing (and the inhibitor switch) and lock it in position with a twist drill of the correct diameter (see illustration). With the lever in this position, it will be aligned with the flange on the inhibitor switch body. This will ensure that the lever is in the "N" position.
4 On early models, with both the selector and transmission levers correctly positioned, slacken the locknut and rotate the adjuster nut to remove all freeplay from the selector cable without placing the cable under any tension. Once the cable is correctly adjusted, securely tighten the locknut.
5 On later models, remove the split pin and washer and detach the cable from the transmission selector lever. With both the selector and transmission levers correctly positioned, the cable end fitting should be correctly aligned with the transmission selector lever pin. If adjustment is necessary, slacken the locknut and alter the length of the cable using the adjuster. Securely tighten the locknut then reconnect the cable to the lever and secure it in position with a washer and new split pin.
6 Remove the twist drill from the selector lever then check the operation of the starter inhibitor/reversing light switch (Section 10). Refit any components removed to improve access.

3 Selector cable - removal and refitting

Removal

Early models

1 Firmly apply the handbrake, then jack up the front of the vehicle and support it on axle stands (see "Jacking and Vehicle Support").
2 Inside the vehicle position the selector lever in the "N" position. Undo the retaining screw and remove the handle from the top of the lever (see illustration).
3 Remove the centre console as described in Chapter 11.

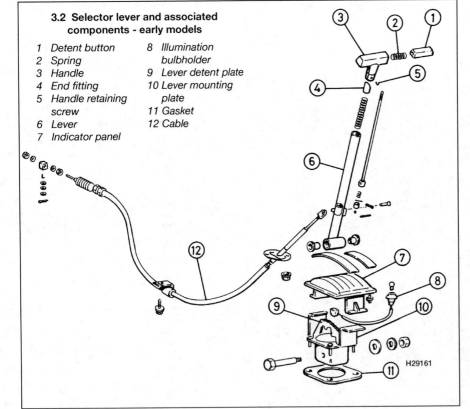

3.2 Selector lever and associated components - early models

1 Detent button
2 Spring
3 Handle
4 End fitting
5 Handle retaining screw
6 Lever
7 Indicator panel
8 Illumination bulbholder
9 Lever detent plate
10 Lever mounting plate
11 Gasket
12 Cable

4 Undo the retaining screws and remove the indicator panel from the selector lever, disconnecting the wiring connector from the illumination light.

5 Where applicable remove the rear heater duct.

6 Remove the split pin then withdraw the clevis pin and detach the selector cable from the lever.

7 In the engine compartment, remove the split pin and detach the cable from the transmission lever noting the correct fitted location of the cable fitting washers.

8 Working beneath the vehicle, if necessary, remove the exhaust system heatshield(s) to gain access to the base of the selector lever assembly (see Chapter 4).

9 Unscrew the nuts securing the cable bracket to the floor and unscrew the support bolt from the floor, then withdraw the cable assembly from the vehicle.

10 Examine the cable, looking for worn end fittings or a damaged outer casing, and for signs of fraying of the inner cable. Check the cable operation; the inner cable should move smoothly and easily through the outer casing. Remember that a cable that appears service-able when tested off the car may well be much heavier in operation when compressed into its working position. Renew the cable if it shows any signs of excessive wear or any damage.

Later models

11 To improve access on fuel-injected models, remove the air cleaner assembly and air duct (see Chapter 4B).

12 Remove the centre console as described in Chapter 11.

13 Working in the engine compartment extract the split pin and remove the washer then disconnect the inner cable adapter from the transmission lever. If necessary, the adapter may be removed from the end of the inner cable by unscrewing the adjuster nut, but note its position if the same cable is to be refitted **(see illustration)**.

14 Pull out the clip and disconnect the selector outer cable from the bracket on the transmission.

15 Inside the vehicle position the selector lever in the "N" position. Undo the retaining screw and remove the handle from the top of the lever. Undo the retaining screws and remove the indicator panel from the selector lever, disconnecting the wiring connector from the illumination light.

16 Extract the split pin and remove the washer then pull out the clevis pin and disconnect the inner cable from the selector lever. Pull out the retaining clip securing the outer cable to the bracket.

17 Unscrew and remove the cable support bracket nut.

18 Unscrew and remove the bolts securing the grommet bracket to the bulkhead and withdraw the cable from the vehicle.

19 Examine the cable as described in paragraph 10.

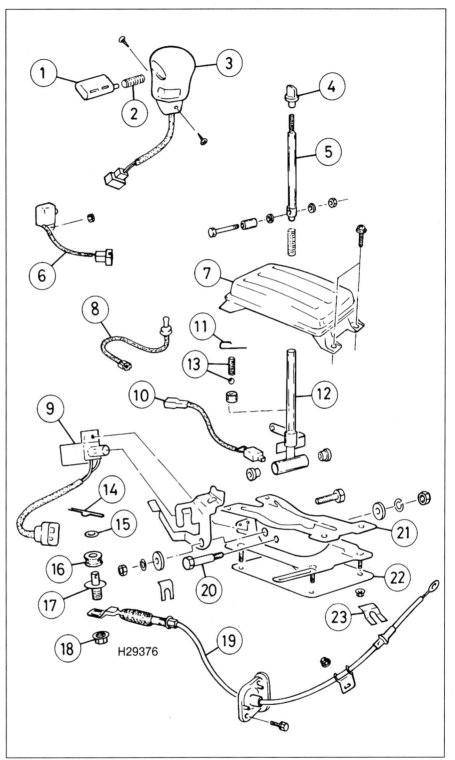

H29376

3.13 Selector lever and associated components - late models

1 Push button	7 Indicator panel	11 Pin	18 Flange nut
2 Spring	8 Illumination wiring	12 Lower lever	19 Selector cable
3 Knob	9 Shift lock	13 Ball and spring	20 Pivot bolt
4 Cam rod	solenoid	14 Clip	21 Bracket
adjustment	assembly	15 Washer	22 Gasket
5 Upper lever	10 Parking position	16 Bush	23 Spring clip
6 Overdrive switch	switch	17 Adjuster	

Refitting

Early models

20 Apply a smear of molybdenum disulphide grease to the cable end fittings and to the pivots of the selector lever.

21 Ensuring that the cable is correctly routed, locate the cable bracket to the floor and tighten the nuts. Also tighten the cable support bolt.

22 If removed, refit the exhaust system heatshield(s).

23 Locate the transmission end of the outer cable in its mounting bracket on the transmission and securely tighten its retaining nuts.

24 Connect the inner cable to the transmission lever, ensuring that the washers are correctly positioned, and secure it in position with a new split pin.

25 Inside the vehicle, connect the inner cable to the selector lever, refit the clevis pin and secure with a new split pin.

26 Where applicable, refit the rear heater duct.

27 Reconnect the illumination light wiring and refit the indicator panel to the selector lever. Tighten the retaining screws.

28 Refit the centre console with reference to Chapter 11.

29 Refit the handle to the top of the selector lever and tighten the retaining screw. Check the operation of the handle detent button ensuring that there is a small amount of freeplay in the button. If necessary adjustments can be made by removing the handle and screwing the end fitting into/out of the selector lever.

30 Check and, if necessary, adjust the selector cable as described in Section 2.

31 Lower the vehicle to the ground.

Later models

32 Apply a smear of molybdenum disulphide grease to the cable end fittings and to the pivots of the selector lever.

33 Ensuring that the cable is correctly routed, locate the cable through the bulkhead, then insert and tighten the bracket retaining bolts.

34 Locate the cable support bracket and tighten the nut.

35 Locate the outer cable on the bracket and fit the retaining clip, then reconnect the inner cable to the selector lever and insert the clevis pin together with the washer and new split pin.

36 Reconnect the illumination light wiring and refit the indicator panel to the selector lever. Tighten the retaining screws.

37 Refit the handle to the top of the selector lever and tighten the retaining screw. Check the operation of the handle detent button ensuring that there is a small amount of freeplay in the button. If necessary adjustments can be made by removing the handle and screwing the end fitting into/out of the selector lever.

38 In the engine compartment, locate the outer cable on the transmission bracket and secure with the retaining clip.

39 If removed, refit the adapter to the end of the inner cable. Reconnect the inner cable adapter to the transmission lever together with the washer and new split pin.

40 Refit the centre console with reference to Chapter 11.

41 On fuel-injected models, refit the air cleaner assembly and air duct with reference to Chapter 4B.

4 Selector lever assembly - removal and refitting

Removal

1 Firmly apply the handbrake, then jack up the front of the vehicle and support it on axle stands (see "Jacking and Vehicle Support").

2 Inside the vehicle position the selector lever in the "N" position. Undo the retaining screw and remove the handle from the top of the lever.

3 Remove the centre console as described in Chapter 11.

4 Undo the retaining screws and remove the indicator panel from the selector lever, disconnecting the wiring connector from the illumination light.

5 Where applicable remove the rear heater duct.

6 Remove the split pin then withdraw the clevis pin and detach the selector cable from the lever.

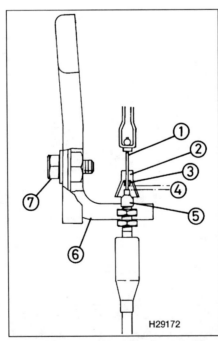

5.1 Kickdown cable adjustment details

1 Cable	5 Outer cable end
2 Dust cover	cover
3 Stopper	6 Mounting bracket
4 Adjustment	7 Mounting bracket
measuring point	bolt

7 Working beneath the vehicle, if necessary, remove the exhaust system heatshield(s) to gain access to the base of the selector lever assembly (see Chapter 4).

8 Unscrew the mounting nuts then withdraw the selector lever assembly from inside the vehicle. Recover the gasket which is fitted between the lever and body and renew it if it shows signs of damage.

Refitting

9 Refitting is the reverse of removal, noting the following points.

a) Check the operation of the handle detent button ensuring that there is a small amount of freeplay in the button. If necessary adjustments can be made by removing the handle and screwing the end fitting into/out of the selector lever.

b) On completion, check and, if necessary, adjust the selector cable as described in Section 2.

5 Kickdown cable - adjustment

Note: The kickdown cable is fitted to the 3-speed transmission only. The 4-speed transmission uses the throttle position switch fitted to the fuel injection system (see Chapter 4B).

1 Locate the kickdown cable attachment on the carburettor/throttle housing and slide the rubber dust cover along the inner cable to reveal the inner cable stopper **(see illustration)**.

2 Measure the distance between the end of the stopper and the outer cable end cover; this should be 1 ± 0.5 mm. If adjustment is necessary, slacken the cable mounting bracket retaining bolt and move the bracket to set the correct clearance then securely tighten the bracket bolt.

3 Slide the dust cover back into position then have an assistant fully depress the accelerator pedal whilst you check the operation of the cable. Ensure that the cable moves smoothly and easily and returns quickly, if not renew the cable as described in Section 6.

6 Kickdown cable - removal and refitting

Note: The kickdown cable is fitted to the 3-speed transmission only. The 4-speed transmission uses the throttle position switch fitted to the fuel injection system (see Chapter 4B). A new transmission sump gasket will be required on refitting.

Removal

1 Detach the upper end of the kickdown inner cable from the throttle linkage and free the outer cable from its mounting bracket.

2 Work along the length of the cable, freeing it from any retaining clips and ties, whilst noting its correct routing. If necessary, on fuel-injected models remove the air cleaner assembly to improve access to the transmission end of the cable (see Chapter 4B).

3 Drain the transmission fluid as described in Chapter 1.

4 Unscrew and remove the retaining bolts and remove the sump from the base of the automatic transmission. Recover the gasket and discard it.

 Whilst the sump is removed, check the transmission filter gauze for signs of debris or damage. If the filter is dirty, unbolt it from the base of the valve block and wash it in solvent to clean the gauze. Renew the filter if it is badly clogged or damaged in anyway. Fit the filter to the base of the valve block and tighten its retaining bolts to the specified torque.

5 Free the lower end of the kickdown cable from the cam on the valve block then unscrew the outer cable from the top of the transmission and remove the cable from the vehicle. Recover the sealing ring which is fitted to the cable end fitting.

Refitting

6 Fit a new sealing ring to the kickdown cable lower end fitting and lubricate it with a smear of oil to ease installation.

7 Manoeuvre the cable into position, ensuring it is correctly routed, and screw the cable end fitting into position in the transmission, tightening it securely.

8 Connect the lower end of the cable to the valve block cam.

9 Ensure that the cable is securely held in position then connect the upper end of the cable to the throttle linkage and secure the outer cable to its mounting bracket.

10 Check the operation of the kickdown cable and adjust it as described in Section 5.

11 Ensure that the sump and transmission mating surfaces are clean and dry and position the new gasket on top of the sump. Refit the sump to the vehicle and tighten its retaining bolts to the specified torque setting.

12 Refill the transmission (see Chapter 1) and refit any components removed for access.

7 Speedometer drive - removal and refitting

Refer to Chapter 7A.

8 Oil seals - renewal

Differential oil seals

1 Refer to Chapter 7A.

Torque converter oil seal

2 Remove the transmission as described in Section 11.

3 Carefully slide the torque converter off the transmission shaft whilst being prepared for fluid spillage.

4 Note the correct fitted depth of the seal in the transmission casing then carefully lever the seal out of position using a flat-bladed screwdriver.

5 Remove all traces of dirt from the area around the oil seal aperture, then apply a smear of grease to the outer lip of the new oil seal, and locate it in its aperture ensuring its sealing lip is facing inwards. Drive the seal squarely into position, using a tubular drift (such as a socket) which bears only on the hard outer edge of the seal, until it is positioned at the same depth the original was prior to removal.

6 Lubricate the seal lip with clean transmission fluid then carefully ease the torque converter into position.

7 Refit the transmission as described in Section 11.

9 Fluid cooler - general information

The transmission fluid cooler is an integral part of the radiator assembly. Refer to Chapter 3 for removal and refitting details, if the cooler is damaged the complete radiator assembly must be renewed.

10 Starter inhibitor/reversing light switch - information, removal, refitting and adjustment

General information

1 The starter inhibitor/reversing light switch is a dual-function switch which is fitted to the selector shaft on the top of the transmission housing. The inhibitor function of the switch ensures that the engine can only be started with the selector lever in either the "N" or "P" positions, therefore preventing the engine being started with the transmission in gear. This is achieved by the switch cutting the supply to the starter motor solenoid. If at any time it is noted that the engine can be started with the selector lever in any position other than "P" or "N", then it is likely that the inhibitor function of the switch is faulty. The switch also performs the function of the reversing light switch, illuminating the reversing lights whenever the selector lever is in the "R" position. If either function of the switch is faulty, the complete switch must be renewed as a unit.

Removal

2 To improve access to the switch, remove the battery as described in Chapter 5.

3 Unscrew and remove the retaining nut and washer and release the selector lever from the transmission shaft.

4 Trace the wiring back from the switch, and disconnect it at the wiring connector.

5 Unscrew and remove the retaining bolts and remove the switch from the top of the transmission housing.

Refitting and adjustment

6 Slide the switch into position and refit its retaining bolts, tighten them lightly only at this stage.

7 Ensure that the switch wiring is correctly routed and reconnect the wiring connector.

8 Engage the selector lever with the transmission shaft then refit the washer and retaining nut, tightening it to the specified torque.

9 Ensure that the selector lever is in the "N" (neutral) position then align the short end of the lever with the flange on the switch body **(see illustration 2.3)**. Ensure both tabs are correctly aligned then tighten the switch retaining bolts to the specified torque.

10 Where necessary, refit the battery as described in Chapter 5, and test the operation of the switch.

11 Automatic transmission - removal and refitting

Removal

1 Chock the rear wheels, apply the handbrake, and place the selector lever in the "N" (neutral) position. Jack up the front of the vehicle, and securely support it on axle stands (see *"Jacking and Vehicle Support"*). Remove both front roadwheels then undo the retaining bolts and remove the plastic liner from beneath the right-hand wheelarch. Also remove the splash guard from under the engine compartment, and on early models remove the transmission sump guard.

2 Drain the transmission fluid as described in Chapter 1, then refit the drain plugs, tightening them securely.

3 Remove the battery as described in Chapter 5.

4 Disconnect the kickdown cable from the throttle linkage and release it from its retaining clips so the cable is free to be removed with the transmission (see Section 6).

5 Disconnect the selector cable from the transmission with reference to Section 3.

6 Trace the wiring back from the starter inhibitor/reversing light switch on the top of the transmission and disconnect it at the wiring connector. Undo the retaining nut/bolt and disconnect the earth strap from the transmission housing (where necessary). Where necessary, disconnect the vacuum hose(s).

7 Make identification marks between the oil cooler hoses and their unions on the top of

the transmission housing. Clamp the hoses to minimise fluid loss then slacken the hose clamps and disconnect the hoses from the transmission. Plug the hose and transmission union ends to prevent the entry of dirt into the hydraulic system.

8 Unscrew the retaining ring and disconnect the speedometer cable from the transmission.

9 Remove the starter motor as described in Chapter 5.

10 On the 4-speed transmission only, the centre crossmember mounting bolts must be unscrewed and the crossmember temporarily moved to one side while the bellhousing lower cover and torque converter bolts are removed **(see illustration)**. To do this, temporarily support the transmission with a trolley jack and piece of wood.

11 Undo the retaining bolts and remove the lower cover from the transmission, to gain access to the torque converter retaining bolts. Mark the driveplate in relation to the torque converter **(see illustration)**. Unscrew and remove the visible bolt then, using a socket and extension bar to rotate the crankshaft pulley, undo the remaining bolts securing the torque converter to the driveplate as they become accessible. There are three bolts.

12 On the 4-speed transmission, refit the centre crossmember and tighten the mounting bolts to the specified torque (see Chapter 2A).

13 Referring to Chapter 8, remove the right-hand driveshaft and disconnect the left-hand driveshaft from the transmission. Note that it is not necessary to remove the left-hand driveshaft completely, it can be left attached to the hub assembly and released from the transmission as the hub is pulled outwards. **Note:** *Do not allow the shaft to hang down under its own weight as this could damage the constant velocity joints/gaiters.*

14 To ensure that the torque converter does not fall out as the transmission is removed, push it fully towards the transmission. If necessary, secure it in position using a length of metal strip bolted to one of the starter motor bolt holes.

15 Place a jack and block of wood beneath the transmission, and raise the jack to take the weight of the transmission.

16 Slacken and remove the through-bolt and nut from the right-hand engine/transmission mounting then undo the retaining bolts and remove the mounting bracket from the top of the transmission housing.

17 With the jack positioned beneath the transmission taking the weight, unscrew and remove the remaining bolts securing the transmission housing to the engine. Note the correct fitted positions of each bolt and the brackets (where applicable) as they are removed, to use on refitting. Make a final check that all components have been disconnected, and are positioned clear of the transmission so that they will not hinder the removal procedure.

18 With the bolts removed, move the trolley jack and transmission to the right, to free it from its locating dowels, ensuring that the torque converter moves with the transmission housing. Once the transmission is free, lower the jack and manoeuvre the unit out from under the car. Remove the locating dowels from the transmission or engine if they are loose, and keep them in a safe place.

Refitting

19 The transmission is refitted by a reversal of the removal procedure, bearing in mind the following points.

a) Ensure that the engine/transmission locating dowels are correctly positioned prior to installation.

b) Once the transmission and engine are correctly joined, refit the securing bolts, tightening them to the specified torque setting noting that the torque setting for each bolt varies according to its size and grade (number stamped onto the bolt head) and sometimes the bolt length.

c) Tighten all nuts and bolts to the specified torque (where given).

d) Renew the driveshaft oil seals (see Chapter 7A) and refit the driveshafts to the transmission as described in Chapter 8.

e) Adjust the selector cable, kickdown cable and starter inhibitor/reversing light switch as described in Sections 2, 5 and 10 of this Chapter.

f) On completion, refill the transmission with the specified type and quantity of fluid as described in Chapter 1.

12 Automatic transmission overhaul - general information

In the event of a fault occurring with the transmission, it is first necessary to determine whether it is of a mechanical or hydraulic nature, and to do this, special test equipment is required. It is therefore essential to have the work carried out by an automatic transmission specialist if a fault is suspected. On the four-speed version, any fault codes are stored in the ECU and may be retrieved using specialist equipment.

Do not remove the transmission for possible repair before professional fault diagnosis has been carried out, since most tests require the transmission to be in the vehicle.

11.10 The centre crossmember mounting bolts

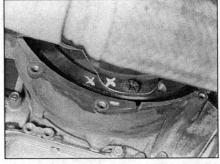

11.11 Mark the driveplate in relation to the torque converter to ensure correct reassembly

Chapter 8
Driveshafts

Contents

Driveshaft overhaul - general information 4
Driveshaft rubber gaiter and constant velocity
  (CV) joint check . . . . .See Chapter 1
Driveshaft rubber gaiters - renewal 3
Driveshafts - removal and refitting 2
General information 1

Degrees of difficulty

Easy, suitable for novice with little experience		Fairly easy, suitable for beginner with some experience		Fairly difficult, suitable for competent DIY mechanic		Difficult, suitable for experienced DIY mechanic		Very difficult, suitable for expert DIY or professional	

Specifications

Lubrication (overhaul only - see text)

Lubricant type/specification . . . .   Use only special grease supplied in sachets with gaiter kits - joints are otherwise pre-packed with grease and sealed

Torque wrench settings	Nm	lbf ft
Driveshaft retaining nut	200 to 260	148 to 192
Roadwheel nuts:		
Early (pre 1991) models:		
Steel wheels	75	54
Alloy wheels	90	66
Later (1991 on) models	100	74

1 General information

1 Drive is transmitted from the differential to the front wheels by means of two solid-steel driveshafts of unequal length.

2 Both driveshafts are splined at their outer ends, to accept the wheel hubs, and are threaded so that each hub can be fastened by a large nut. The inner end of each driveshaft is splined, to accept the differential sun gear.

3 Constant velocity (CV) joints are fitted to each end of the driveshafts, to ensure the smooth and efficient transmission of power at all suspension and steering angles. Both the inner and outer constant velocity joints are of the ball-and-cage type. A damper assembly is fitted to the longer, left-hand driveshaft to dampen out vibration.

2 Driveshafts - removal and refitting

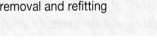

Note: *A new driveshaft inner joint circlip will be required on refitting; all split pins should also be renewed. It is also likely that a puller will be required to free the outer constant velocity joint from the hub assembly.*

Removal

1 Remove the wheel trim/hub cap (as applicable). Extract the split pin and slacken the driveshaft nut with the vehicle resting on its wheels **(see illustration)**. Also slacken the wheel nuts.

2 Chock the rear wheels of the car, firmly apply the handbrake, then jack up the front of the car and support it on axle stands. Remove the appropriate front roadwheel.

3 Drain the transmission oil/fluid as described in Chapter 1.

4 On early (pre 1991) models, slacken and remove the nuts and washers securing the balljoint and radius arm to the lower

2.1 Extract the split pin and slacken the driveshaft nut

2.8 Carefully lever the driveshaft inner joint out from the transmission, taking care not to damage the oil seal (see text)

2.9 If the driveshaft is a tight fit in the hub assembly, use a legged-puller to draw the hub assembly off the outer joint

2.11 The driveshaft inner joint circlip should be renewed every time the driveshaft is removed

suspension arm and withdraw the bolts (refer to Chapter 10 for further information).

5 On later (1991 on) models, slacken and remove the nuts and washers securing the balljoint to the lower suspension arm and withdraw the bolts. Slacken and remove the nut and washer then withdraw the link bolt and washer securing the anti-roll bar to the lower arm. Remove the anti-roll bar spacer and mounting rubbers, noting each components correct fitted location (refer to Chapter 10 for further information). **Note:** *A new anti-roll bar link bolt nut will be needed on refitting.*

6 On all models, remove the split pin then unscrew the retaining nut and washer and free the track rod balljoint from the hub. If necessary, a balljoint separator can be used to free the track rod end (see Chapter 10).

7 Slacken and remove the driveshaft retaining nut and washer, noting which way around the washer is fitted.

8 Using a large, flat-bladed screwdriver or suitable bar carefully lever the driveshaft inner constant velocity joint out of the transmission **(see illustration)**. Once the inner joint retaining clip has been released, pull the hub assembly outwards and free the driveshaft from the transmission. Support the driveshaft to avoid placing any strain on the constant velocity joints/gaiters.

Caution: Do not insert the screwdriver/bar more than 7 mm in behind the driveshaft joint otherwise the driveshaft oil seal will be damaged.

2.14 Refitting the driveshaft outer joint to the hub assembly

9 Free the outer constant velocity joint from the hub assembly and remove the driveshaft from underneath the vehicle. The shaft can be tapped out of the hub using a soft-faced mallet or, if necessary, the hub assembly can be drawn off the joint using a legged-puller **(see illustration)**. **Note:** *Do not allow the vehicle to rest on its wheels with one or both driveshafts removed, as damage to the wheel bearing(s) may result. If moving the vehicle is unavoidable, temporarily insert the outer end of the driveshaft(s) in the hub(s) and tighten the driveshaft nut(s). Support the inner end(s) of the driveshaft(s) to avoid damage.*

Refitting

10 Before installing the driveshaft, examine the driveshaft oil seal in the transmission for signs of damage or deterioration and, if necessary, renew it, referring to Chapter 7 for further information (Having got this far it is worth renewing the seal as a matter of course).

11 Thoroughly clean the driveshaft splines, and the apertures in the transmission and hub assembly. Remove the circlip from the inner constant velocity and fit the new one making sure it is correctly located in the joint groove **(see illustration)**.

12 Apply a thin film of grease to the oil seal lips, and to the driveshaft splines and shoulders. Check that all gaiter clips are securely fastened.

13 Offer up the driveshaft, and locate the joint splines with those of the differential sun gear, taking great care not to damage the oil seal. Push the joint fully into position and check that it is securely retained by the circlip.

14 Locate the outer constant velocity joint splines with those of the swivel hub, and slide the joint back into position in the hub **(see illustration)**.

15 On early (pre 1991) models, referring to Chapter 10, align the balljoint and radius arm with the lower suspension arm and refit the retaining bolts and washers. Refit the washers and retaining nuts and tighten them to the specified torque.

16 On later (1991 on) models, referring to Chapter 10, align the balljoint with the lower suspension arm then refit its retaining bolts,

washers and nuts, tightening them to the specified torque. Ensure that the anti-roll bar spacer and mounting rubbers are correctly positioned then refit the link bolt, washers and fit the new nut. Tighten the link bolt nut until 24 to 26 mm of the link bolt threads are exposed.

17 Engage the track rod balljoint with the hub then refit the washer and nut. Tighten the nut to the specified torque setting and secure it in position with a new split pin.

18 Refit the driveshaft nut washer, making sure its tapered edge is facing outwards, and screw on the hub nut. Tighten the nut securely at this stage, it can be tightened to the specified torque once the vehicle is resting on its wheels.

19 Refit the roadwheel then lower the vehicle to the ground and tighten the wheel nuts to the specified torque.

20 Tighten the driveshaft nut to the specified torque setting so that the nut slots align with the split pin hole in the driveshaft joint. Secure the nut in position with a new split pin then refit the wheel trim/hub cap (as applicable).

3 Driveshaft rubber gaiters - renewal

Inner joint

1 Remove the driveshaft from the car as described in Section 2 **(see illustration)**.

2 Secure the driveshaft in a vice equipped with soft jaws and release the two inner joint gaiter retaining clips **(see illustration)**. If necessary, the retaining clips can be cut to release them.

3 Slide the rubber gaiter down the shaft to expose the constant velocity joint and scoop out excess grease. Using paint or a suitable marker pen, make alignment marks between the driveshaft and joint inner and outer members.

4 Using a flat-bladed screwdriver, prise out the large circlip from the inside of the inner joint outer member and remove the member from the end of the driveshaft **(see illustrations)**.

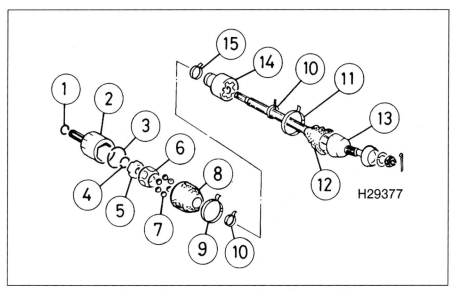

3.2 Bend up the retaining tabs and release the gaiter retaining clips

3.1 Exploded view of a typical driveshaft assembly

1 Circlip
2 Inner constant velocity joint outer member
3 Circlip
4 Circlip
5 Inner race

6 Cage
7 Balls
8 Gaiter
9 Outer retaining clip
10 Inner retaining clip
11 Outer retaining clip
12 Gaiter

13 Outer constant velocity joint/driveshaft
14 Dynamic damper (where fitted)
15 Damper retaining clip (where fitted)

3.4a Carefully prise out the large circlip . . .

5 Using circlip pliers, remove the circlip from the inner end of the driveshaft. Slide off the inner member, noting which way around it is fitted (see illustration).

3.4b . . . and remove the inner joint outer member from the driveshaft

6 Slide the rubber gaiter off the driveshaft and discard it. If necessary, remove the outer joint gaiter as described below.
7 Thoroughly clean the constant velocity joint(s) using paraffin, or a suitable solvent, and dry thoroughly. Carry out a visual inspection as follows.
8 Examine the constant velocity joint balls for cracks, flat spots or signs of surface pitting and inspect the ball tracks on the inner and outer members (see illustration). If the tracks have widened, the balls will no longer be a tight fit. At the same time check the ball cage windows for wear or cracking between the windows.
9 If on inspection any of the constant velocity joint components are found to be worn or damaged, it will be necessary to renew the complete joint assembly. If the joint is in satisfactory condition, obtain a new gaiter and retaining clips, a constant velocity joint circlip

and the correct type and quantity of grease. All components are available in a kit from Hyundai dealers.
10 Tape over the splines on the end of the driveshaft.
11 Slide the new gaiter and inner retaining clip onto the end of the driveshaft then remove the tape from the driveshaft splines.
12 Fit the inner member to the end of the driveshaft, making sure it is fitted the correct way around and the marks made prior to removal are correctly aligned. Secure the inner member in position with a new circlip, making sure the clip is correctly located in the driveshaft groove.
13 Pack the inner member with the specified type of grease (see illustration). Work the grease well into the bearing tracks whilst twisting the joint, and fill the outer member and gaiter with any excess.

3.5 Remove the circlip and slide the inner member off the driveshaft

3.8 Clean the inner member and inspect for signs of wear or damage as described

3.13 Work the grease fully into the inner member ball tracks and place the excess in the outer member and gaiter

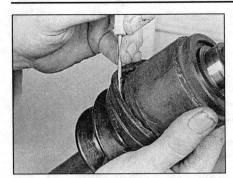

3.15 Carefully lift the outer lip to equalise air pressure in the gaiter

14 Slide the outer member into position, aligning the marks made prior to removal, and secure it in position with the large circlip. Ensure that the circlip is correctly located in the outer member groove and check that the joint is free to move easily.

15 Ease the gaiter over the joint and ensure that the gaiter lips are correctly located on both the driveshaft and constant velocity joint member. Lift the outer sealing lip of the gaiter to equalize air pressure within the gaiter **(see illustration)**.

16 Locate the inner retaining clip correctly on the gaiter and secure it in position by folding down the end of the clip and locking it in position by bending down the retaining tabs. Fit the large, outer retaining clip and secure it in position in the same way **(see illustrations)**.

17 Check the constant velocity joint move freely in all directions then refit the driveshaft to the vehicle, as described in Section 2.

Outer joint

18 Remove the inner joint as described in paragraphs 1 to 6.

19 If work is being carried out on the left-hand shaft it will be necessary to remove the dynamic damper (where fitted). Prior to removal, make alignment marks between the damper and driveshaft (these can be used on refitting to ensure that the damper is correctly positioned) then release the retaining clip and slide the damper off the shaft.

20 Release the retaining clips then slide the outer joint gaiter off from the driveshaft and discard it.

21 Inspect the outer joint as described in paragraphs 7 to 9. If the joint assembly is worn, the complete joint/ driveshaft assembly must be renewed. Obtain the necessary components required and proceed as follows.

22 Tape over the splines on the end of the driveshaft. Pack the outer joint with the specified type of grease. Work the grease well into the bearing tracks whilst twisting the joint, and fill the rubber gaiter with any excess.

23 Slide the new gaiter and inner retaining clip along the driveshaft and locate it on the outer joint assembly. Secure the gaiter in position as described in paragraphs 15 and 16 then check the joint is free to move in all directions.

24 Where necessary, slide the dynamic damper onto the driveshaft making sure it is fitted the correct way around. Align the marks made prior to removal and secure the damper in position with a new retaining clip.

25 Fit the new inner gaiter as described in paragraphs 11 to 17.

4 Driveshaft overhaul - general information

1 If any of the checks described in Chapter 1 reveal wear in any driveshaft joint, first remove the roadwheel trim or centre cap (as appropriate).

2 If the split pin is fitted, the driveshaft nut should be correctly tightened; if in doubt, remove the pin, and use a torque wrench to check that the nut is securely fastened. Once tightened, secure the nut in position with a new split pin then refit the centre cap or trim. Repeat this check on the remaining driveshaft nut.

3 Road test the vehicle, and listen for a metallic clicking from the front as the vehicle is driven slowly in a circle on full-lock. If a clicking noise is heard, this indicates wear in the outer constant velocity joint. This means

3.16a Locate the retaining clips correctly on the gaiter and secure each one in position by folding the end of the clip . . .

3.16b . . . and by bending down the retaining tabs

that the joint must be renewed; reconditioning is not possible.

4 If vibration, consistent with road speed, is felt through the car when accelerating, there is a possibility of wear in the inner constant velocity joints.

5 To check the joints for wear, remove the driveshafts, then dismantle them as described in Section 3; if any wear or free play is found, the affected joint must be renewed. In the case of the outer joints, this means that the complete joint/driveshaft assembly must be renewed, as the joints are not available separately. Refer to your Hyundai dealer for information on the availability of driveshaft components.

Chapter 9
Braking system

Contents

Brake pedal - adjustment 11
Front brake caliper - removal, overhaul and refitting 8
Front brake disc - inspection, removal and refitting 6
Front brake pad wear check .... .See Chapter 1
Front brake pads - renewal 4
General information 1
Handbrake - adjustment 14
Handbrake cables - removal and refitting 16
Handbrake lever - removal and refitting 15
Hydraulic fluid level check .... .See "Weekly checks"
Hydraulic fluid renewal .... .See Chapter 1
Hydraulic pipes and hoses - renewal 3

Hydraulic system - bleeding 2
Master cylinder - removal, overhaul and refitting 10
Rear brake drum - removal, inspection and refitting 7
Rear brake pressure-regulating valve - testing,
    removal and refitting 17
Rear brake shoe wear check .... .See Chapter 1
Rear brake shoes - renewal 5
Rear wheel cylinder - removal, overhaul and refitting 9
Stop-light switch - removal, refitting and adjustment 18
Vacuum servo unit - testing, removal and refitting 12
Vacuum servo unit check valve - removal, testing and refitting 13

Degrees of difficulty

Easy, suitable for novice with little experience	Fairly easy, suitable for beginner with some experience	Fairly difficult, suitable for competent DIY mechanic	Difficult, suitable for experienced DIY mechanic	Very difficult, suitable for expert DIY or professional

Specifications

Front brakes

Disc diameter:
    Early models .... 229 mm
    Later models .... 242 mm
Disc thickness:
    Early models:
        New .... 13.0 mm
        Minimum .... 11.4 mm
    Later models:
        New .... 19.0 mm
        Minimum .... 17.0 mm
Maximum disc run-out .... 0.15 mm
Brake pad friction material minimum thickness .... 1.0 mm

Rear drum brakes

Drum internal diameter:
    New .... 180 mm
    Maximum diameter after machining .... 182 mm
Brake shoe friction material minimum thickness .... 1.0 mm
Maximum drum run-out .... 0.15 mm

Adjustment data

Early models:
    Master cylinder piston-to servo pushrod clearance .... 0 to 0.075 mm
    Brake pedal:
        Height .... 182 to 187 mm
        Freeplay .... 10 to 15 mm
        Pedal-to-bulkhead clearance .... More than 15 mm
Later models:
    Brake pedal:
        Height .... 163 to 168 mm
        Freeplay .... 3 to 8 mm
        Pedal-to-floor clearance .... More than 50 mm

Torque wrench settings

	Nm	lbf ft
Bleed screw	9	6
Front disc to hub bolts	55	40
Front brake caliper:		
Early models:		
Mounting bolts	60	44
Body bolts	60	44
Later models:		
Retaining bolt	27	20
Guide pin-to-mounting bracket	40	30
Mounting bracket bolts	70	51
Hydraulic pipe/hose union nut	15	11
Hydraulic pipe union bolt	27	20
Master cylinder retaining nuts	12	8
Pressure regulating valve mounting nut	10	7
Rear hub nut:		
Early models (castellated nut and split pin - see text):		
Stage 1	20	14
Fully slacken the nut then:		
Stage 2	5	4
Later models	175	127
Rear wheel cylinder bolts	11	8
Roadwheel nuts:		
Early (pre-1991) models:		
Steel wheels	75	54
Alloy wheels	90	66
Later (1991-on) models	100	74
Vacuum servo unit mounting nuts	12	8

1 General information

The braking system is of the servo-assisted, dual-circuit hydraulic type. The arrangement of the hydraulic system is such that each circuit operates one front and one rear brake from a tandem master cylinder. Under normal circumstances, both circuits operate in unison. However, in the event of hydraulic failure in one circuit, full braking force will still be available at two wheels.

All models are fitted with front disc brakes and rear drum brakes. The front disc brakes are actuated by single-piston sliding type calipers, which ensure that equal pressure is applied to each disc pad. The rear drum brakes, the rear brakes incorporate leading and trailing shoes, which are actuated by twin-piston wheel cylinders. A self-adjust mechanism is incorporated, to automatically compensate for brake shoe wear. As the brake shoe linings wear, the footbrake operation automatically operates the adjuster mechanism, which effectively lengthens the shoe strut and repositions the brake shoes, to remove the lining-to-drum clearance.

A pressure-regulating valve arrangement is situated in the hydraulic circuit to each rear brake. The valve controls the hydraulic pressure applied to the rear brakes to help to prevent rear wheel lock-up during emergency braking.

The handbrake provides an independent mechanical means of rear brake application.

Note: *When servicing any part of the system, work carefully and methodically; also observe scrupulous cleanliness when overhauling any part of the hydraulic system. Always renew components (in axle sets, where applicable) if in doubt about their condition, and use only genuine Hyundai replacement parts, or at least those of known good quality. Note the warnings given in "Safety first" and at relevant points in this Chapter concerning the dangers of asbestos dust and hydraulic fluid.*

2 Hydraulic system - bleeding

⚠️ *Warning: Hydraulic fluid is poisonous; wash off immediately and thoroughly in the case of skin contact, and seek immediate medical advice if any fluid is swallowed or gets into the eyes. Certain types of hydraulic fluid are inflammable, and may ignite when allowed into contact with hot components; when servicing any hydraulic system, it is safest to assume that the fluid is inflammable, and to take precautions against the risk of fire as though it is petrol that is being handled. Hydraulic fluid is also an effective paint stripper, and will attack plastics; if any is spilt, it should be washed off immediately, using copious quantities of fresh water. Finally, it is hygroscopic (it absorbs moisture from the air) - old fluid may be contaminated and unfit for further use. When topping-up or renewing the fluid, always use the recommended type, and ensure that it comes from a freshly-opened sealed container.*

General

1 The correct operation of any hydraulic system is only possible after removing all air from the components and circuit; this is achieved by bleeding the system.

2 During the bleeding procedure, add only clean, unused hydraulic fluid of the recommended type; never re-use fluid that has already been bled from the system. Ensure that sufficient fluid is available before starting work.

3 If there is any possibility of incorrect fluid being already in the system, the brake components and circuit must be flushed completely with uncontaminated, correct fluid, and new seals should be fitted to the various components.

4 If hydraulic fluid has been lost from the system, or air has entered because of a leak, ensure that the fault is cured before proceeding further.

5 Park the vehicle on level ground, switch off the engine and select first or reverse gear (Park on automatic transmission models), then chock the wheels and release the handbrake.

6 Check that all pipes and hoses are secure, unions tight and bleed screws closed. Clean any dirt from around the bleed screws.

7 Unscrew the master cylinder reservoir cap, and top the master cylinder reservoir up to the "MAX" level line; refit the cap loosely, and remember to maintain the fluid level at least above the "MIN" level line throughout the procedure, or there is a risk of further air entering the system.

8 There are a number of one-man, do-it-yourself brake bleeding kits currently available from motor accessory shops. It is recommended that one of these kits is used

whenever possible, as they greatly simplify the bleeding operation, and also reduce the risk of expelled air and fluid being drawn back into the system. If such a kit is not available, the basic (two-man) method must be used, which is described in detail below.

9 If a kit is to be used, prepare the vehicle as described previously, and follow the kit manufacturer's instructions, as the procedure may vary slightly according to the type being used; generally, they are as outlined below in the relevant sub-section.

10 Whichever method is used, the same sequence must be followed (paragraphs 11 and 12) to ensure the removal of all air from the system.

Bleeding sequence

11 If the system has been only partially disconnected, and suitable precautions were taken to minimise fluid loss, it should be necessary only to bleed that part of the system (ie the primary or secondary circuit).

12 If the complete system is to be bled, then it should be done working in the following sequence:

a) Left-hand rear brake.
b) Right-hand front brake.
c) Right-hand rear brake.
d) Left-hand front brake.

Bleeding - basic (two-man) method

13 Collect a clean glass jar, a suitable length of plastic or rubber tubing which is a tight fit over the bleed screw, and a ring spanner to fit the screw. The help of an assistant will also be required.

14 Remove the dust cap from the first screw in the sequence. Fit the spanner and tube to the screw, place the other end of the tube in the jar, and pour in sufficient fluid to cover the end of the tube.

15 Ensure that the master cylinder reservoir fluid level is maintained at least above the "MIN" level line throughout the procedure.

16 Have the assistant fully depress the brake pedal several times to build up pressure, then maintain it on the final downstroke.

17 While pedal pressure is maintained, unscrew the bleed screw (approximately one turn) and allow the compressed fluid and air to flow into the jar. The assistant should maintain pedal pressure, following it down to the floor if necessary, and should not release it until instructed to do so. When the flow stops, tighten the bleed screw again, have the assistant release the pedal slowly, and recheck the reservoir fluid level.

18 Repeat the steps given in paragraphs 16 and 17 until the fluid emerging from the bleed screw is free from air bubbles. If the master cylinder has been drained and refilled, and air is being bled from the first screw in the sequence, allow approximately five seconds between cycles for the master cylinder passages to refill.

19 When no more air bubbles appear, tighten the bleed screw securely, remove the tube and spanner, and refit the dust cap. Do not overtighten the bleed screw.

20 Repeat the procedure on the remaining screws in the sequence, until all air is removed from the system and the brake pedal feels firm again.

Bleeding - using a one-way valve kit

21 As their name implies, these kits consist of a length of tubing with a one-way valve fitted, to prevent expelled air and fluid being drawn back into the system; some kits include a translucent container, which can be positioned so that the air bubbles can be more easily seen flowing from the end of the tube.

22 The kit is connected to the bleed screw, which is then opened. The user returns to the driver's seat, depresses the brake pedal with a smooth, steady stroke, and slowly releases it; this is repeated until the expelled fluid is clear of air bubbles.

23 Note that these kits simplify work so much that it is easy to forget the master cylinder reservoir fluid level; ensure that this is maintained at least above the "MIN" level line at all times.

Bleeding - using a pressure-bleeding kit

24 These kits are usually operated by the reservoir of pressurised air contained in the spare tyre. However, note that it will probably be necessary to reduce the pressure to a lower level than normal; refer to the instructions supplied with the kit.

25 By connecting a pressurised, fluid-filled container to the master cylinder reservoir, bleeding can be carried out simply by opening each screw in turn (in the specified sequence), and allowing the fluid to flow out until no more air bubbles can be seen in the expelled fluid.

26 This method has the advantage that the large reservoir of fluid provides an additional safeguard against air being drawn into the system during bleeding.

27 Pressure-bleeding is particularly effective when bleeding "difficult" systems, or when bleeding the complete system at the time of routine fluid renewal.

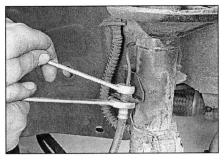

3.2a Retain the pipe with an open-ended spanner whilst slackening the union nut with a brake pipe spanner . . .

All methods

28 When bleeding is complete, and firm pedal feel is restored, wash off any spilt fluid, tighten the bleed screws securely, and refit their dust caps.

29 Check the hydraulic fluid level in the master cylinder reservoir, and top-up if necessary (see "Weekly checks").

30 Discard any hydraulic fluid that has been bled from the system; it will not be fit for re-use.

31 Check the feel of the brake pedal. If it feels at all spongy, air must still be present in the system, and further bleeding is required. Failure to bleed satisfactorily after a reasonable repetition of the bleeding procedure may be due to worn master cylinder seals.

3 Hydraulic pipes and hoses - renewal

Note: *Before starting work, refer to the note at the beginning of Section 2 concerning the dangers of hydraulic fluid.*

1 If any pipe or hose is to be renewed, minimise fluid loss by first removing the master cylinder reservoir cap, then tightening it down onto a piece of polythene to obtain an airtight seal. Alternatively, flexible hoses can be sealed, if required, using a proprietary brake hose clamp; metal brake pipe unions can be plugged (if care is taken not to allow dirt into the system) or capped immediately they are disconnected. Place a wad of rag under any union that is to be disconnected, to catch any spilt fluid.

2 If a flexible hose is to be disconnected, unscrew the brake pipe union nut before removing the spring clip which secures the hose to its mounting bracket **(see illustrations)**.

3 To unscrew the union nuts, it is preferable to obtain a brake pipe spanner of the correct size; these are available from most large motor accessory shops. Failing this, a close-fitting open-ended spanner will be required, though if the nuts are tight or corroded, their flats may be rounded-off if the spanner slips.

3.2b . . . then slide out the pipe retaining clip

4.2 On early models carefully prise out the access cover from the top of the caliper

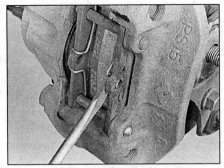

4.3a Unclip the M-clip from the outer pad . . .

4.3b . . . and free it from the pad retaining pins

In such a case, a self-locking wrench is often the only way to unscrew a stubborn union, but it follows that the pipe and the damaged nuts must be renewed on reassembly. Always clean a union and surrounding area before disconnecting it. If disconnecting a component with more than one union, make a careful note of the connections before disturbing any of them.

4 If a brake pipe is to be renewed, it can be obtained, cut to length and with the union nuts and end flares in place, from Hyundai dealers. All that is then necessary is to bend it to shape, following the line of the original, before fitting it to the car. Alternatively, most motor accessory shops can make up brake pipes from kits, but this requires very careful measurement of the original, to ensure that the replacement is of the correct length. The safest answer is usually to take the original to the shop as a pattern.

4.4 Unhook the K-spring from the inner pad and remove it from the caliper

5 On refitting, do not overtighten the union nuts. It is not necessary to exercise brute force to obtain a sound joint.
6 Ensure that the pipes and hoses are correctly routed, with no kinks, and that they are secured in the clips or brackets provided. After fitting, remove the polythene from the reservoir, and bleed the hydraulic system as described in Section 2. Wash off any spilt fluid, and check carefully for fluid leaks.

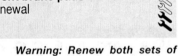

4 Front brake pads - renewal

Warning: Renew both sets of front brake pads at the same time - never renew the pads on only one wheel, as uneven braking may result. Note that the dust created by wear of the pads may contain asbestos, which is a health hazard. Never blow it out with compressed air, and don't inhale any of it. An approved filtering mask should be worn when working on the brakes. DO NOT use petrol or petroleum-based solvents to clean brake parts; use brake cleaner or methylated spirit only.

1 Chock the rear wheels, apply the handbrake, then jack up the front of the vehicle and support it on axle stands. Remove the front roadwheels and proceed as described under the relevant sub-heading.

Early models

2 Using a flat-bladed screwdriver, carefully

unclip the access cover from the top of the caliper (see illustration). Note the correct fitted locations of the pad spring, clip and pins.
3 Carefully unclip the M-clip from the centre of the outer brake pad then release the clip from the pad retaining pin holes and remove it from the caliper (see illustrations).
4 Using a pair of pliers, unhook the K-spring from the inner pad and remove the spring from the caliper (see illustration).
5 Withdraw the pad retaining pins and slide the pads out from the caliper, along with the anti-squeak shim which is fitted between the outer pad and the caliper (see illustrations).
6 First measure the thickness of each brake pad's friction material. If either pad is worn at any point to the specified minimum thickness or less, all four pads must be renewed. Also, the pads should be renewed if any are fouled with oil or grease; there is no satisfactory way of degreasing friction material, once contaminated. If any of the brake pads are worn unevenly, or are fouled with oil or grease, trace and rectify the cause before reassembly. Note that the pad shim, clip and spring should also be renewed every time new pads are installed.
7 If the brake pads are still serviceable, carefully clean them using a clean, fine wire brush or similar, paying particular attention to the sides and back of the metal backing. Clean out the grooves in the friction material, and pick out any large embedded particles of dirt or debris. Carefully clean the pad locations in the caliper mounting bracket.

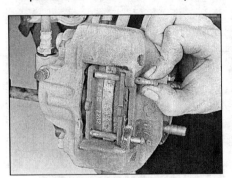

4.5a Slide out the retaining pins . . .

4.5b . . . then withdraw the brake pads . . .

4.5c . . . and the anti-squeak shim from the caliper

4.13 On refitting, ensure that the M-clip is correctly engaged in the retaining pin holes

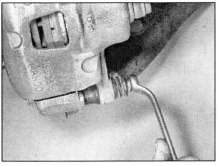

4.19a On later models slacken and remove the caliper retaining bolt . . .

4.19b . . . then pivot the caliper upwards and away from the brake disc

8 Prior to fitting the pads, check that the caliper is free to slide easily on the caliper mounting bracket. Brush the dust and dirt from the caliper and piston, but **do not** inhale it, as it is injurious to health. Inspect the dust seal around the piston for damage, and the piston for evidence of fluid leaks, corrosion or damage. If attention to any of these components is necessary, refer to Section 8.

9 If new brake pads are to be fitted, the caliper piston must be pushed back into the cylinder to make room for them. Either use a G-clamp or similar tool, or use suitable pieces of wood as levers. Provided that the master cylinder reservoir has not been overfilled with hydraulic fluid, there should be no spillage, but keep a careful watch on the fluid level while retracting the piston. If the fluid level rises above the "MAX" level line at any time, the surplus should be siphoned off or ejected via a plastic tube connected to the bleed screw (see Section 2). **Note:** *Do not syphon the fluid by mouth, as it is poisonous; use a syringe or an old poultry baster.*

10 Ensuring that the friction material of each pad is against the brake disc, slide the pads into position making sure the anti-squeak shim is correctly positioned between the outer pad and the caliper.

11 Slide the pad retaining pins into position ensuring they pass through the holes in the pads and shim.

12 Hook the ends of the K-spring behind the pad retaining pins and hook the spring over the inner pad.

13 Locate one end of the M-clip in the lower pad retaining pin hole, then rotate the upper retaining pin slightly and locate the upper end of the clip with the upper pin **(see illustration)**. Ensure the clip ends are correctly located then hook the clip into the hole in the centre of the outer pad backing plate.

14 Depress the brake pedal repeatedly, until the pads are pressed into firm contact with the brake disc, and normal (non-assisted) pedal pressure is restored.

15 Repeat the above procedure on the remaining front brake caliper.

16 Refit the roadwheels, then lower the vehicle to the ground and tighten the roadwheel nuts to the specified torque setting.

17 Check the hydraulic fluid level as described in *"Weekly checks"*.

> **HAYNES HiNT**
> *New pads will not give full braking efficiency until they have bedded in. Be prepared for this, and avoid hard braking as far as possible for the first hundred miles or so after pad renewal.*

Later models

18 Push the piston into its bore by pulling the caliper outwards.

19 Slacken and remove the caliper retaining bolt and pivot the caliper upwards and away from the brake pads and mounting bracket **(see illustrations)**. Tie the caliper to the suspension strut using a suitable piece of wire.

4.20a Lift out the brake pads and shims . . .

20 Remove the brake pads, complete with their shims then, noting their correct fitted locations, remove the pad springs from the caliper mounting bracket **(see illustrations)**.

21 Inspect the brake pads as described in paragraphs 6 to 9. If new pads are to be fitted, the pad shims and springs should also be renewed. Whilst the pads are removed check the caliper guide pin and bush for signs of wear or damage **(see Section 8)**.

22 Fit a new shim to the backing plate of each pad then fit the shim cover to the back of the inner pad and shim assembly; the inner pad is the pad with the wear indicator on it **(see illustration)**.

23 Locate the pad springs correctly in the caliper mounting bracket then fit the pad and shim assemblies **(see illustration)**. Ensure the pad with the wear indicator is fitted as the inner pad and both pads are fitted with their friction material facing the disc.

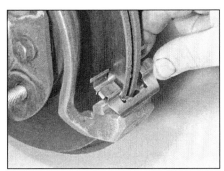

4.20b . . . and recover the pad springs from the caliper mounting bracket

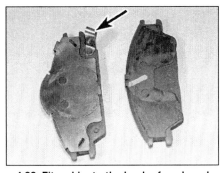

4.22 Fit a shim to the back of each pad then fit the shim cover to the inner pad (arrowed)

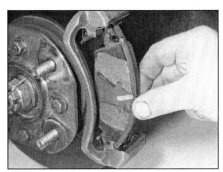

4.23 Ensure that the pad springs are correctly positioned and fit the pads to the caliper mounting bracket

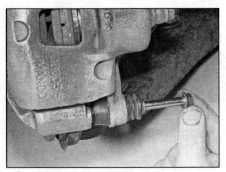

4.24 Pivot the caliper down into position and refit the retaining bolt

24 Ensure the pads, shims and springs are correctly located in the mounting bracket then pivot the caliper down into position over the pads. Press the caliper into position, then install the retaining bolt and tighten it to the specified torque setting **(see illustration)**.

25 Depress the brake pedal repeatedly, until the pads are pressed into firm contact with the brake disc, and normal (non-assisted) pedal pressure is restored.

26 Repeat the above procedure on the remaining front brake caliper.

27 Refit the roadwheels, then lower the vehicle to the ground and tighten the roadwheel nuts to the specified torque setting.

28 Check the hydraulic fluid level as described in "*Weekly checks*".

> **HAYNES HiNT** *New pads will not give full braking efficiency until they have bedded in. Be prepared for this, and avoid hard braking as far as possible for the first hundred miles or so after pad renewal.*

5 Rear brake shoes - renewal

> ⚠ *Warning: Brake shoes must be renewed on both rear wheels at the same time - never renew the shoes on only one wheel, as uneven braking may result. Also, the dust created by wear of the shoes may contain asbestos, which is a health hazard. Never blow it out with compressed air, and don't inhale any of it. An approved filtering mask should be worn when working on the brakes. DO NOT use petrol or petroleum-based solvents to clean brake parts; use brake cleaner or methylated spirit only.*

1 Remove the brake drum as described in Section 7.

2 Working carefully, and taking the necessary precautions, remove all traces of brake dust from the brake drum, backplate and shoes.

3 Measure the thickness of the friction material of each brake shoe at several points; if either shoe is worn at any point to the specified minimum thickness or less, all four shoes must be renewed as a set. The shoes should also be renewed if any are fouled with oil or grease; there is no satisfactory way of degreasing friction material, once contaminated.

4 If any of the brake shoes are worn unevenly, or fouled with oil or grease, trace and rectify the cause before reassembly.

5 To renew the brake shoes, proceed as described under the relevant sub-heading. If all the components are in good condition, refit the brake drum as described in Section 7.

Early models

6 Note the position of each shoe, and the location of each of the springs **(see illustration)**. Also make a note of the self-adjuster component locations, to aid refitting later.

7 Using a flat-bladed screwdriver, carefully prise off the return spring retaining clip from the base of the large shoe return spring **(see illustration)**.

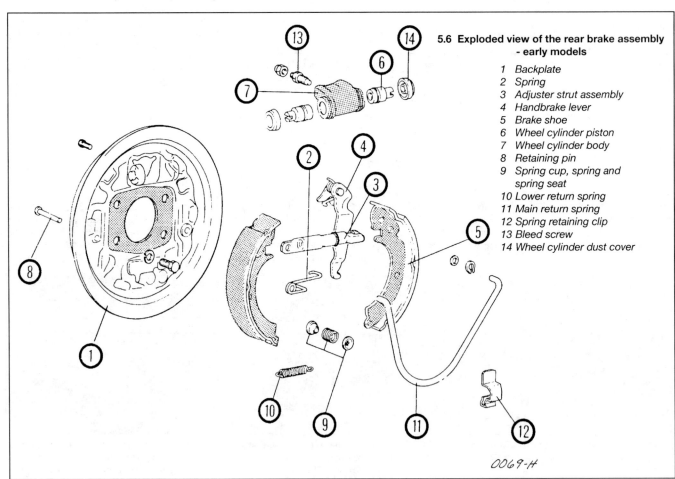

5.6 Exploded view of the rear brake assembly - early models

1 Backplate
2 Spring
3 Adjuster strut assembly
4 Handbrake lever
5 Brake shoe
6 Wheel cylinder piston
7 Wheel cylinder body
8 Retaining pin
9 Spring cup, spring and spring seat
10 Lower return spring
11 Main return spring
12 Spring retaining clip
13 Bleed screw
14 Wheel cylinder dust cover

0069-H

5.7 On early models, prise the retaining clip off from the base of the large return spring . . .

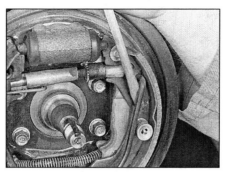

5.8 . . . then carefully lever the spring out from the shoes

5.9 Remove the retainer cup, lift off the spring and spring seat and withdraw the shoe retainer pin

5.10a Ease the shoe assembly away from the backplate . . .

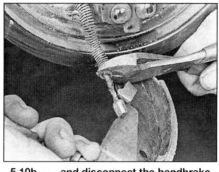

5.10b . . . and disconnect the handbrake cable

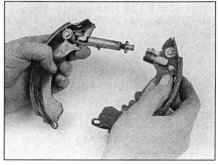

5.11 With the shoes on a bench, separate them at the adjuster strut

8 Using a pair of pliers, unhook the lower return spring from the base of the shoes then carefully unhook the large main return spring

5.12a Slide out the retaining clip . . .

and remove it from the shoe assembly (see illustration).

9 Using a pair of pliers, remove the shoe retainer spring cups by depressing and turning them through 90° (see illustration). With the cups removed, lift off the springs and spring seats then withdraw the retainer pins.

10 Ease the shoes out one at a time from the lower pivot point then ease the upper end of both shoes out from their wheel cylinder locations, taking care not to damage the wheel cylinder seals. Disconnect the handbrake cable from the trailing shoe and manoeuvre the shoe and adjuster strut assembly out of position and away from the backplate (see illustrations). Do not depress the brake pedal until the brakes are

reassembled; wrap a strong elastic band around the wheel cylinder pistons to retain them.

11 With the shoe and adjuster strut assembly on a bench, make a note of the correct fitted positions of the springs and adjuster strut, to use as a guide on reassembly. Separate the brake shoes at the adjuster strut (see illustration).

12 Working on the trailing shoe first, slide out the retaining clip from the handbrake lever assembly pivot pin (remove the clip on the side opposite the handbrake lever) and remove the washer. Unhook the return spring then disengage the adjuster strut end piece from the pivot lever. The handbrake lever assembly can then be removed from the shoe (see illustrations).

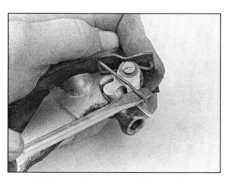

5.12b . . . then unhook the return spring . . .

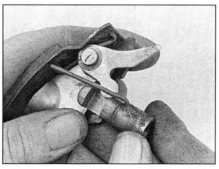

5.12c . . . and detach the adjuster strut end piece . . .

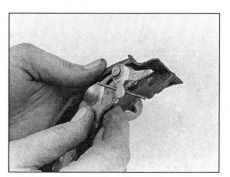

5.12d . . . and the handbrake lever from the trailing shoe

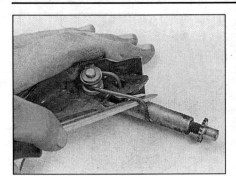

5.13a Unhook the spring from the adjuster strut body . . .

5.13b . . . then remove the retaining clip, washer and pin and separate the leading shoe and adjuster strut

5.19 Apply a light coat of high-temperature brake grease to the contact areas of the backplate and shoes

13 Working on the leading shoe, disengage the spring from the adjuster strut body. Slide out the retaining clip then remove the washer and separate the strut and shoe. Withdraw the retaining pin and remove the spring assembly from the shoe **(see illustrations)**.

14 Unscrew the knurled wheel from the strut body and examine the adjuster strut assembly for signs of wear or damage and renew if necessary. Also note that all springs and retaining clips should also be renewed, regardless of their apparent condition; spring kits are available from Hyundai dealers.

15 Peel back the rubber protective caps, and check the wheel cylinder for fluid leaks or other damage; check that both cylinder pistons are free to move easily. Refer to Section 9, if necessary, for information on wheel cylinder renewal.

16 Slide the spring and retaining pin assembly into position in the leading shoe. Fit the adjuster strut body and washer and secure it in position with a new retaining clip. Hook the spring into position underneath the strut body.

17 Slide the handbrake lever assembly into position on the trailing shoe. Engage the adjuster strut end piece with the pivot lever and hook the end of the return spring over the

pivot lever. Refit the washer to the retaining pin and secure it in position with the new retaining clip.

18 Ensure the threads of the adjuster strut knurled wheel are clean and apply a little high-melting-point grease to its threads. Screw the knurled wheel into the body until only a small gap exists between the wheel and body.

19 Prior to installation, clean the backplate, and apply a thin smear of high-temperature brake grease or anti-seize compound (eg Duckhams Copper 10) to all those surfaces of the backplate which bear on the shoes, particularly the wheel cylinder pistons and lower pivot point **(see illustration)**. Do not allow the lubricant to foul the friction material.

20 Reassemble the shoes and remove the elastic band from the wheel cylinder. Manoeuvre the shoe and strut assembly into position and reconnect the handbrake cable to the trailing shoe.

21 Locate the upper end of both shoes with the wheel cylinder pistons and locate the lower ends on the pivot.

22 Centralise the shoes on the backplate, then refit the shoe retainer pins, spring seats and springs, and secure them in position with the spring cups.

23 Fit the lower return spring to the base of the shoes then install the large return spring. Secure the large return spring in position with the retaining clip, making sure it is securely clipped onto the lower pivot **(see illustrations)**.

24 Using a screwdriver, turn the strut adjuster wheel to expand the shoes until the brake drum just slides over the shoes.

25 Refit the brake drum as described in Section 7.

26 Repeat the above procedure on the remaining rear brake.

27 Once both sets of rear shoes have been renewed, adjust the lining-to-drum clearance by alternately depressing the brake pedal then applying the handbrake. Do this repeatedly until the brake pedal action returns to normal.

28 Check and, if necessary, adjust the handbrake as described in Section 14. On completion, check the hydraulic fluid level as described in "Weekly checks".

> **HAYNES HiNT** *New shoes will not give full braking efficiency until they have bedded in. Be prepared for this, and avoid hard braking as far as possible for the first hundred miles or so after shoe renewal.*

5.23a Ensure that the large return spring ends are correctly engaged in the brake shoe holes . . .

5.23b . . . and secure it in position with the retaining clip

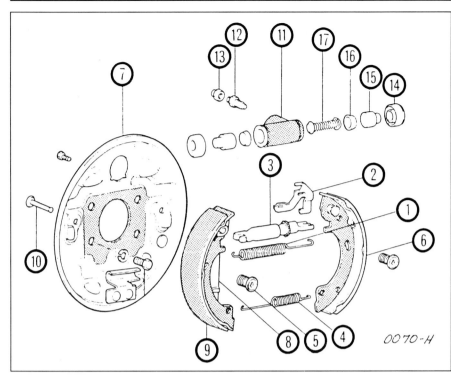

5.29b Correct fitted locations of Mando rear brake assembly components

5.29a Exploded view of the rear brake assembly - later models (Bendix arrangement shown, Mando similar)

1 Upper return spring	6 Leading shoe	12 Bleed screw
2 Adjuster strut lever	7 Backplate	13 Dust cap
3 Adjuster strut	8 Handbrake lever	14 Dust cover
4 Lower return spring	9 Trailing shoe	15 Piston
5 Retainer spring and cup	10 Retainer pin	16 Fluid seal
	11 Wheel cylinder body	17 Spring

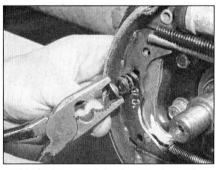

5.30 On later models, remove the spring cup and spring and withdraw the shoe retainer pin

Later models

Note: *There are two different manufacturers of the brake assemblies fitted to later models; Bendix (see illustration 5.29a), and Mando (see illustration 5.29b and the accompanying photos). Both assemblies are very similar with only minor differences but components are not interchangeable.*

29 Note the position of each shoe, and the location of each of the springs. Also make a note of the self-adjuster component locations, to aid refitting later **(see illustrations)**.

30 Using a pair of pliers, remove the shoe retainer spring cups by depressing and turning them through 90°. With the cups removed, lift off the springs and (where fitted) washers and withdraw the retainer pins **(see illustration)**.

31 Ease the shoes out one at a time from the lower pivot point, to release the tension of the return spring, then disconnect the lower return spring from both shoes **(see illustration)**.

32 Ease the upper end of both shoes out from their wheel cylinder locations, taking care not to damage the wheel cylinder seals, and disconnect the handbrake cable from the

trailing shoe. The brake shoe and adjuster strut assembly can then be manoeuvred out of position and away from the backplate. Do not depress the brake pedal until the brakes are reassembled; wrap a strong elastic band around the wheel cylinder pistons to retain them **(see illustrations)**.

33 With the shoe and adjuster strut assembly on a bench, make a note of the correct fitted positions of the springs and adjuster strut, to use as a guide on reassembly.

34 Disconnect the upper return spring, noting which way around it is fitted, then detach the trailing shoe and return spring from the leading shoe and strut assembly **(see illustration)**. Unhook the adjuster strut lever spring (where fitted) then separate the strut, adjusting lever and leading shoe.

5.31 Ease the shoe lower ends out from the pivot then remove the lower return spring

5.32a Ease the shoe assembly away from the backplate and detach it from the handbrake cable

5.32b Wrap a stout elastic band around the wheel cylinder to prevent the pistons being expelled

5.34 Note which way around the upper return spring is fitted on removal (Mando assembly shown)

35 Depending on the type of brake shoes being installed, it may be necessary to remove the handbrake lever from the original trailing shoe, and install it on the new shoe. Secure the lever in position with a new retaining clip. All return springs should be renewed, regardless of their apparent condition; spring kits are available from Hyundai dealers.

36 Separate the two halves of the adjuster strut, and carefully examine the assembly for signs of wear or damage. Pay particular attention to the threads of the adjuster bolt and the knurled adjuster wheel, and renew if necessary.

37 Apply a little high-melting-point grease to the threads of the adjuster bolt. Screw the adjuster wheel in so that the strut is set to its smallest possible length.

38 Fit the adjuster strut lever to the leading shoe. Engage the adjuster strut with the shoe and lever assembly and (where necessary) fit the lever spring.

39 Engage the trailing shoe with the opposite end of the adjuster strut. Ensure that both shoes and the handbrake lever are correctly positioned then fit the upper return spring to assembly, making sure it is the right way around.

40 Peel back the rubber protective caps, and check the wheel cylinder for fluid leaks or other damage; check that both cylinder pistons are free to move easily. Refer to Section 9, if necessary, for information on wheel cylinder renewal.

41 Prior to installation, clean the backplate, and apply a thin smear of high-temperature

6.3 Using a micrometer to measure brake disc thickness

brake grease or anti-seize compound (eg Duckhams Copper 10) to all those surfaces of the backplate which bear on the shoes, particularly the wheel cylinder pistons and lower pivot point. Do not allow the lubricant to foul the friction material.

42 Remove the elastic band from the wheel cylinder and manoeuvre the shoe and strut assembly into position. Attach the handbrake cable to the trailing shoe then locate the upper end of both shoes with the wheel cylinder pistons. Fit the lower return spring to both shoes, and ease the shoes into position on the lower pivot point.

43 Tap the shoes to centralise them with the backplate, then refit the shoe retainer pins, springs and (where fitted) washers, and secure them in position with the spring cups.

44 Using a screwdriver, turn the strut adjuster wheel to expand the shoes until the brake drum just slides over the shoes.

45 Refit the brake drum as described in Section 7.

46 Repeat the above procedure on the remaining rear brake.

47 Once both sets of rear shoes have been renewed, adjust the lining-to-drum clearance by alternately depressing the brake pedal then applying the handbrake. Do this repeatedly until the brake pedal action returns to normal.

48 Check and, if necessary, adjust the handbrake as described in Section 14.

49 On completion, check the hydraulic fluid level as described in "Weekly checks".

 HAYNES HiNT *New shoes will not give full braking efficiency until they have bedded in. Be prepared for this, and avoid hard braking as far as possible for the first hundred miles or so after shoe renewal.*

6 Front brake disc - inspection, removal and refitting

Note: *Before starting work, refer to the note at the beginning of Section 4 concerning the dangers of asbestos dust.*

Inspection

Note: *If either disc requires renewal, BOTH should be renewed at the same time, to ensure even and consistent braking. New brake pads should also be fitted.*

1 Apply the handbrake, then jack up the front of the car and support it on axle stands. Remove the appropriate front roadwheel.

2 Slowly rotate the brake disc so that the full area of both sides can be checked; remove the brake pads if better access is required to the inboard surface. Light scoring is normal in the area swept by the brake pads, but if heavy scoring or cracks are found, the disc must be renewed.

3 It is normal to find a lip of rust and brake dust around the disc's perimeter; this can be

scraped off if required. If, however, a lip has formed due to excessive wear of the brake pad swept area, then the disc's thickness must be measured using a micrometer **(see illustration)**. Take measurements at several places around the disc, at the inside and outside of the pad swept area; if the disc has worn at any point to the specified minimum thickness or less, the disc must be renewed.

4 If the disc is thought to be warped, it can be checked for run-out. Either use a dial gauge mounted on any convenient fixed point, while the disc is slowly rotated, or use feeler blades to measure (at several points all around the disc) the clearance between the disc and a fixed point, such as the caliper mounting bracket **(see illustration)**. If the measurements obtained are at the specified maximum or beyond, the disc is excessively warped, and must be renewed; however, it is worth checking first that the hub bearing is in good condition (Chapters 1 and/or 10).

5 Check the disc for cracks, especially around the wheel stud holes, and any other wear or damage, and renew if necessary.

Removal and refitting

6 To remove the brake disc, the front suspension swivel hub assembly must be removed from the vehicle and dismantled. Dismantling the hub assembly will almost certainly damage the hub bearings, so these should be renewed on refitting. Refer to Chapter 10, Sections 2 and 3 for further information.

7 Rear brake drum - removal, inspection and refitting

Note: *Before starting work, refer to the note at the beginning of Section 5 concerning the dangers of asbestos dust.*

Removal

1 Chock the front wheels, then jack up the rear of the vehicle and support it on axle stands. Remove the appropriate rear wheel.

2 Using a large flat-bladed screwdriver, carefully prise/tap out the hub cap from the centre of the brake drum **(see illustration)**. If

6.4 Using a dial gauge to measure brake disc runout

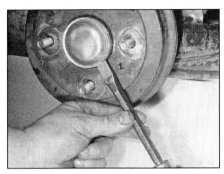

7.2 Tap/lever out the hub cap from the centre of the brake drum

the cap is damaged or disfigured on removal, a new one should be used on refitting. Proceed as described under the relevant sub-heading.

Early models

3 Extract the split pin and remove the locking cap from the hub nut **(see illustrations)**. Discard the split pin; a new one will be needed on refitting.
4 Slacken and remove the hub nut then remove the toothed washer and outer bearing from the stub axle **(see illustrations)**.
5 Ensure the handbrake is fully release then withdraw the brake drum from the hub. It may be difficult to remove the drum due the brake shoes binding on the inner circumference of the drum. If the drum is tight, tap the periphery of the drum using a hide or plastic mallet. If the brake shoes are binding, slacken the handbrake cable adjustment as described in Section 14.

Later models

Note: *A new hub nut will be required on refitting.*
6 Slacken and remove the hub nut and discard it; a new one should be used on refitting.
7 Remove the drum (see paragraph 5).

Inspection

Note: *If either drum requires renewal, BOTH should be renewed at the same time, to ensure even and consistent braking. New brake shoes should also be fitted.*

8 Working carefully, remove all traces of brake dust from the drum, but *avoid inhaling the dust, as it is injurious to health.*
9 Clean the outside of the drum, and check it for obvious signs of wear or damage, such as cracks around the roadwheel stud holes; renew the drum if necessary. The wheel studs can be renewed individually; they are a press-fit in the drum.
10 Examine carefully the inside of the drum. Light scoring of the friction surface is normal, but if heavy scoring is found, the drum must be renewed. It is usual to find a lip on the drum's inboard edge which consists of a mixture of rust and brake dust; this should be scraped away, to leave a smooth surface which can be polished with fine (120- to 150-grade) emery paper. If, however, the lip is due to the friction surface being recessed by excessive wear, then the drum must be renewed.
11 If the drum is thought to be excessively worn, or oval, its internal diameter must be measured at several points using an internal micrometer. Take measurements in pairs, the second at right-angles to the first, and compare the two, to check for signs of ovality. Provided that it does not enlarge the drum to beyond the specified maximum diameter, it may be possible to have the drum refinished by skimming or grinding; if this is not possible, the drums on both sides must be renewed. Note that if the drum is to be skimmed, BOTH drums must be refinished, to maintain a consistent internal diameter on both sides.

Refitting

12 If a new brake drum is to be installed, use a suitable solvent to remove any preservative coating that may have been applied to its interior. If necessary, install the bearing races, inner bearing and oil seal as described in Chapter 10 and thoroughly grease the outer bearing.
13 Using a screwdriver, turn the brake shoe adjuster strut wheel to expand the shoes until the brake drum just slides over the shoes.
14 Apply a smear of grease to the drum oil seal and carefully slide the assembly onto the

7.3 Remove the locking cap from the hub nut

stub axle. Proceed as described under the relevant heading.

Early models

15 Fit the outer bearing and toothed thrust washer, ensuring its tooth is correctly engaged in the axle slot.
16 Refit the hub nut and tighten it to the Stage 1 torque setting whilst rotating the brake drum to settle the hub bearings in position. Fully slacken the hub nut then tighten it to the specified Stage 2 torque. If the nut slots are not correctly aligned with the split hole, back the nut off slightly (do not tighten it) until the slots and hole are in alignment. **Note:** *The nut should not be backed off more than 15°.* When the hub nut is correctly positioned, refit the locking cap and secure the nut in position with a new split pin.
17 Pack the hub with grease then fit the cap to the centre of the brake drum, driving it fully into position **(see illustration)**.
18 Adjust the lining-to-drum clearance by alternately depressing the brake pedal then applying the handbrake. Do this repeatedly until the brake pedal action returns to normal.
19 Repeat the above procedure on the remaining rear brake assembly (if necessary), then check and, if necessary, adjust the handbrake cable as described in Section 14.
20 On completion, refit the roadwheel(s), then lower the vehicle to the ground and tighten the wheel nuts to the specified torque.

7.4a Unscrew the hub nut then remove the toothed washer . . .

7.4b . . . and bearing before withdrawing the brake drum

7.17 Ensure that the hub cap is securely fitted to the centre of the brake drum

Later models

21 Fit the outer bearing to the drum and screw on the nut hub nut. Tighten the hub nut to the specified torque whilst rotating the drum to settle the bearings in position (**see illustrations**).

22 Carry out the operations described in paragraphs 17 to 20.

8 Front brake caliper - removal, overhaul and refitting

Note: *Before starting work, refer to the note at the beginning of Section 2 concerning the dangers of hydraulic fluid, and to the warning at the beginning of Section 4 concerning the dangers of asbestos dust.*

7.21a On later models, fit the drum assembly and locate the outer bearing in position . . .

7.21b . . . then fit the new hub nut . . .

7.21c . . . and tighten it to the specified torque setting

Removal

1 Apply the handbrake, then jack up the front of the vehicle and support it on axle stands. Remove the appropriate roadwheel.

2 Minimise fluid loss by first removing the master cylinder reservoir cap, and then tightening it down onto a piece of polythene, to obtain an airtight seal. Alternatively, use a brake hose clamp, a G-clamp or a similar tool to clamp the flexible hose. Proceed as described under the relevant sub-heading.

Early models

3 Remove the brake pads (see Section 4).
4 Clean the area around the caliper hose union, then loosen the union.
5 Prior to removal, slacken the bolts which secure the two halves of the caliper body together.
6 Slacken and remove the bolts securing the caliper to the hub assembly. Lift the caliper away from the brake disc, then unscrew the caliper from the end of the brake hose. Plug/cover the hose end to minimise fluid loss and prevent dirt entry.

Later models

7 Slacken and remove the brake hose union bolt and detach the hose from the caliper. Plug/cover the hose end to minimise fluid loss and prevent dirt entry; discard the sealing washers, new ones should be used on refitting.

8 Slacken and remove the caliper mounting bolt then pivot the caliper upwards and away from the disc and slide it off its guide pin. The brake pads can be left in position in the mounting bracket.

Overhaul

Early models

9 With the caliper on the bench, wipe away all traces of dust and dirt, but *avoid inhaling the dust, as it is injurious to health* (**see illustration**).
10 Unscrew the bolts and separate the two halves of the caliper. The caliper main body and mounting bracket can then be separated (**see illustrations**).
11 Carefully prise out the dust seal retaining clip.
12 Withdraw the partially ejected piston from the caliper body, and remove the dust seal.

> **HAYNES HiNT** *If the piston cannot be withdrawn by hand, it can be pushed out by applying compressed air to the brake hose union hole. Only low pressure should be required, such as is generated by a foot pump, and position the caliper piston-side down to ensure it is not forcibly expelled.*

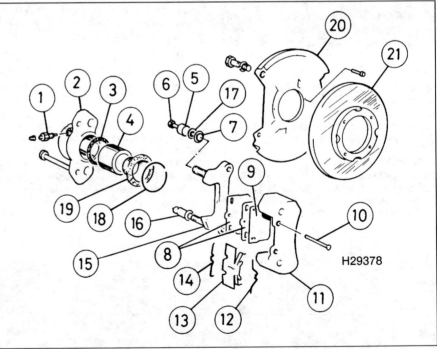

8.9 Exploded view of the front brake caliper - early models

1 *Bleed screw*	8 *Brake pads*
2 *Caliper main body*	9 *Anti-squeak shim*
3 *Piston (fluid) seal*	10 *Pad retaining pin*
4 *Piston*	11 *Caliper outer body*
5 *Mounting bracket pin bush*	12 *M-clip*
6 *Plug*	13 *Access cover*
7 *Seal*	14 *K-spring*

15 *Mounting bracket*
16 *Mounting bracket pin bush*
17 *Retainer*
18 *Retaining clip*
19 *Dust seal*
20 *Backplate*
21 *Brake disc*

H29378

8.10a On early models, unscrew the retaining bolts and separate the caliper halves . . .

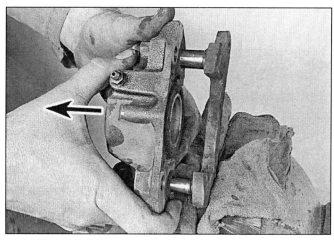

8.10b . . . and slide the main body off the mounting bracket

13 Using a small screwdriver, extract the piston hydraulic seal, taking great care not to damage the caliper bore (see illustration).
14 Thoroughly clean all components, using only methylated spirit, isopropyl alcohol or clean hydraulic fluid as a cleaning medium. Never use mineral-based solvents such as petrol or paraffin, as they will attack the hydraulic system's rubber components. Dry the components immediately, using compressed air or a clean, lint-free cloth. Use compressed air to blow clear the fluid passages.
15 Check all components, and renew any that are worn or damaged. Check particularly the cylinder bore and piston; these should be

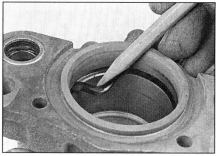

8.13 Carefully remove the piston seal, taking great care not to mark the caliper bore

renewed (note that this means the renewal of the complete body assembly) if they are scratched, worn or corroded in any way. Similarly check the condition of the mounting bracket pins and their bushes/seals; both pins should be undamaged and (when cleaned) a reasonably tight sliding fit in the caliper body. If there is any doubt about the condition of any component, renew it.
16 If the assembly is fit for further use, obtain the appropriate repair kit; the components are available from Hyundai dealers in various combinations. All rubber seals should be renewed as a matter of course; these should never be re-used.
17 On reassembly, ensure that all components are clean and dry.
18 Soak the piston and the new piston (fluid) seal in clean hydraulic fluid. Smear clean fluid on the cylinder bore surface.
19 Fit the new piston (fluid) seal, using only your fingers (no tools) to manipulate it into the cylinder bore groove.
20 Fit the new dust seal to the piston and carefully ease the piston squarely into the cylinder bore using a twisting motion. Press the piston fully into position then seat the outer lip of the dust seal in the caliper body.
21 Secure the dust seal in position with the retaining clip (see illustration).

22 If the mounting bracket pin bushes are being renewed, push/lever out the old bush components noting each ones correct fitted location. Press the new bush, end cap, retainer and seal into position in the caliper body and lubricate all components with high-temperature brake grease. Ensure the mounting bracket pins are adequately lubricated then slide the bracket into position in the caliper body (see illustrations).
23 Reassemble the caliper halves and tighten the retaining bolts to the specified torque.

Later models

24 With the caliper on the bench, wipe away all traces of dust and dirt, but *avoid inhaling the dust, as it is injurious to health* (see illustration).
25 Withdraw the partially ejected piston from the caliper body, and remove the dust seal.

> **HAYNES HiNT** *If the piston cannot be withdrawn by hand, it can be pushed out by applying compressed air to the brake hose union hole. Only low pressure should be required, such as is generated by a foot pump. As the piston is expelled take great care not to trap your fingers between the piston and caliper.*

8.21 Secure the dust seal in position with the retaining clip

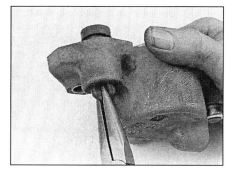

8.22a The caliper mounting bracket bush can be pushed out using pointed-nose pliers

8.22b Lubricate the mounting bracket pins and slide the bracket back into position in the main caliper body

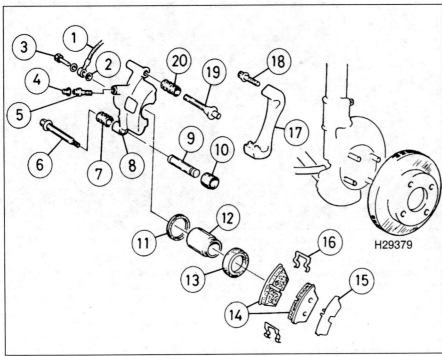

8.24 Exploded view of the front brake caliper - later models

1	Brake hose	6	Retaining bolt	11	Piston (fluid) seal
2	Sealing washer	7	Gaiter	12	Piston
3	Union bolt	8	Caliper	13	Dust seal
4	Dust cap	9	Guide bush	14	Brake pads
5	Bleed screw	10	Gaiter	15	Shim

16	Pad spring
17	Mounting bracket
18	Mounting bolt
19	Guide pin
20	Gaiter

26 Using a small screwdriver, extract the piston hydraulic seal, taking great care not to damage the caliper bore.

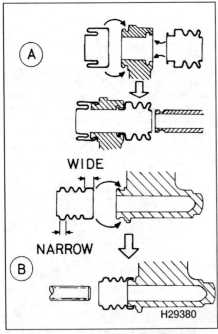

8.34 On later models, ensure that the guide bush gaiters (A) and guide pin gaiter (B) are correctly positioned on reassembly

27 Thoroughly clean all components, using only methylated spirit, isopropyl alcohol or clean hydraulic fluid as a cleaning medium. Never use mineral-based solvents such as petrol or paraffin, as they will attack the hydraulic system's rubber components. Dry the components immediately, using compressed air or a clean, lint-free cloth. Use compressed air to blow clear the fluid passages.

28 Check all components, and renew any that are worn or damaged. Check particularly the cylinder bore and piston; these should be renewed (note that this means the renewal of the complete body assembly) if they are scratched, worn or corroded in any way. Similarly check the condition of the guide pin/bush and their gaiters; the pin and bush should be undamaged and (when cleaned) a reasonably tight sliding fit in the caliper. If there is any doubt about the condition of any component, renew it.

29 If the assembly is fit for further use, obtain the appropriate repair kit; the components are available from Hyundai dealers in various combinations. All rubber seals should be renewed as a matter of course; these should never be re-used.

30 On reassembly, ensure that all components are clean and dry.

31 Soak the piston and the new piston (fluid) seal in clean hydraulic fluid. Smear clean fluid on the cylinder bore surface.

32 Fit the new piston (fluid) seal, using only your fingers (no tools) to manipulate it into the cylinder bore groove.

33 Fit the new dust seal to the rear of the piston and seat the outer lip of the seal in the caliper body groove. Carefully ease the piston squarely into the cylinder bore using a twisting motion. Press the piston fully into position and seat the inner lip of the dust seal in the piston groove.

34 With the guide bush removed from the caliper, locate the new gaiters in the caliper body grooves, making sure the guide pin gaiter is fitted the correct way around **(see illustration)**. Lubricate the bush with high-temperature brake grease and slide it into position in the caliper, making sure the gaiters are correctly located in the bush grooves.

35 If necessary, unscrew the guide pin from the mounting bracket and renew it. Fit the new pin, tightening it to the specified torque, and lubricate it with high-temperature brake grease.

Refitting

Early models

36 Screw the caliper body fully onto the flexible hose union then refit the caliper to the hub and tighten its mounting bolts to the specified torque.

37 Tighten the brake hose union nut to the specified torque and remove the clamp/polythene (as applicable).

38 Refit the brake pads as described in Section 4.

39 Bleed the hydraulic system as described in Section 2. Note that, providing the precautions described were taken to minimise brake fluid loss, it should only be necessary to bleed the relevant front brake.

40 Refit the roadwheel, then lower the vehicle to the ground and tighten the roadwheel nuts to the specified torque.

Later models

41 Ensure that the brake pads are still correctly fitted in the caliper mounting bracket (see Section 4).

42 Slide the caliper fully onto its guide pin making sure the gaiter is correctly located in both the guide pin and caliper body grooves.

43 Pivot the caliper down over the pads then refit the retaining bolt and tighten it to the specified torque setting.

44 Position a new sealing washer on each side of the brake hose union then refit the union bolt and tighten it to the specified torque setting.

45 Remove the brake hose clamp or polythene (where fitted) and bleed the hydraulic system as described in Section 2. Note that, providing the precautions described were taken to minimise brake fluid loss, it should only be necessary to bleed the relevant front brake.

46 Refit the roadwheel, then lower the vehicle to the ground and tighten the roadwheel nuts to the specified torque.

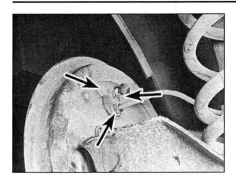

9.4 Rear wheel cylinder retaining bolts and brake pipe union nut (arrowed)

9 Rear wheel cylinder - removal, overhaul and refitting

Note: *Before starting work, refer to the note at the beginning of Section 2 concerning the dangers of hydraulic fluid, and to the warning at the beginning of Section 5 concerning the dangers of asbestos dust.*

Removal

1 Remove the brake drum as described in Section 7.
2 Minimise fluid loss by first removing the master cylinder reservoir cap, and then tightening it down onto a piece of polythene, to obtain an airtight seal. Alternatively, use a brake hose clamp, a G-clamp or a similar tool to clamp the flexible hose at the nearest convenient point to the wheel cylinder.
3 On early models, carefully unhook the large return spring from the brake shoes and on later models, carefully unhook the upper brake shoe return spring, and remove it from both brake shoes noting which way around it is fitted (see Section 5). Pull the upper ends of the shoes away from the wheel cylinder to disengage them from the pistons.
4 Wipe away all traces of dirt around the brake pipe union at the rear of the wheel cylinder, and unscrew the union nut **(see illustration)**. Carefully ease the pipe out of the wheel cylinder, and plug or tape over its end to prevent dirt entry. Wipe off any spilt fluid immediately.
5 Unscrew the two wheel cylinder retaining bolts from the rear of the backplate, and remove the cylinder, along with its sealing ring (where fitted), taking great care not to allow surplus hydraulic fluid to contaminate the brake shoe linings.

Overhaul

6 Brush the dirt and dust from the wheel cylinder, but take care not to inhale it.
7 Pull the rubber dust seals from the ends of the cylinder body.
8 The pistons will normally be ejected by the pressure of the coil spring, but if they are not, tap the end of the cylinder body on a piece of wood, or apply low air pressure - eg, from a

foot pump - to the hydraulic fluid union hole to eject the pistons from their bores.
9 Inspect the surfaces of the pistons and their bores in the cylinder body for scoring, or evidence of metal-to-metal contact. If evident, renew the complete wheel cylinder assembly.
10 If the pistons and bores are in good condition, discard the seals and obtain a repair kit, which will contain all the necessary renewable items.
11 Remove the seals from the pistons noting their correct fitted orientation. Lubricate the new piston seals with clean brake fluid, and fit them onto the pistons.
12 Dip the pistons in clean brake fluid, then fit the spring to the cylinder.
13 Insert the pistons into the cylinder bores using a twisting motion.
14 Fit the dust seals, and check that the pistons can move freely in their bores.

Refitting

15 Ensure that the backplate and wheel cylinder mating surfaces are clean and dry. On models where a sealing ring is fitted to the cylinder, use a new sealing ring. Where no sealing ring is fitted, apply a smear of sealing compound to the wheel cylinder mating surface.
16 Spread the brake shoes and manoeuvre the wheel cylinder into position. Engage the brake pipe, and screw in the union nut two or three turns to ensure that the thread has started.
17 Insert the two wheel cylinder retaining bolts, tightening them to the specified torque, then tighten the brake pipe union nut to the specified torque.
18 Remove the clamp from the flexible brake hose, or the polythene from the master cylinder reservoir (as applicable).
19 Ensure that the brake shoes are correctly located in the cylinder pistons, then carefully refit the brake shoe return spring, ensuring it is correctly located in both shoes.
20 Refit the brake drum as described in Section 7.
21 Bleed the brake hydraulic system as described in Section 2. Providing suitable precautions were taken to minimise loss of fluid, it should only be necessary to bleed the relevant rear brake.

10.3 Slacken the union nuts (arrowed) and disconnect the brake pipes from the master cylinder

10 Master cylinder - removal, overhaul and refitting

Note: *Before starting work, refer to the warning at the beginning of Section 2 concerning the dangers of hydraulic fluid.*

Removal

1 Remove the master cylinder reservoir cap and, where necessary, the diaphragm and float, and syphon the hydraulic fluid from the reservoir. **Note:** *Do not syphon the fluid by mouth, as it is poisonous; use a syringe or an old poultry baster.* Alternatively, open any convenient bleed screw in the system, and gently pump the brake pedal to expel the fluid through a plastic tube connected to the screw (see Section 2).
2 Disconnect the wiring connector from the brake fluid level sender unit.
3 Wipe clean the area around the brake pipe unions on the side of the master cylinder, and place absorbent rags beneath the pipe unions to catch any surplus fluid. Make a note of the correct fitted positions of the unions, then unscrew the union nuts and carefully withdraw the pipes **(see illustration)**. Plug or tape over the pipe ends and master cylinder orifices, to minimise the loss of brake fluid, and to prevent the entry of dirt into the system. Wash off any spilt fluid immediately with cold water.
4 Slacken and remove the nuts and washers securing the master cylinder to the vacuum servo unit **(see illustration)**. Free the pressure regulating valve mounting bracket from the studs then remove the master cylinder from the engine compartment.

Overhaul

5 Remove all traces of dirt from the master cylinder body then proceed as described under the relevant sub-heading.

Early models

6 Slacken and remove the retaining screw then remove the fluid reservoir from the top of the master cylinder and remove the mounting seals from the master cylinder ports **(see illustrations)**.

10.4 Remove the nuts and washers (arrowed) securing the master cylinder to the vacuum servo unit

10.6a On early models, remove the retaining screw . . .

10.6b . . . then remove the fluid reservoir and its mounting seals from the master cylinder

10.7 Push the pistons fully into position then slacken and remove the piston retaining screw and washer

7 Carefully grip the master cylinder body in a vice equipped with soft-jaws. Using a suitable punch, press the piston into the cylinder then slacken and remove the piston retaining screw and sealing washer from the side of the body (see illustration).

8 Press the piston into the cylinder again and remove the piston retaining circlip from the rear of the master cylinder (see illustration).

9 Noting each components correct fitted location, withdraw the primary and secondary piston assemblies from the cylinder. If necessary, tap the master cylinder body on a clean wooden surface to release the pistons (see illustrations).

10 Thoroughly clean all components using only methylated spirit, isopropyl alcohol or clean hydraulic fluid as a cleaning medium. Never use mineral-based solvents such as petrol or paraffin which will attack the hydraulic system's rubber components. Dry the components immediately using compressed air or a clean, lint-free cloth.

11 Check all components and renew any that are worn or damaged. Check particularly the cylinder bores and pistons; the complete assembly should be renewed if these are scratched, worn or corroded. If there is any doubt about the condition of the assembly or of any of its components, renew it. Check that the body's fluid passages are clear.

12 If the assembly is fit for further use, obtain a repair kit from your Hyundai dealer. Renew all seals disturbed on dismantling as a matter

of course; these should never be re-used.

13 Prior to reassembly, soak the piston assemblies and all new seals in clean hydraulic fluid. Smear clean fluid into the cylinder bore.

14 Insert the secondary piston assembly into the master cylinder body, making sure the piston assembly is the correct way around. Fit the piston assembly using a twisting motion whilst ensuring the piston seals do not become trapped as they enter the cylinder.

15 Fit a new sealing washer to the piston retaining screw then press the piston assembly into the master cylinder bore. Fit the retaining screw to the master cylinder body and tighten it securely.

16 Ensure the secondary piston is securely retained by the screw then fit the new primary piston assembly as described in paragraph 14.

17 Press the primary piston into the cylinder and refit the circlip. Make sure that the circlip is correctly located in the master cylinder groove.

18 Press the reservoir seals into the master cylinder ports and refit the fluid reservoir, tightening its retaining screw securely.

Later models

19 Remove the fluid reservoir from the top of the master cylinder and ease the mounting seals out from the ports.

20 Dismantle and examine the cylinder assembly as described in paragraphs 8 to 13.

21 Insert the secondary piston assembly into the master cylinder body, making sure the piston assembly is the correct way around. Fit the piston assembly using a twisting motion whilst ensuring the piston seals do not become trapped as they enter the cylinder.

22 Fit the primary piston assembly using the same method then press the piston into the cylinder and refit the circlip. Make sure that the circlip is correctly located in the master cylinder groove.

23 Press the reservoir seals into the master cylinder ports and securely refit the fluid reservoir.

Refitting

24 On early models, prior to refitting the master cylinder it is necessary to ensure the master cylinder piston-to-servo unit pushrod clearance is correctly set; if the clearance is excessive the brake pedal travel will be excessive and if it is insufficient the brakes may drag. **Note:** *On later models the pushrod length is preset and is not adjustable.* Referring to **illustration 10.24**, on the master cylinder measure the distance from the primary piston seat to the rear of the cylinder body (B) and the distance from the rear of the mating surface to the rear of the body (C). On the servo unit measure the distance from the end of the pushrod to the mating surface (D). Using the above measurements, calculate the piston-to-rod clearance A by subtracting the measurements C and D from B, ie. A = B - C - D. If this distance is not within the

10.8 Depress the pistons again and remove the circlip from the master cylinder bore

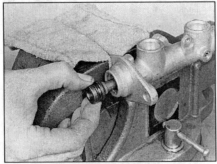

10.9a Withdraw the primary piston assembly . . .

10.9b . . . then free the secondary piston assembly from the body

specified range, adjust it by screwing the end nut onto/off the pushrod as necessary until the pushrod length is correctly set.

25 On all models, remove all traces of dirt from the master cylinder and servo unit mating surfaces and carefully fit the master cylinder to the servo unit, ensuring that the servo unit pushrod enters the master cylinder bore centrally.

26 Locate the pressure regulating valve bracket on the studs then refit the washers and mounting nuts, tightening them to the specified torque.

27 Wipe clean the brake pipe unions and refit them to the master cylinder ports, tightening them to the specified torque.

28 Reconnect the fluid level sender unit wiring connector then refill the master cylinder reservoir with new fluid. Bleed the complete hydraulic system as described in Section 2.

11 Brake pedal - adjustment

1 The brake hydraulic system is self-adjusting and therefore requires no checking or manual adjustment other than ensuring that the fluid level remains correct. The following is a check of the pedal action which should only be necessary should the pedal/servo unit be disturbed or a fault be suspected.

2 If necessary, to improve access to the pedal remove the lower panel from the driver's side of the facia (see Chapter 11).

3 Peel back the carpet from underneath the brake pedal, and ensure that there are no obstructions between the pedal and floor panel. Measure the distance from the centre of the brake pedal pad to the floor **(see**

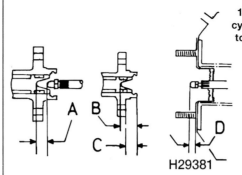

10.24a On early models, set the master cylinder-to-servo pushrod clearance prior to refitting the master cylinder - see text

A   *Piston-to-pushrod clearance*
B   *Primary piston seat-to-body measurement*
C   *Master cylinder mating surface-to-body measurement*
D   *Servo pushrod-to-mating surface measurement*

illustration). **Note:** *This measurement can be taken with the carpet in position, so long as the thickness of the carpet is added onto the pedal height measurement.* The pedal height should be as given in the Specifications at the start of this Chapter. If adjustment is necessary, slacken the servo unit pushrod clevis locknut and adjust the pedal height by rotating the pushrod with a pair of pliers. Whilst adjusting the pedal, note that it may be necessary to unscrew the stop-light switch slightly if it stops the pedal movement (see Section 18). Once the pedal height is correctly set, securely tighten the pushrod clevis locknut.

4 Adjust the stop-light switch as described in Section 18.

5 With the pedal height and stop-light switch correctly adjusted, slowly depress the brake pedal, and measure the distance that the pedal pad travels from the at-rest position to the point where resistance in the hydraulic circuit is felt **(see illustration)**. This is the pedal free play, and should be within the

range given in the Specifications. If the freeplay is not within the specified range, then it is likely that there is air in the hydraulic system and the system should be bled as described in Section 2. On early models, if this fails to cure the problem then the master cylinder-to-servo unit pushrod clearance is likely to be incorrect and will need adjustment (see Section 10, paragraph 24).

6 With all adjustments correctly set, with the engine idling, fully depress the brake pedal. On early (pre 1991) models measure the distance between the pedal and the front bulkhead and on later (1991 on) models measure the distance between the pedal pad and the floor **(see illustration)**. Compare the results to those given in the Specifications. If the clearance is less than specified, it is likely that there is air present in the hydraulic system. Bleed the system as described in Section 2 and repeat the check. If the clearance is still less than specified then it is likely that the master cylinder is faulty.

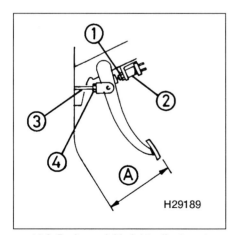

11.3 Brake pedal height adjustment details

A   *Brake pedal height measurement*
1   *Stop-light switch locknut*
2   *Stop-light switch*
3   *Servo unit pushrod*
4   *Clevis locknut*

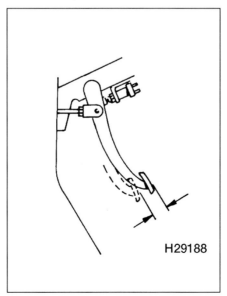

11.5 Brake pedal freeplay measurement

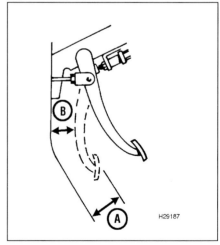

11.6 Brake pedal clearance measurement

A   *Pedal-to-bulkhead clearance - early models*
B   *Pedal pad-to-floor clearance - later models*

12 Vacuum servo unit - testing, removal and refitting

Testing

1 To test the operation of the servo unit, depress the footbrake several times to exhaust the vacuum, then start the engine whilst keeping the pedal firmly depressed. As the engine starts, there should be a noticeable "give" in the brake pedal as the vacuum builds up. Allow the engine to run for at least two minutes, then switch it off. If the brake pedal is now depressed it should feel normal, but further applications should result in the pedal feeling firmer, with the pedal stroke decreasing with each application.

2 If the servo does not operate as described, first inspect the servo unit check valve as described in Section 13.

3 If the servo unit still fails to operate satisfactorily, the fault lies within the unit itself. Repairs to the unit are not possible - if faulty, the servo unit must be renewed.

Removal

4 Remove the master cylinder (see Section 10).

5 Release the retaining clip and disconnect the vacuum hose from the servo unit check valve.

6 From inside the vehicle, extract the split pin from the servo unit pushrod clevis then remove the washer and withdraw the split pin securing the pushrod to the brake pedal.

7 On early models, slacken and remove the lower nuts securing the servo unit mounting bracket to the bulkhead then return to the engine compartment. Slacken and remove the mounting bracket upper nuts then manoeuvre the servo unit out of position. Recover the gasket which is fitted between the mounting bracket and bulkhead. If necessary, the servo unit and mounting bracket can then be separated.

8 On later models, slacken and remove the servo unit retaining nuts then return to the engine compartment and lift the servo unit assembly out of position. Slide the spacer off from the servo unit mounting studs noting the gasket which is fitted on either side of it.

9 On all models, if the servo unit is faulty it must be renewed; overhaul of the unit is not possible.

Refitting

10 Ensure all mating surfaces are clean and dry.

11 On early models, where necessary, fit a new gasket to the rear of the servo unit then reassembly the unit and mounting bracket, tightening the nuts and washers to the specified torque. Fit a new gasket to the rear of the mounting bracket and manoeuvre the servo unit assembly into position.

12 On later models slide the first gasket onto the rear of the servo unit then refit the spacer followed by the second gasket. Manoeuvre the servo unit into position in the engine compartment.

13 On all models ensure that the servo unit is correctly engaged with the brake pedal then refit the mounting nuts and tighten them to the specified torque setting.

14 Align the pushrod clevis with the brake pedal and slide in the clevis pin. Refit the washer and secure the pin in position with a new split pin.

15 Reconnect the vacuum hose to the servo unit and secure it in position with the retaining clip.

16 Refit the master cylinder as described in Section 10 and bleed the complete hydraulic system as described in Section 2.

13 Vacuum servo unit check valve - removal, testing and refitting

Removal

1 Release the retaining clips and disconnect the hoses from the servo unit check valve which is mounted onto the engine compartment bulkhead.

2 Slacken the retaining bolts and slide the valve out from its mounting bracket, noting which way around the valve is fitted.

Testing

3 Examine the check valve for signs of damage, and renew if necessary. The valve may be tested by blowing through it in both directions. Air should flow through the valve in one direction only - when blown through from the servo unit end of the valve (in the direction of the arrow marked on the side of the valve). Renew the valve if this is not the case.

4 Examine the vacuum hoses for signs of damage or deterioration, and renew as necessary.

Refitting

5 Slide the valve into position in the mounting bracket ensuring that the arrow stamped on the valve is pointing towards the engine.

14.4 On early models adjust the handbrake cables by slackening the locknuts and rotating the adjuster nuts (arrowed)

6 Securely tighten the retaining bolts then reconnect the vacuum hoses, securing them in position with the retaining clips.

7 On completion, start the engine and check the check valve connections for signs of air leaks.

14 Handbrake - adjustment

1 To check the handbrake adjustment, fully release the handbrake then apply the footbrake firmly several times to establish correct shoe-to-drum clearance then apply and release the handbrake several times to ensure that the self-adjust mechanism is fully adjusted. Applying normal moderate pressure, pull the handbrake lever to the fully-applied position, counting the number of clicks emitted from the handbrake ratchet mechanism. If adjustment is correct, there should be between 5 and 7 clicks before the handbrake is fully applied. If this is not the case, adjust as follows.

2 Chock the front wheels, then jack up the rear of the vehicle and support it on axle stands.

3 To gain access to the handbrake adjuster, remove the centre console as described in Chapter 11.

4 On early models, with the handbrake lever fully released, slacken the locknut and rotate the adjuster nut on each cable to adjust the lever travel (see illustration). When adjust the cables, ensure that the equalizer mechanism on the lever remains square and does not tilt; do this by adjusting each cable an equal amount. Check the handbrake adjustment by applying the handbrake fully, counting the clicks emitted from the handbrake ratchet and, if necessary, re-adjust. Once the lever is correctly adjusted securely tighten the locknuts.

5 On later models, with the handbrake lever fully released, adjust the cables by rotating the adjuster nut which is fitted to the rear of the handbrake lever; the equalizer plate ensures that the cables are equally adjusted. Check the handbrake adjustment by applying the handbrake fully, counting the clicks emitted from the handbrake ratchet and, if necessary, re-adjust.

6 Once the handbrake is correctly adjusted, check the operation of the warning light switch. The warning light should illuminate after the lever is pulled onto the first notch of its ratchet mechanism. If adjustment is necessary, slacken the retaining screw and reposition the switch correctly before tightening the screw securely (see illustration).

7 Once both the handbrake and warning light switch are correctly adjusted refit the centre console as described in Chapter 11.

15 Handbrake lever - removal and refitting

Removal

1 Chock the front wheels then jack up the rear of the vehicle and support it on axle stands.
2 Remove the centre console as described in Chapter 11.
3 Disconnect the wiring connector from the handbrake warning light switch.
4 On early models, slacken the locknuts then remove the adjuster nuts and detach the handbrake cables from the handbrake lever.
5 On later models, unscrew the adjusting nut and free the equalizer plate from the rear of the handbrake lever.
6 On all models unbolt the handbrake lever and remove it from the vehicle.

Refitting

7 Refitting is a reversal of removal tightening the lever retaining bolts securely and adjusting the handbrake as described in Section 14.

16 Handbrake cables - removal and refitting

Removal

1 The handbrake cable consists of two sections, a right- and left-hand section which connect the rear brakes to the handbrake lever. Each section can be removed individually as follows.
2 Firmly chock the front wheels, then jack up the rear of the vehicle and support it on axle stands.

3 Remove the centre console and rear seat cushion as described in Chapter 11.
4 On early models, slacken the locknut then remove the adjuster nut and detach the relevant handbrake cable from the handbrake lever.
5 On later models, unscrew the adjusting nut then detach the relevant handbrake cable from the handbrake lever equalizer plate.
6 On all models, slacken and remove the bolts securing the cable retaining clamp to the floor.
7 Remove the relevant set of brake shoes as described in Section 5.
8 Remove the retaining clip (where fitted) then tap the handbrake cable end fitting out from the brake backplate (see illustration).
9 Work back along the cable, noting its correct routing whilst freeing it from any clips or ties, and slacken and remove the cable retaining clip bolt. Free the outer cable grommet from the vehicle body and remove the cable from the vehicle.

Refitting

10 Refitting is a reversal of the removal procedure ensuring that the cable is correctly routed and retained by all the relevant clips and ties. Prior to refitting the console, adjust the handbrake as described in Section 14.

17 Rear brake pressure-regulating valve - testing, removal and refitting

Testing

1 A pressure-regulating valve is fitted into the hydraulic circuit to each rear brake. The valve is located directly underneath the master cylinder assembly. The valve measures the pressure being applied to the front brakes and regulates the hydraulic pressure being applied

to the rear brakes accordingly to help prevent rear wheels locking up under hard braking.
2 Specialist equipment is required to check the performance of the valve(s), therefore if the valve is thought to be faulty the car should be taken to a suitably equipped Hyundai dealer for testing. Repairs are not possible and, if faulty, the valve must be renewed.

Removal

Note: Before starting work, refer to the warning at the beginning of Section 2 concerning the dangers of hydraulic fluid.
3 Minimise fluid loss by first removing the master cylinder reservoir cap, and then tightening it down onto a piece of polythene, to obtain an airtight seal.
4 Wipe clean the area around the brake pipe unions on the valve, and place absorbent rags beneath the pipe unions to catch any surplus fluid. To avoid confusion on refitting, make alignment marks between the pipes and valve assembly.
5 Slacken the union nuts and disconnect the brake pipes from the valve. Plug or tape over the pipe ends and valve orifices, to minimise the loss of brake fluid, and to prevent the entry of dirt into the system. Wash off any spilt fluid immediately with cold water.
6 Slacken and remove the retaining nut and remove the valve assembly from underneath the master cylinder.

Refitting

7 Manoeuvre the valve assembly into position and tighten its retaining nut to the specified torque.
8 Refit the brake pipes to their specific unions on the valve and tighten the union nuts to the specified torque setting.
9 Remove the polythene from the master cylinder reservoir and bleed the complete hydraulic system as described in Section 2.

14.6 To adjust the handbrake warning light switch, slacken the retaining screw and reposition as necessary

16.8 Remove the retaining clip and free the handbrake cable from the rear of the brake backplate

18.3 Disconnect the wiring connector then slacken the locknut (arrowed) and unscrew the switch

18 Stop-light switch - removal, refitting and adjustment

Removal

1 The stop-light switch is located on the pedal bracket behind the facia.

2 To improve access to the switch, remove the lower panel from the driver's side of the facia (see Chapter 11).

3 Disconnect the wiring connector then slacken the locknut and unscrew the switch from the bracket **(see illustration)**.

Refitting and adjustment

4 Screw the switch back into position in the mounting bracket, until the gap between the end of the main body of the switch and the lug on the brake pedal is approximately 0.5 to 1 mm.

5 Once the stop-light switch is correctly positioned, securely tighten the locknut and reconnect the wiring connector. Check the operation of the stop-lights. The stop-lights should illuminate after the brake pedal has travelled approximately 5 mm. Adjust the switch as necessary then refit the lower facia panel.

Chapter 10
Suspension and steering

Contents

Front hub bearings - renewal 3
Front suspension and steering check .... See Chapter 1
Front suspension anti-roll bar - removal and refitting 9
Front suspension lower arm - removal, overhaul and refitting 6
Front suspension lower arm balljoint - removal and refitting 7
Front suspension radius arm (early models) - removal and refitting . 8
Front suspension strut - overhaul 5
Front suspension strut - removal and refitting 4
Front swivel hub assembly - removal and refitting 2
General information 1
Ignition switch/steering column lock - removal and refitting 18
Power steering fluid level check .... See "Weekly checks"
Power steering pump - removal and refitting 22
Power steering pump drivebelt - check, adjustment
    and renewal ....See Chapter 1
Power steering system - bleeding 21

Rear axle assembly - removal, overhaul and refitting 14
Rear hub assembly - removal and refitting 10
Rear hub bearings - renewal 11
Rear suspension coil spring - removal and refitting 13
Rear suspension shock absorber - removal, testing and refitting ... 12
Steering column - removal, inspection and refitting 16
Steering column intermediate shaft - removal, inspection and
    refitting 17
Steering gear assembly - removal, overhaul and refitting 19
Steering gear rubber gaiters - renewal 20
Steering wheel - removal and refitting 15
Track rod - removal and refitting 24
Track rod balljoint - removal and refitting 23
Wheel alignment and steering angles - general information 25
Wheel and tyre maintenance and
    tyre pressure checks .... See "Weekly checks"

Degrees of difficulty

Easy, suitable for novice with little experience	**Fairly easy,** suitable for beginner with some experience	**Fairly difficult,** suitable for competent DIY mechanic	**Difficult,** suitable for experienced DIY mechanic	**Very difficult,** suitable for expert DIY or professional

Specifications

Wheel alignment and steering angles

Front wheel:
Toe setting	4.0 mm toe-in to 2.0 mm toe-out
Camber	0° to 1°

Castor:
Early (pre 1991) models	0° 30' to 1° 10'

Later (1991-on) models:
Models with manual steering	1° 2' to ± 30'
Models with power steering	1° 40' to ± 30'

King pin inclination:
Early (pre 1991) models	12° 42'
Later (1991-on) models	12° 59'

Steering angle:

Early (pre 1991) models:
Inner wheel	34° 10' to 37° 10'
Outer wheel	29° 17'

Later (1991-on) models:
Inner wheel	37° 24' ± 1° 30'
Outer wheel	31° 31'

Rear wheel:
Toe setting	6.0 mm toe-in to 3 mm toe-out
Camber	-40'

Roadwheels

Type	Pressed-steel or aluminium alloy (depending on model)
Size	4.5J x 13 or 5J x 13 (depending on model)
Tyre pressures	See "Weekly checks"

Torque wrench settings

	Nm	lbf ft
Front suspension		
Anti-roll bar:		
Early (pre 1991) models:		
Mounting clamp bolts	35	26
Radius arm clamp bolts	6	4
Later (1991-on) models:		
Mounting clamp bolts	22	16
Link bolt nut	Tighten until the correct amount thread is exposed (see text)	
Driveshaft retaining nut	200 to 260*	148 to 192*
Lower arm:		
Early (pre 1991) models:		
Inner pivot bolt	110	80
Later (1991-on) models:		
Front mounting bracket bolts	175	127
Rear mounting bracket bolts	70	51
Front mounting bracket pivot shaft nut	110	80
Lower arm balljoint:		
Balljoint nut	65	48
Balljoint-to-lower arm bolt nut	110	80
Radius arm - early (pre 1991) models only:		
Locknut	80	59
Front mounting nut	80	59
Radius arm-to-lower arm bolt nut	110	80
Suspension strut:		
Upper mounting nuts	15	11
Upper mounting plate nut	45	33
Strut-to-swivel hub bolt nuts:		
Early (pre 1991) models	80	59
Later (1991-on) models	95	70
Subframe mounting bolts	120	88
Tighten until it is possible to insert a split pin		
Rear suspension		
Axle assembly:		
Mounting bracket bolts	60	44
Trailing arm shaft nuts:		
Early (pre 1991) models	60	44
Later (1991-on) models	140	101
Bump stop nut	22	16
Hub nut	See Chapter 9	
Shock absorber mounting bolts	75	55
Steering		
Column mounting bolts/nuts:		
Early (pre 1991) models	10	7
Later (1991-on) models	15	11
Intermediate shaft clamp bolt	18	13
Power steering pipe union nuts:		
Steering gear unions	15	11
Pump union	20	15
Steering gear mounting bolts:		
Early (pre 1991) models	35	26
Later (1991-on) models	70	51
Steering wheel nut	40	30
Track rod:		
Balljoint-to-swivel hub nut	15 to 34*	11 to 25*
Balljoint locknut	50	37
Inner balljoint-to-steering rack	90	66
Tighten until it is possible to insert a split pin		
Roadwheels		
Wheel nuts:		
Early (pre 1991) models:		
Steel wheels	75	54
Alloy wheels	90	66
Later (1991-on) models	100	74

1 General information

The independent front suspension is of the MacPherson strut type, incorporating coil springs and integral telescopic shock absorbers. The MacPherson struts are located by transverse lower suspension arms, which utilise rubber inner mounting bushes, and incorporate a balljoint at the outer ends. The front swivel hubs, which carry the wheel bearings, brake calipers and the hub/disc assemblies, are bolted to the MacPherson struts, and connected to the lower arms via the balljoints. A front anti-roll bar is fitted to all models. The anti-roll bar is rubber-mounted onto the subframe, and is connected directly to the front suspension struts. On early (pre 1991) models, radius arms are also fitted linking the lower arms to the front vehicle body **(see illustration)**.

The independent rear suspension is of the semi-independent beam axle type, incorporating coil springs and shock absorbers. The axle assembly consists of the left- and right-hand trailing arm assemblies which are bolted together and allowed to pivot at the centre of the axle crossmember. An anti-roll bar links the left- and right-hand arms and the axle assembly is mounted onto the vehicle body by rubber bushes on the side **(see illustration)**.

The steering column is connected to the steering gear by an intermediate shaft. The intermediate shaft has a universal joint at each end and is clamped to the steering column and gear pinion by means of clamp bolts.

The steering gear is mounted onto the front subframe, and is connected by two track rods, with balljoints at their outer ends, to the steering arms projecting rearwards from the swivel hubs. The track rod ends are threaded, to facilitate adjustment. On models with power-assisted steering, the hydraulic steering system is powered by a belt-driven pump, which is driven off the crankshaft pulley.

2 Front swivel hub assembly - removal and refitting

Note: *A new lower arm balljoint nut will be required on refitting; all split pins should also be renewed. On later (1991 on) models a new anti-roll bar link bolt nut will also be needed. It is also likely that a puller will be required to free the outer constant velocity joint from the hub assembly.*

Removal

1 Remove the wheel trim/hub cap (as applicable). Extract the split pin and slacken the driveshaft nut with the vehicle resting on its wheels. Also slacken the wheel nuts.

1.1 Front suspension and steering components (early model shown)

1 Anti-roll bar	4 Lower arm balljoint	7 Steering gear gaiter
2 Suspension strut	5 Track rod balljoint	8 Steering gear
3 Lower arm	6 Track rod	

2 Chock the rear wheels of the car, firmly apply the handbrake, then jack up the front of the car and support it on axle stands (see "*Jacking and Vehicle Support*"). Remove the appropriate front roadwheel.
3 Unscrew the two bolts securing the brake

caliper assembly to the swivel hub, and slide the caliper assembly off the disc. Using a piece of wire or string, tie the caliper to the front suspension coil spring, to avoid placing any strain on the hydraulic brake hose.
4 On early (pre 1991) models, slacken and

1.2 Rear suspension components

1 Trailing arm	2 Anti-roll bar	3 Coil spring

2.10 Removing the swivel hub assembly

remove the nuts and washers securing the radius arm to the lower suspension arm and withdraw the bolts.

5 On later (1991 on) models, slacken and remove the nut, washer and mounting rubber securing the anti-roll bar link bolt to the lower arm. Withdraw the anti-roll bar link bolt and washer and remove the spacer and mounting rubbers, noting each components correct fitted location. Discard the nut, a new one should be used on refitting.

6 On all models, remove the split pin then unscrew the retaining nut and washer and free the track rod balljoint from the hub. If necessary, a balljoint separator can be used to free the track rod end.

7 Unscrew the lower arm balljoint nut and free the balljoint shank from the swivel hub, if necessary, using a balljoint separator. Discard the nut, a new one should be used on refitting.

8 Slacken and remove the driveshaft retaining nut and washer, noting which way around the washer is fitted.

9 Slacken and remove the nuts and washers

and withdraw the bolts securing the swivel hub to the suspension strut.

10 Free the swivel hub assembly from the driveshaft outer constant velocity joint and remove the hub from the vehicle **(see illustration)**. The shaft can be tapped out of the hub using a soft-faced mallet or, if necessary, the hub assembly can be drawn off the joint using a legged-puller. With the hub removed, support the driveshaft to avoid placing any strain on the constant velocity joints/gaiters.

Refitting

11 Ensure that the driveshaft outer constant velocity joint and hub splines are clean, then slide the hub fully onto the driveshaft splines.

12 Engage the hub with the suspension strut then insert the bolts and refit the washers and nuts.

13 Engage the lower arm balljoint shank in the swivel hub and fit the new retaining nut, tightening it to the specified torque.

14 Locate the track rod balljoint in the hub then refit the washer and retaining nut. Tighten the nut to the specified torque and secure it in position with a new split pin.

15 On early (pre 1991) models align the radius arm with the lower arm and refit the retaining bolts. Fit the washers and nuts and tighten them to the specified torque.

16 On later (1991 on) models, refit the anti-roll bar spacer and mounting rubbers, ensuring that the rubbers are correctly positioned. Insert the link bolt and washer then fit the washer and new nut, tighten the nut until 24 to 26 mm of the link bolt threads are exposed (see Section 9).

17 Tighten the strut-to-swivel hub bolts to the specified torque setting.

18 Slide the brake caliper into position, making sure the pads pass either side of the disc, and tighten the caliper bracket bolts to the specified torque setting (see Chapter 9).

19 Refit the driveshaft nut washer, making sure its tapered edge is facing outwards, and screw on the hub nut. Tighten the nut securely at this stage, it can be tightened to the specified torque once the vehicle is resting on its wheels.

20 Refit the roadwheel then lower the vehicle to the ground and tighten the wheel nuts to the specified torque.

21 Tighten the driveshaft nut to the specified torque setting so that the nut slots align with the split pin hole in the driveshaft joint. Secure the nut in position with a new split pin then refit the wheel trim/hub cap (as applicable).

3 Front hub bearings - renewal

Note: *Never overtighten the driveshaft nut beyond the specified torque wrench setting in an attempt to "adjust" the bearing.*

Note: *A press will be required to dismantle and rebuild the assembly; if such a tool is not available, a large bench vice and spacers (such as large sockets) will serve as an adequate substitute. The bearing inner races are an interference fit on the hub and a bearing puller will be required to remove the outer one. Also a length of threaded rod complete with nuts and suitable tubular spacers will also be required on refitting to draw the hub flange back into position.*

1 Remove the swivel hub assembly as described in Section 2.

2 Support the swivel hub securely on blocks or in a vice **(see illustration)**. Using a tubular spacer which bears only on the inner end of the hub flange, press the hub flange/disc out of the bearing. Alternately, securely mount the swivel hub in a vice and extract the hub flange/disc using a slide hammer. Remove the brake disc shield from the swivel hub.

3 Remove the outer bearing inner race from the hub flange using a bearing puller.

4 If necessary, slacken and remove the retaining bolts and washers and separate the brake disc and hub flange. If the original disc is to be refitted, make alignment marks between the disc and hub prior to removal.

5 Lever out the inner and outer oil seals from the swivel hub and lift out the bearing inner race.

6 Securely mount the swivel hub in a vice and tap the inner and outer bearing outer races out of position.

7 Thoroughly clean the hub and swivel hub, removing all traces of dirt and grease, and polish away any burrs or raised edges which might hinder reassembly. Check both for cracks or any other signs of wear or damage, and renew them if necessary.

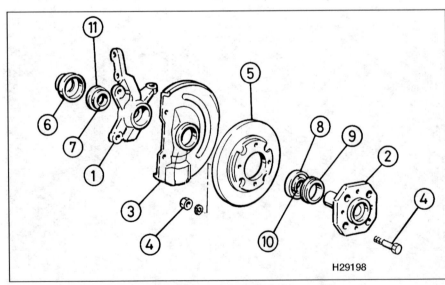

H29198

3.2 Exploded view of the front hub assembly

1 Swivel hub	5 Brake disc	9 Oil seal
2 Hub flange	6 Oil seal	10 Outer bearing inner race
3 Disc shield	7 Inner bearing inner race	11 Inner bearing outer race
4 Nut/bolt	8 Outer bearing outer race	

3.16 Refitting the hub flange using a length of threaded bar

4.3a Slacken and remove the nuts and washers . . .

4.3b . . . and withdraw the bolts securing the strut to the swivel hub assembly

8 On reassembly, apply a light film of oil to the bearing outer races to aid installation of the bearings.
9 Securely support the rear of the swivel hub, and locate the outer bearing outer race in the hub.
10 Press/tap the outer race fully into position, ensuring that it enters the hub squarely, using a tubular spacer which bears only on the outer edge of the race.
11 Turn the swivel hub assembly over and fit the inner bearing outer race in the same way.
12 Thoroughly grease the new bearing inner races with a lithium-based, multi-purpose grease (such as Duckhams LB10), working the grease well into the rollers. Apply grease to the outer races and inner surface of the swivel hub assembly bearing area.
13 Fit the outer bearing inner race to the swivel hub then fit the new oil seal. Ensure that the seal lip is facing inwards and press/tap it squarely into position until it is flush with the swivel hub face.
14 Ensure that the hub flange and disc mating surfaces are clean and dry; if a new disc is being installed, clean the disc with solvent to remove all traces of grease/oil. Fit the disc to the hub flange, aligning the marks made on dismantling if the original is being fitted. Refit the retaining bolts and washers and tighten them to the specified torque.
15 Mount the swivel hub assembly vertically in a vice and fit the inner bearing inner race and brake disc shield.
16 Fit a nut and large washer/tubular spacer to one end of the threaded bar then carefully engage the hub flange assembly with the outer bearing inner race. Pass the threaded bar through the centre then slide the second washer/tubular spacer onto the rear of the bar and fit the second nut. Ensure that the washers/spacers are correctly located against the hub flange and bearing inner race then draw the hub flange into position using the nuts whilst rotating the brake disc to settle the bearings in position **(see illustration)**. Once the hub flange is fully seated (this may mean tightening the nuts right up to the driveshaft nut specified torque), check the brake disc rotates freely then unscrew one of the nuts and remove the threaded bar.
17 Refit the swivel hub assembly as described in Section 2.

4 Front suspension strut - removal and refitting

Removal

1 Chock the rear wheels, apply the handbrake, then jack up the front of the vehicle and support on axle stands (see *"Jacking and Vehicle Support"*). Remove the appropriate roadwheel.
2 Unscrew the bolt and free the brake hose mounting bracket from the suspension strut. Where the bracket is welded to the strut, slide out the retaining clips and free the hose (see Chapter 9).
3 Slacken and remove the nuts and washers and withdraw the bolts securing the strut to the swivel hub **(see illustrations)**.
4 Working in the engine compartment, slacken and remove the suspension strut upper mounting nuts, then withdraw the strut from under the wheel arch.

Refitting

5 Manoeuvre the strut assembly into position, ensuring that the top mounting plate is correctly located in the body, and engage the lower end of the strut with the hub assembly.
6 Insert the strut lower bolts then refit the washers and retaining nuts.
7 Refit the upper mounting nuts, tightening them to the specified torque, then tighten the lower bolt nuts to the specified torque.

5.2 Slacken the upper mounting plate nut whilst preventing rotation by retaining the mounting

8 Refit the brake hose clamp to the strut and securely tighten its retaining bolt. Alternately, locate the brake hose in the brackets and secure it in position with the retaining clips (as applicable).
9 Refit the roadwheel, then lower the vehicle to the ground and tighten the roadwheel nuts to the specified torque.

5 Front suspension strut - overhaul

⚠ *Warning: Before attempting to dismantle the front suspension strut, a suitable tool to hold the coil spring in compression must be obtained. Adjustable coil spring compressors are readily-available, and are recommended for this operation. Any attempt to dismantle the strut without such a tool is likely to result in damage or personal injury.*
Note: *A new mounting plate nut will be required.*
1 With the strut removed from the car, clean away all external dirt, then mount it upright in a vice. Fit the spring compressor to the coil spring and compress it until all tension is relieved from the spring seats.
2 Remove the dust cap then slacken the mounting plate nut. If necessary, prevent rotation by retaining the shock upper mounting plate with a suitable pair of grips or a C-spanner whilst the nut is slackened **(see illustration)**.
3 Remove the nut and (where fitted) washer and lift off the upper mounting plate.
4 On early models lift off the upper spring seat and coil spring and slide the bump stop/dust cover off the strut piston.
5 On later models, remove the upper spring seat and its rubber damper then lift off the coil spring and slide the bump stop and dust cover off the strut piston.
6 Examine the shock absorber for signs of fluid leakage. Check the piston for signs of pitting along its entire length, and check the shock body for signs of damage. While holding it in an upright position, test the operation of the shock absorber by moving the piston through a full stroke, and then

through short strokes of 50 to 100 mm. In both cases, the resistance felt should be smooth and continuous. If the resistance is jerky, or uneven, or if there is any visible sign of wear or damage to the shock absorber, renewal is necessary.

7 Inspect all other components for signs of damage or deterioration, and renew any that are suspect.

8 On reassembly, slide the bump stop and dust cover onto the piston then fit the coil spring. Ensure that the end of the spring is correctly located against its stop on the lower seat **(see illustration)**.

9 Fit the upper spring seat, complete with rubber damper (where fitted), aligning the seat stop with the upper end of the coil spring **(see illustration)**.

10 Fit the mounting plate assembly, making sure it is correctly engaged with the piston, then fit the washer (where fitted) and screw on the new nut. Tighten the nut to the specified torque setting whilst retaining the mounting plate.

11 Pack the area around the mounting plate with multi-purpose grease then refit the dust cap.

6 Front suspension lower arm - removal, overhaul and refitting

Removal

1 Chock the rear wheels, firmly apply the handbrake, then jack up the front of the vehicle and support on axle stands (see "*Jacking and Vehicle Support*"). Remove the appropriate front roadwheel.

Early (pre 1991) models

2 Unscrew the retaining nuts and washers and withdraw the bolts securing the radius arm and balljoint to the lower arm.

3 Slacken and remove the lower arm pivot bolt and washer and remove the arm from the vehicle, taking care not to damage the balljoint **(see illustration)**.

Later (1991-on) models

Note: *A new lower balljoint nut and anti-roll bar link bolt nut will be required on refitting.*

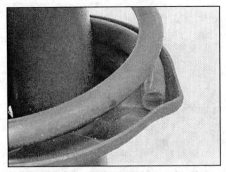

5.8 Ensure that the spring ends are correctly seated against the stops in the lower . . .

4 Unscrew the lower arm balljoint nut and free the balljoint shank from the swivel hub, if necessary, using a balljoint separator. Discard the nut, a new one should be used on refitting.

5 Slacken and remove the nut, washer and mounting rubber securing the anti-roll bar link bolt to the lower arm. Withdraw the anti-roll bar link bolt and washer and remove the spacer and mounting rubbers, noting each components correct fitted location. Discard the nut, a new one should be used on refitting.

6 Slacken and remove the bolts securing the lower arm rear mounting bracket in position. Unscrew the front mounting bracket bolts and manoeuvre the lower arm assembly out of position **(see illustrations)**.

Overhaul

7 Thoroughly clean the lower arm and the area around the arm mountings, removing all traces of dirt and underseal if necessary, then check carefully for cracks, distortion or any other signs of wear or damage, paying particular attention to the pivot bush(es), and renew components as necessary.

8 Renewal of the pivot bush(es) and/or mounting bracket (as applicable) will require the use of a hydraulic press, a bearing puller (later models only) and several spacers and should therefore be entrusted to a Hyundai dealer with access to the necessary equipment.

Refitting

Early (pre 1991) models

9 Manoeuvre the arm into position, engaging

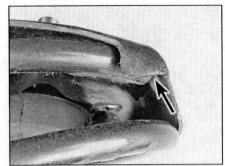

5.9 . . . and upper spring seat

it with the balljoint and radius arm, and refit the pivot bolt. Tighten the bolt lightly only at this stage.

10 Align the balljoint and radius arm with the lower arm and refit the bolts. Fit the washers and nuts to the bolts and tighten them to their specified torque settings.

11 Refit the roadwheel then lower the vehicle to the ground and tighten the wheel nuts to the specified torque setting. Rock the vehicle to settle the lower arm in position then, with the vehicle resting on its wheels, tighten the lower arm pivot bolt to the specified torque.

Later (1991-on) models

12 Manoeuvre the lower arm into position, engaging the balljoint shank with the swivel hub.

13 Refit the front mounting bracket bolts then offer up the rear mounting bracket and screw in its retaining bolts. Tighten both the front and rear mounting bracket bolts to the specified torque setting.

14 Refit the anti-roll bar spacer and mounting rubbers, ensuring that the rubbers are correctly positioned. Insert the link bolt and washer then fit the washer and new nut, tighten the nut until 24 to 26 mm of the link bolt threads are exposed (see Section 9).

15 Fit the new nut to the lower arm balljoint shank and tighten it to the specified torque setting.

16 Refit the roadwheel then lower the vehicle to the ground and tighten the wheel nuts to the specified torque.

6.3 Slacken and remove the lower arm inner pivot bolt and nut

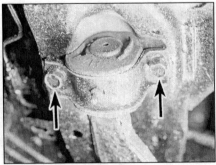

6.6a Remove the lower arm rear mounting bracket bolts (arrowed) . . .

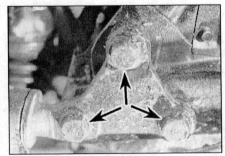

6.6b . . . and the front mounting bracket bolts (arrowed) then remove the lower arm assembly

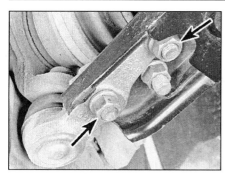

7.2 Remove the nuts and bolts securing the balljoint to the lower arm (early model shown)

8.3 On early models, remove the nut, washer and mounting rubber securing the radius arm to the body . . .

8.4 . . . then undo the nuts and bolts securing the arm to the lower arm (arrowed)

7 Front suspension lower arm balljoint - removal and refitting

Removal

Note: *A new lower balljoint nut will be required on refitting.*

1 Chock the rear wheels, firmly apply the handbrake, then jack up the front of the vehicle and support on axle stands (see *"Jacking and Vehicle Support"*). Remove the appropriate front roadwheel.
2 Unscrew the retaining nuts and washers and withdraw the bolts securing the balljoint to the lower arm **(see illustration)**.
3 Unscrew the lower arm balljoint nut and free the balljoint shank from the swivel hub, if necessary, using a balljoint separator. Discard the nut, a new one should be used on refitting, and remove the balljoint.
4 Inspect the balljoint for signs of wear or damage and renew if necessary. The balljoint gaiter is available separately and should be renewed if it shows signs of damage or deterioration.

Refitting

5 Manoeuvre the balljoint into position and locate it in the swivel hub.
6 Refit the balljoint retaining bolts then fit the washers and nuts and tighten them to the specified torque setting.
7 Fit the new nut to the balljoint shank and tighten it to the specified torque setting.
8 Refit the roadwheel then lower the vehicle to the ground and tighten the wheel nuts to the specified torque.

8 Front suspension radius arm (early models) - removal and refitting

Removal

1 Chock the rear wheels, firmly apply the handbrake, then jack up the front of the vehicle and support on axle stands (see *"Jacking and Vehicle Support"*). Remove the appropriate front roadwheel.

2 Unscrew the retaining bolt then disengage the mounting clamp securing the radius arm to the anti-roll bar.
3 Slacken and remove the nut and washer securing the front end of the radius arm to the body **(see illustration)**.
4 Unscrew the nuts and washers and withdraw the bolts securing the radius arm to the lower arm **(see illustration)**.
5 Manoeuvre the arm out of position and recover the front washer and mounting rubber from body. With the arm removed, slide the rear mounting rubber, spacer and washer off from the radius arm and remove the anti-roll bar mounting clamp rubber. **Note:** *Do not disturb the locknut and adjuster nut on the radius arm as these adjust the front wheel caster.*
6 Inspect all components for signs of wear or damage, paying particular attention to the mounting rubbers, and renew as necessary.

Refitting

7 If a new radius arm is being installed, measure the distance from the adjuster nut face to the end of the radius arm. Slacken the locknut then unscrew both the adjuster nut and locknut from the original arm and fit them to the new arm. Position the adjuster nut the same distance from the rod end as was noted prior to removal; Hyundai recommend that the adjuster nut is initially set 80.3 mm from the end of the arm. With the adjuster nut correctly positioned, tighten the locknut to the specified torque.

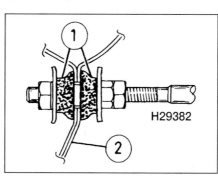

8.8 The radius arm front mounting rubbers (1) and washers must be correctly positioned on either side of the body (2)

8 Slide the rear washer onto the radius arm, with its concave surface facing the adjuster nut. Fit the spacer followed by the rear mounting rubber, ensuring its smaller end is against the washer. Fit the anti-roll bar mounting rubber **(see illustration)**.
9 Manoeuvre the arm into position ensuring it is correctly engaged with the anti-roll bar clamp and vehicle body.
10 Insert the bolts securing the radius arm to the lower arm and refit the washers and retaining nuts.
11 Slide on the front mounting rubber, ensuring its larger end is against the vehicle body, then fit the front washer with its convex surface facing the rubber. Refit the washer and mounting nut to the front of the radius arm and tighten it lightly only at this stage.
12 Tighten the radius arm-to-lower arm bolts to the specified torque.
13 Refit the mounting clamp securing the arm to the anti-roll bar and tighten its bolt to the specified torque.
14 Refit the roadwheel then lower the vehicle to the ground and tighten the wheel nuts to the specified torque setting. Rock the suspension to settle the arm in position then tighten its front mounting nut to the specified torque.

9 Front suspension anti-roll bar - removal and refitting

Removal

1 Chock the rear wheels, firmly apply the handbrake, then jack up the front of the vehicle and support on axle stands (see *"Jacking and Vehicle Support"*). Remove both front roadwheels.

Early (pre 1991) models

2 Slacken and remove the clamp bolts and remove the mounting clamps securing the left- and right-hand ends of the anti-roll bar to the radius arms **(see illustration)**.
3 Undo the bolts securing the anti-roll bar mounting clamps to the front of the vehicle body and remove the clamps **(see illustration)**.

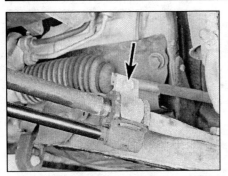

9.2 Unscrew the bolt (arrowed) and free the mounting clamp from each side of the anti-roll bar . . .

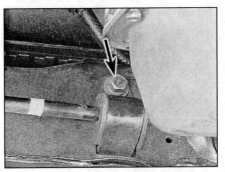

9.3 . . . then undo the retaining bolts (arrowed) and free the mounting clamps from the vehicle body

4 Free the anti-roll bar from the radius arms and manoeuvre it out from underneath the vehicle. Remove the mounting rubbers and examine them for signs of damage or deterioration, renewing as necessary.

Later (1991-on) models

Note: *New link bolt nuts will be needed on refitting. The track rod nut split pins should also be renewed.*

5 Remove the split pin then unscrew the retaining nut and washer and free the left-hand track rod balljoint from the hub. If necessary, a balljoint separator can be used to free the track rod end. Free the right-hand balljoint in the same way.

6 Referring to Chapter 2, slacken and remove the through-bolt then undo the mounting bolts and remove the engine/transmission rear mounting from the centre member.

9.18a Refit the link bolt complete with mounting rubber and upper washer

7 Noting each components correct fitted location, slacken and remove the anti-roll bar left-hand link bolt nut and washer and remove the mounting rubber. Withdraw the link bolt, washer and mounting rubber from the top of the anti-roll bar then remove the spacer and mounting rubbers which are fitted between the anti-roll bar and lower arm. Repeat the operation on the right-hand link bolt arrangement.

8 Undo the bolts securing the mounting clamps to the body then manoeuvre the anti-roll bar out of position.

9 With the anti-roll bar removed, noting their correct fitted locations, unclip the mounting clamp halves and remove the mounting rubbers; the mounting clamps should be marked "L" and "R" (left and right) to avoid confusion on refitting, if not make your own marks.

10 Inspect the mounting clamp and link components for signs of damage or deterioration, paying particular attention to the mounting rubbers, renewing any that are worn.

Refitting

Early (pre 1991) models

11 Fit the mounting rubbers to the anti-roll bar and position them so their flats are facing forwards. Fit the mounting rubbers to the radius arm and position them so that their flat surfaces are facing downwards.

12 Manoeuvre the anti-roll bar into position and engage it with the radius arms. Refit the mounting clamps, ensuring that the flats of the mounting rubbers are against the vehicle

body, and tighten the bolts to the specified torque setting.

13 Ensure that the mounting rubbers are correctly positioned then refit the radius arm clamps and tighten the clamp bolts to the specified torque.

14 Refit the roadwheels then lower the vehicle to the ground and tighten the wheel nuts to the specified torque.

Later (1991-on) models

15 Fit the mounting rubbers to the anti-roll bar, positioning their splits at the bottom. Clip the upper and lower mounting clamp halves onto the rubber peg on each rubber.

16 Ensure that the mounting rubbers and clamps are correctly assembled and manoeuvre the anti-roll bar into position.

17 Locate the mounting clamps on the vehicle body and refit the retaining bolts, tightening them lightly only at this stage.

18 Refit the left-hand spacer, position a mounting rubber at its upper and lower end, between the anti-roll bar and lower arm. Fit a mounting rubber to the top of the anti-roll bar and insert the link bolt and washer. Fit a mounting rubber to the base of the link bolt then fit the washer and new nut. Repeat the procedure on the right-hand side then tighten both link bolt nuts until 24 to 26 mm of the link bolt threads are exposed **(see illustrations)**.

19 Tighten the anti-roll bar mounting clamp bolts to the specified torque.

20 Refit the engine/transmission rear mounting assembly, tightening the mounting and through-bolts to their specified torque settings (see Chapter 2).

21 Refit the track rod balljoints to the swivel hubs then refit the retaining nuts, tighten them to the specified torque. Secure each nut in position with a new split pin.

22 Refit the roadwheels then lower the vehicle to the ground and tighten the wheel nuts to the specified torque.

10 Rear hub assembly - removal and refitting

The rear hub assembly is an integral part of the brake drum. See Chapter 9 for brake drum removal and refitting details.

9.18b Fit the mounting rubber and lower washer to the bolt . . .

9.18c . . . then fit the new nut and tighten it . . .

9.18d . . . until 24 to 26 mm of the link bolt threads are exposed

11 Rear hub bearings - renewal

1 Remove the brake drum (see Chapter 9).
2 Using a large screwdriver, lever out the oil seal from the rear of the drum and lift out the bearing inner race.
3 Support the rear of the drum on blocks of wood and tap the inner bearing outer race out of position using a hammer and suitable drift. Turn the drum over and remove the outer bearing inner race in the same way.
4 Thoroughly clean the brake drum hub, removing all traces of dirt and grease, and polish away any burrs or raised edges which might hinder reassembly. Check for cracks or any other signs of wear or damage, and renew if necessary.
5 On reassembly, apply a light film of oil to the bearing outer races to aid installation of the bearings.
6 Securely support the rear of the brake drum and locate the outer bearing outer race in the hub. Press/tap the outer race fully into position, ensuring that it enters the hub squarely, using a tubular spacer which bears only on the outer edge of the race.
7 Turn the drum assembly over and fit the inner bearing outer race in the same way.
8 Thoroughly grease the new bearing inner races with a lithium-based, multi-purpose grease (such as Duckhams LB10), working the grease well into the rollers. Apply grease to the outer races and inner surface of the drum hub bearing area.
9 Fit the inner bearing inner race to the drum then fit the new oil seal. Ensure that the seal lip is facing inwards and press/tap it squarely into position until it is flush with the drum face.
10 Fit the outer bearing inner race then refit the drum as described in Chapter 9.

12 Rear suspension shock absorber - removal, testing and refitting

Removal

1 Chock the front wheels then jack up the rear of the vehicle and support it on axle

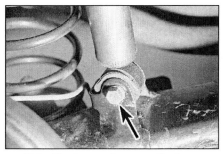

12.3a Slacken and remove the lower mounting bolt (arrowed) . . .

stands (see *"Jacking and Vehicle Support"*). Remove the relevant rear roadwheel.
2 Position a jack underneath the trailing arm and raise the jack until the coil spring is slightly compressed.
3 Slacken and remove the lower mounting bolt then remove the upper mounting bolt and nut and remove the shock absorber from the rear of the vehicle **(see illustrations)**.

Testing

4 Examine the shock absorber for signs of fluid leakage or damage. Test the operation of the shock absorber, while holding it in an upright position, by moving the piston through a full stroke and then through short strokes of 50 to 100 mm. In both cases, the resistance felt should be smooth and continuous. If the resistance is jerky, or uneven, or if there is any visible sign of wear or damage, renewal is necessary. Also check the rubber mountings for damage and deterioration. Renew worn comp-onents as necessary. Inspect the shank of the mounting bolt for signs of wear or damage, and renew as necessary. The self-locking nuts should be renewed as a matter of course.

Refitting

5 Prior to refitting the shock absorber, mount it upright in the vice, and operate it fully through several strokes in order to prime it.
6 Manoeuvre the shock absorber into position and refit the upper mounting bolt, washer and nut. Refit the lower mounting bolt, tightening both bolts lightly only at this stage.
7 Remove the jack from underneath the trailing arm and refit the roadwheel.
8 Lower the vehicle to the ground and tighten

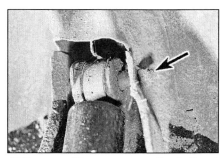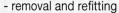

12.3b . . . and the upper mounting bolt and nut, then remove the rear shock absorber

the wheel nuts to the specified torque. Rock the vehicle to settle the shock absorber in position then, with the vehicle resting on its wheels, tighten both the upper and lower mounting bolts to the specified torque setting.

13 Rear suspension coil spring - removal and refitting

Removal

1 Chock the front wheels then jack up the rear of the vehicle and support it on axle stands (see *"Jacking and Vehicle Support"*). Remove the relevant rear roadwheel.
2 Position a jack underneath the trailing arm and raise the jack until the coil spring is slightly compressed.
3 Slacken and remove the shock absorber lower mounting bolt **(see illustration)**.
4 Slowly lower the jack until it is possible to manoeuvre the spring out of position, complete with its upper spring seat **(see illustration)**. If necessary, push down on the trailing arm assembly to gain the required clearance.
5 Inspect the coil spring and upper seat for signs of wear or damage and renew if necessary. Whilst the spring is removed, examine the bump stop on the trailing arm and renew if necessary; the bump stop is retained by a nut, on refitting tighten the nut to the specified torque.

Refitting

6 Fit the upper spring seat to the coil spring, aligning the stop on the seat with the spring end **(see illustration)**.

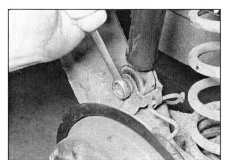

13.3 Slacken and remove the shock absorber lower mounting bolt . . .

13.4 . . . then lower the trailing arm and remove the coil spring and spring seat

13.6 Ensure that the spring upper end is correctly located against the spring seat stop

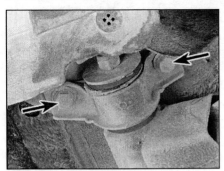

14.6 Rear axle assembly mounting bolts (arrowed)

7 Ensure that the bump stop is securely tightened and manoeuvre the spring and seat into position. Position the lower end of the spring against its stop on the trailing arm.

8 Carefully raise the trailing arm, aligning the spring upper seat with the body, and refit the shock absorber lower mounting bolt. Tighten the bolt lightly only at this stage.

9 Remove the jack from underneath the trailing arm and refit the roadwheel.

10 Lower the vehicle to the ground and tighten the wheel nuts to the specified torque. Rock the vehicle to settle the shock absorber in position then, with the vehicle resting on its wheels, tighten the shock absorber lower mounting bolt to the specified torque setting.

14 Rear axle assembly - removal, overhaul and refitting

Removal

1 Chock the front wheels then jack up the rear of the vehicle and support it on axle stands (see "*Jacking and Vehicle Support*"). Remove the rear roadwheels.

2 Remove the exhaust system tailpipe as described in Chapter 4.

3 Referring to Chapter 9, carry out the following operations.

a) *Remove the left- and right-hand rear brake shoe assemblies; note that there is no need to dismantle the shoe assemblies.*

b) *Disconnect the brake pipes from the rear of the wheel cylinders and free both pipes from their clips on the axle assembly.*

c) *Free the handbrake cables from the backplates and axle retaining clips.*

4 Remove the left- and right-hand coil springs as described in Section 13.

5 Check that the hoses/pipes and cables are positioned clear of the axle then support the axle crossmember with a jack.

6 Slacken and remove the bolts securing the axle mounting bush brackets to the floor then carefully lower the axle assembly out of position and remove it from underneath the vehicle **(see illustration)**.

Overhaul

Note: *New trailing arm shaft nuts will be required.*

7 With the axle removed from the vehicle, remove all traces of dirt from the axle assembly **(see illustration)**.

8 Using paint or a suitable marker pen, make alignment marks between each of the mounting brackets and left- and right-hand trailing arm assemblies **(see illustration)**. These marks can then be used on refitting to reposition the bracket correctly.

9 Unscrew the right-hand nut from the trailing arm shaft and remove the dished washer. Noting each components correct fitted orientation, slide the mounting bracket off the shaft, along with its inner and outer mounting bush.

10 Remove the left-hand mounting assembly as described in paragraph 9.

11 On models with a rear anti-roll bar, make alignment marks between each end of the bar and the punch marks on the trailing arms; these marks can be used on refitting to ensure that the anti-roll bar is correctly positioned **(see illustration)**.

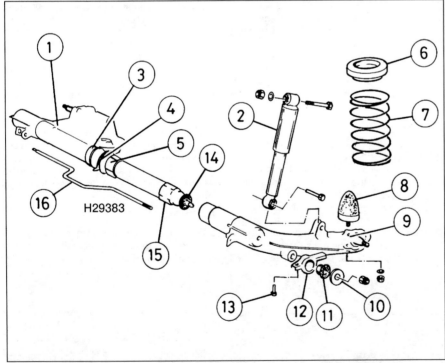

14.7 Exploded view of the rear axle assembly and associated components

1 *Right-hand trailing arm*	6 *Spring seat*	12 *Mounting bracket*
2 *Shock absorber*	7 *Coil spring*	13 *Mounting bolt*
3 *Dust cover*	8 *Bump stop*	14 *Rubber stopper*
4 *Retaining clip*	9 *Left-hand trailing arm*	15 *Bush*
5 *Bush*	10 *Washer*	16 *Anti-roll bar*
	11 *Mounting bush*	

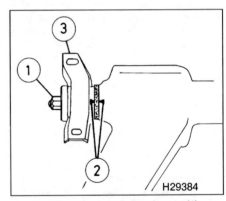

14.8 Prior to removing the nut (1), make alignment marks (2) between the mounting bracket (3) and trailing arm to use on refitting

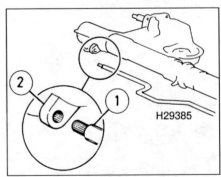

14.11 Prior to separating the trailing arms, make alignment marks between the anti-roll bar (1) and trailing arm punch marks (2)

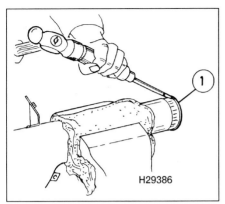

14.15a Tap the inner bush (1) out of position using a hammer and screwdriver . . .

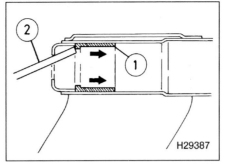

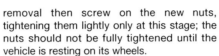

14.15b . . . then tap out the outer bush (1) with a suitable punch (2)

14.21 Ensure that the dust cover (2) is correctly seated and secured in position with the retaining clip (1)

12 On all models, release the retaining clip and slide the dust cover to the right to free it from the left-hand trailing arm. The left- and right-hand trailing arm assemblies can then be separated and, where necessary, the anti-roll bar removed.

13 Slide the rubber stopper ring off from the inner end of the right-hand arm.

14 Examine all components, paying particular attention to the rubber bushes, and renew components as necessary.

15 If the trailing arm bushes are to be renewed, using a hammer and screwdriver, tap out the inner bush from the end of the left-hand trailing arm. Prior to removing the outer bush, measure the correct fitted depth of the bush in the tube and mark its location. The bush can then be tapped out using a hammer and drift **(see illustrations)**. Thoroughly lubricate the arm inner surface and the bush outer surfaces with a lithium-based grease (such as Duckhams LBM10). Locate the outer bush in the trailing arm tube, ensuring it is fitted the correct way around, and tap it into position using a suitable tubular drift which bears only on the bushes outer edge. Position the outer bush so that it is aligned with the marks/at the same depth as the original was prior to removal. Once the outer bush is correctly positioned, fit the inner bush to the trailing arm end.

16 On refitting, ensure that the dust cover and retaining clip are in position on the right-hand arm and fit the rubber stopper ring.

17 Where necessary, refit the anti-roll bar to the left-hand arm, aligning the marks made prior to removal.

18 Apply the specified grease to the inner surfaces of the bushes in the left-hand arm and to the outer surface of the right-hand arm.

19 Carefully assemble the left- and right-hand arms and press firmly together. On models with an anti-roll bar as the arms join, ensure that the marks made prior to removal are correctly aligned as the bar locates with the right-hand arm.

20 Refit the mounting bracket and bush assemblies to the ends of the shaft and fit the dished washer. Align the marks made prior to

removal then screw on the new nuts, tightening them lightly only at this stage; the nuts should not be fully tightened until the vehicle is resting on its wheels.

21 Remove excess grease from the trailing arm joint then slide the dust cover into position and secure it in position with the retaining clip **(see illustration)**.

Refitting

22 Raise the axle assembly into position and refit the mounting bracket bolts, tightening them to the specified torque setting.

23 Refit the coil springs (see Section 13) and install the shock absorber lower mounting bolts, tighten them lightly only at this stage.

24 Working as described in Chapter 9, carry out the following.

a) Reconnect the handbrake cables to the backplates, secure them in position with all the relevant clips and ties.
b) Refit the brake shoes assemblies.
c) Reconnect the pipes to the wheel cylinders and secure the pipes/hoses in position with all the necessary clips.
d) Refit the brake drums and bleed the hydraulic system.
e) Adjust the handbrake cable.

25 Refit the exhaust system tailpipe as described in Chapter 4.

26 Lower the vehicle to the ground and tighten the wheel nuts to the specified torque. Rock the vehicle to settle the shock absorber

in position then, with the vehicle resting on its wheels, tighten the shock absorber lower mounting bolt to the specified torque setting. If the axle assembly has been overhauled, the trailing arm shaft (axle mounting) nuts should also be tightened to the specified torque.

15 Steering wheel - removal and refitting

Removal

Note: *It is likely that a puller will be needed to release the steering wheel from the end of the column. Threaded holes are supplied in the wheel to bolt the puller to.*

1 Set the front wheels in the straight-ahead position, and engage the steering lock.

2 Slacken the retaining screws (where necessary) then carefully ease the horn pad away from the wheel and disconnect its wiring **(see illustration)**.

3 Slacken and remove the steering wheel retaining nut and washer **(see illustration)**.

4 Mark the steering wheel and steering column shaft in relation to each other, then remove the steering wheel off the column splines. If the wheel is tight (which is likely), attach a puller to the wheel using bolts which screw into the threaded holes provided and draw the steering wheel off the end of the steering column **(see illustration)**.

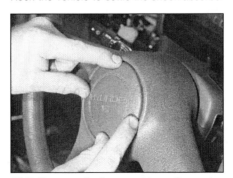

15.2 Remove the horn pad from the centre of the steering wheel and disconnect its wiring . . .

15.3 . . . then slacken and remove the steering wheel retaining nut

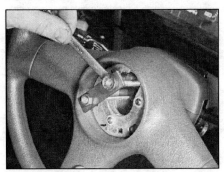

15.4 Using an improvised puller to free the steering wheel from the column

Refitting

5 Refitting is a reversal of removal, noting the following points:
a) *Prior to refitting, ensure that the indicator switch stem is in its central position. Failure to do this could lead to the steering wheel lug breaking the switch tab as the steering wheel is refitted.*
b) *On refitting, align the marks made on removal, and tighten the retaining nut to the specified torque.*

16 Steering column - removal, inspection and refitting

Removal

1 Disconnect the battery negative terminal and proceed as described under the relevant sub-heading.

Early (pre 1991) models

Note: *A splined socket (Hyundai no. 09563-21000) will be needed to remove the steering column mounting bolts.*

2 Remove the steering wheel (see Section 15).
3 Remove the combination switch assembly from the steering column as described in Chapter 12.
4 Using paint or a suitable marked pen, make alignment marks between the column and the intermediate shaft upper universal joint then slacken and remove the clamp bolt and nut **(see illustration)**.

16.4 Make alignment marks between the column and intermediate shaft prior to removing the clamp bolt and nut (arrowed)

5 Slacken and remove the column mounting bolts and remove the assembly from the vehicle, freeing it from the intermediate shaft.

Later (1991-on) models

6 Carry out the operations described in paragraphs 2 and 3.
7 Using paint or a suitable marked pen, make alignment marks between the intermediate shaft lower universal joint and the steering gear pinion then slacken and remove the clamp bolt **(see illustration)**.
8 Slacken and remove the mounting nuts and bolts then free the intermediate shaft from the steering gear pinion and remove the assembly from the vehicle.
9 If necessary, make alignment marks between the intermediate shaft upper universal joint and the column. Slacken and remove the clamp bolt and nut and remove the intermediate shaft, noting which way around it is fitted.

Inspection

10 Before refitting the steering column, examine the column and mountings for signs of damage and deformation, and renew as necessary.
11 Check the steering shaft for signs of free play in the column bushes. If any damage or wear is found, the column must be renewed/overhauled (as applicable). Overhaul of the steering column is only possible on early models, on later models the column is only available as a complete assembly.

Refitting

Early (pre 1991) models

12 Align the marks made prior to removal and engage the column with the intermediate shaft universal joint.
13 Fit the column mounting bolts and tighten them to the specified torque.
14 Refit the intermediate shaft joint clamp bolt and nut and tighten to the specified torque.
15 The remainder of refitting is a direct reversal of the removal procedure, noting the following.
a) *Ensure that all wiring is correctly routed and retained by all the necessary clips and ties.*
b) *Refit the steering wheel as described in Section 15.*

16.7 Make alignment marks between the intermediate shaft and steering gear pinion prior to removing the clamp bolt (arrowed)

Later (1991-on) models

16 Where necessary, align the marks made on removal and refit the intermediate shaft to the steering column. Ensure that the shaft is fitted the right way around (it is not symmetrical - the upper universal joint is the shorter of the two and should be marked with a sticker) then refit the clamp bolt and nut and tighten it to the specified torque.
17 On models with a tilt-adjustable column, lock the adjustment mechanism in the centre of its travel prior to installation.
18 On all models, manoeuvre the steering column assembly into position and engage the intermediate shaft with the steering gear pinion, aligning the marks made prior to removal.
19 Seat the column in position on the bulkhead and refit the mounting nuts and bolts, tightening them to the specified torque setting.
20 Tighten the intermediate shaft lower clamp bolt to the specified torque setting.
21 The remainder of refitting is a direct reversal of the removal procedure, noting the following.
a) *Ensure that all wiring is correctly routed and retained by all the necessary clips and ties.*
b) *Refit the steering wheel as described in Section 15.*

17 Steering column intermediate shaft - removal, inspection and refitting

Early (pre 1991) models

Removal

1 From inside the engine compartment, using paint or a suitable marked pen, make alignment marks between the intermediate shaft lower universal joint and the steering gear pinion then slacken and remove the clamp bolt and nut.
2 From inside the vehicle, make alignment marks between the intermediate shaft upper universal joint and the steering column then slacken and remove the clamp bolt and nut.
3 Slacken and remove the intermediate shaft gaiter retaining bolts then free the shaft from the steering gear and column and manoeuvre it out of position **(see illustration)**.
4 If necessary, ease the shaft bushes out from the centre of the gaiter then separate the gaiter and shaft.

Inspection

5 Inspect the intermediate shaft assembly for signs of wear or damage, paying particular attention to the universal joints. If the shaft or joint show any sign of wear then the complete shaft assembly must be renewed. Renew the rubber gaiter and bushes if they show signs of damage or deterioration.

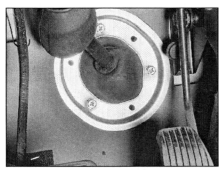

17.3 On early models the steering gaiter is secured to the bulkhead by three bolts

Refitting

6 Where necessary, slide the gaiter onto the intermediate shaft making sure it is fitted the right way around. Apply multi-purpose grease to the bearing surfaces of the shaft bushes then slide them into position in the gaiter. Ensure that the bushes are correctly located and check that the gaiter rotates easily on the shaft.
7 From inside the vehicle, manoeuvre the shaft and gaiter assembly into position. Align the marks made prior to removal and engage the joints with the steering column and gear.
8 Seat the gaiter on the bulkhead and securely tighten its retaining bolts.
9 Refit the universal joint clamp bolts and nuts, tightening them to the specified torque setting.

Later (1991-on) models

10 The intermediate shaft is removed along with the steering column and then separated. See Section 16 for removal and refitting details.

---

18 Ignition switch/steering column lock - removal and refitting

Removal

Note: *New lock assembly shear bolts will be required on refitting.*
1 Remove the steering column as described in Section 16.
2 Using a hammer and suitable punch, loosen the lock assembly screws until it is possible to unscrew them by hand. Remove both screws and lift the lock assembly and clamp away from the steering column.

Refitting

3 Align the lock assembly correctly with the steering column then refit the retaining clamp and screw in the new shear bolts.
4 Tighten the bolts securely by hand then check the operation of the lock assembly. If the lock is working correctly, evenly and progressively tighten the shear bolts until their heads break off.
5 Ensure that the lock assembly is working correctly then refit the steering column as described in Section 16.

---

19 Steering gear assembly - removal, overhaul and refitting

Removal

1 Firmly apply the handbrake then jack up the front of the vehicle and support it on axle stands. Remove both front roadwheels.
2 Withdraw the split pins then slacken and remove the nuts and washers securing the steering gear track rod balljoints to the swivel hubs. Release the balljoint tapered shanks using a universal balljoint separator. Note that new split pins will be needed on refitting.

3 On early models, make alignment marks between the steering gear pinion and the intermediate shaft lower joint then slacken and remove the clamp bolt and nut.
4 On later models, from inside the vehicle, make alignment marks between the intermediate shaft lower joint and the steering gear pinion then slacken and remove the clamp bolt. Return to the engine compartment and release the retaining clip securing the gaiter to the steering gear pinion housing.
5 On models equipped with power steering, using brake hose clamps, clamp both the supply and return hoses near the power steering fluid reservoir to minimise fluid loss. Mark the unions to ensure that they are correctly positioned on reassembly, then unscrew the feed and return pipe union nuts from the steering gear assembly; be prepared for fluid spillage, and position a suitable container beneath the pipes whilst unscrewing the union nuts **(see illustration)**. Disconnect both pipes, and plug the pipe ends and steering gear orifices, to prevent fluid leakage and to keep dirt out of the hydraulic system.
6 On all models, undo the mounting bolts then remove the steering gear mounting clamps **(see illustration)**.
7 Free the steering gear pinion from the intermediate shaft joint and manoeuvre it out towards the driver side of the vehicle. Remove the mounting rubbers from the steering gear; the rubbers should be renewed if they show signs of damage or deterioration.

Overhaul

8 Examine the steering gear assembly for signs of wear or damage, and check that the rack moves freely throughout the full length of its travel, with no signs of roughness or excessive free play between the steering gear pinion and rack. On models with power steering, inspect all the steering gear fluid unions for signs of leakage, and check that all union nuts are securely tightened.

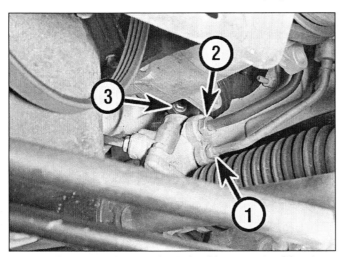

19.5 Power steering gear feed pipe (1), return pipe (2) and intermediate shaft clamp bolt (3)

19.6 Undo the bolts (arrowed) and remove the steering gear mounting clamp

9 It is possible to overhaul the steering gear assembly housing components, but this task should be entrusted to a Hyundai dealer. The only components which can be renewed easily by the home mechanic are the steering gear gaiters, the track rod balljoints and the track rods. Track rod balljoint, steering gear gaiter and track rod renewal procedures are covered elsewhere in this Chapter **(see illustration)**.

Refitting

10 Ensure that the mounting rubbers are correctly positioned and manoeuvre the steering gear into position.
11 Engage the steering gear pinion with the intermediate shaft coupling, aligning the marks made prior to removal, then refit the mounting clamps and bolts. Ensure that the steering gear is correctly located and tighten the mounting bolts to the specified torque.
12 On models with power steering, reconnect the fluid pipes to the steering gear and tighten their union nuts to the specified torque. Secure the pipes in position with all the necessary clips and ties and remove the clamps from the hoses.
13 Refit the clamp bolt and (where fitted) nut, tightening it to the specified torque. On later models, ensure that the gaiter is correctly seated on the pinion housing and secure it in position with the retaining clip.
14 Locate the track rod balljoints in the swivel hubs and refit the washers and retaining nuts. Tighten the nuts to the specified torque setting and secure them in position with new split pins.
15 Fit the roadwheels then lower the vehicle to the ground and tighten the roadwheel nuts to the specified torque.

16 On models with power steering, top-up the fluid reservoir and bleed the hydraulic system as described in Section 21.
17 On completion check and, if necessary, adjust the front wheel alignment as described in Section 25.

20 Steering gear rubber gaiters - renewal

1 Remove the track rod balljoint and locknut as described in Section 23.
2 Mark the correct fitted position of the gaiter on the track rod, then release the retaining clips and slide the gaiter off the steering gear housing and track rod end.
3 Thoroughly clean the track rod and the steering gear housing, using fine abrasive paper to polish off any corrosion, burrs or sharp edges, which might damage the new gaiter's sealing lips on installation. Scrape off all the grease from the old gaiter, and apply it to the track rod inner balljoint. (This assumes that grease has not been lost or contaminated as a result of damage to the old gaiter. Use fresh grease if in doubt.)
4 Carefully slide the new gaiter onto the track rod end, and locate it on the steering gear housing. Align the outer edge of the gaiter with the mark made on the track rod prior to removal, then secure it in position with new retaining clips.
5 Refit the track rod balljoint as described in Section 23.

21 Power steering system - bleeding

1 This procedure will only be necessary when any part of the hydraulic system has been disconnected.
2 Referring to "Weekly checks", remove the fluid reservoir filler cap, and top-up with the specified fluid to the upper level mark.
3 With the engine stopped, slowly move the steering from lock-to-lock several times to purge out the trapped air, then top-up the level in the fluid reservoir. Repeat this procedure until the fluid level in the reservoir does not drop any further.

> **HAYNES HINT** *It will be easier to turn the wheel if the front of the car is raised slightly so that the wheels are off the ground.*

4 Start the engine, then slowly move the steering from lock-to-lock several times to purge out any remaining air in the system. Repeat this procedure until bubbles cease to appear in the fluid reservoir.
5 If, when turning the steering, an abnormal noise is heard from the fluid lines, it indicates that there is still air in the system. Check this by turning the wheels to the straight-ahead position and switching off the engine. If the fluid level in the reservoir rises significantly, then air is present in the system, and further bleeding is necessary.
6 Once all traces of air have been removed from the power steering hydraulic system, check that the fluid level is up to the upper mark on the power steering fluid reservoir, topping-up if necessary.

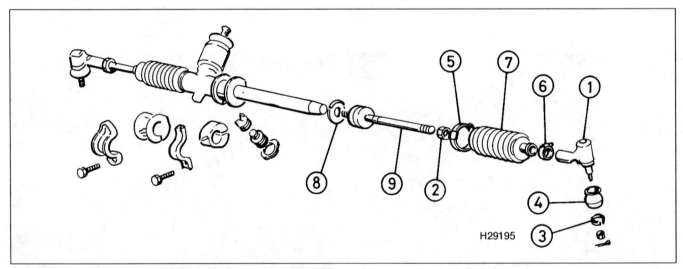

19.9 Steering gear components which can be renewed by the home mechanic

1 Track rod balljoint	4 Balljoint gaiter	6 Steering gear gaiter retaining clip	8 Lockwasher
2 Locknut	5 Steering gear gaiter retaining clip	7 Steering gear gaiter	9 Track rod
3 Balljoint gaiter retaining clip			

H29195

22 Power steering pump - removal and refitting

Removal

1 Release the drivebelt tension (seeChapter 1), and unhook the drivebelt from the pump pulley.
2 To minimise fluid loss, clamp the fluid supply hose as close as possible to the power steering pump.
3 Slacken the retaining clip and disconnect the hose from the fluid supply hose from the pump then unscrew the union nut and washer and disconnect the feed pipe **(see illustration)**. Plug the hose/pipe ends and the pump unions to prevent dirt entering the hydraulic system and wipe up any spilt fluid.
4 Remove the pump mounting bolts and manoeuvre the pump away from the engine, disconnect the wiring connector from the pressure switch (where fitted) as it becomes accessible.

Refitting

5 Manoeuvre the pump into position, reconnecting the switch wiring connector to the pump pressure switch, and install the mounting bolts.
6 Reconnect the feed hose to the pump then refit the washer and union nut, tightening it to the specified torque setting. Reconnect the supply hose, tightening its retaining clip securely, and remove the hose clamp.
7 Refit the drivebelt and tension it as described in Chapter 1, tightening the pump mounting bolts securely.
8 On completion, bleed the hydraulic system as described in Section 21.

23 Track rod balljoint - removal and refitting

Removal

1 Apply the handbrake, then jack up the front of the vehicle and support it on axle stands (see *"Jacking and Vehicle Support"*). Remove the appropriate front roadwheel.

22.3 Power steering pump fluid supply hose retaining clip (1) and feed pipe union nut (2)

2 If the balljoint is to be re-used, use a straight-edge and a scriber, or similar, to mark its relationship to the track rod.
3 Hold the track rod/balljoint and unscrew the balljoint locknut by a quarter of a turn **(see illustration)**. Do not move the locknut from this position, as it will serve as a handy reference mark on refitting.
4 Remove the split pin then slacken and remove the nut and washer securing the track rod balljoint to the swivel hub; discard the split pin, a new one will be needed on refitting. Release the balljoint tapered shank using a universal balljoint separator **(see illustration)**.
5 Counting the **exact** number of turns necessary to do so, unscrew the balljoint from the track rod end. If necessary, count the number of exposed threads on the track rod end then unscrew the locknut from the track rod, again counting the exact number of turns required.
6 Carefully clean the balljoint and the threads. Renew the balljoint if its movement is sloppy or too stiff, if excessively worn, or if damaged in any way; carefully check the stud taper and threads. If only the balljoint gaiter is damaged, this can be renewed separately.

Refitting

7 Where necessary, screw the locknut onto the track rod by the number of turns noted on removal and check that the correct number of threads are exposed.
8 Screw the balljoint into the track rod by the number of turns noted on removal. This should bring the balljoint to within a quarter of

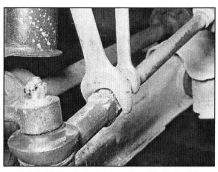

23.3 Hold the track rod balljoint and slacken the locknut by a quarter of a turn

a turn from the locknut, with the alignment marks that were made on removal (if applicable) lined up.
9 Locate the balljoint shank in the swivel hub then refit the washer and retaining nut. Tighten the nut to the specified torque setting and secure it in position with a new split pin **(see illustrations)**.
10 Refit the roadwheel, then lower the vehicle to the ground and tighten the roadwheel nuts to the specified torque.
11 Check and, if necessary, adjust the front wheel alignment as described in Section 25, then securely tighten the balljoint locknut.

24 Track rod - removal and refitting

Removal

Note: *A new lockwasher will be required on refitting.*
1 Remove the track rod balljoint and locknut as described in Section 23.
2 Release the retaining clips and slide the steering gear gaiter off the end of the track rod.
3 Using a hammer and pointed-nose chisel, carefully unstake the track rod lockwasher from the steering rack groove.
4 Unscrew the track rod inner balljoint from the steering rack end, taking great care not to place excess strain on the rack as the joint is unscrewed. If necessary, prevent the steering

23.4 Using a universal balljoint separator to free the balljoint from the hub

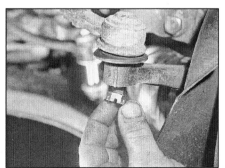

23.9a Refit the balljoint retaining nut . . .

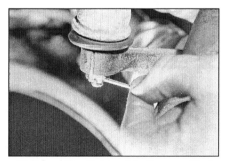

23.9b . . . then tighten it to the specified torque setting and secure it in position with a new split pin

rack from turning by holding it carefully with a pair of grips. Take great care not to mark the surfaces of the rack and balljoint.

5 Remove the track rod assembly and discard the lockwasher.

6 Examine the track rod inner balljoint for signs of slackness or tight spots, and check that the track rod itself is straight and free from damage. If necessary, renew the track rod; it is also recommended that the steering gear gaiter is renewed, regardless of its apparent condition.

Refitting

7 Fit a new lockwasher to the track rod and screw the track rod balljoint into the steering rack, tightening it to the specified torque. If necessary, retain the steering rack with a pair of grips, again taking great care not to damage or mark the track rod balljoint or steering rack. Secure the track rod in position by staking the lockwasher firmly into the steering rack groove.

8 Carefully slide on the new gaiter, and locate it on the steering gear housing. Turn the steering fully from lock-to-lock, to check that the gaiter is correctly positioned on the track rod, then secure it in position with new retaining clips.

9 Refit the locknut and track rod balljoint as described in Section 23.

25 Wheel alignment and steering angles -
general information

Definitions

A car's steering and suspension geometry is defined in four basic settings - all angles are expressed in degrees (toe settings are also expressed as a measurement); the steering axis is defined as an imaginary line drawn through the axis of the suspension strut, extended where necessary to contact the ground.

Camber is the angle between each roadwheel and a vertical line drawn through its centre and tyre contact patch, when viewed from the front or rear of the car. Positive camber is when the roadwheels are tilted outwards from the vertical at the top; negative camber is when they are tilted inwards. The camber angle is not adjustable

Castor is the angle between the steering axis and a vertical line drawn through each roadwheel centre and tyre contact patch, when viewed from the side of the car. Positive castor is when the steering axis is tilted so that it contacts the ground ahead of the vertical; negative castor is when it contacts the ground behind the vertical. The castor angle is adjustable on early models, by altering the length of the radius arms, but is not adjustable on later models.

Toe is the difference, viewed from above, between lines drawn through the roadwheel centres and the car's centre-line. "Toe-in" is when the roadwheels point inwards, towards each other at the front, while "toe-out" is when they splay outwards from each other at the front.

The front wheel toe setting is adjusted by screwing the track rod in or out of its balljoints, to alter the effective length of the track rod assembly. Rear wheel toe setting is not adjustable.

Checking and adjustment

Due to the special measuring equipment necessary to check the wheel alignment and steering angles, and the skill required to use it properly, the checking and adjustment of these settings is best left to a Hyundai dealer or similar expert. Note that most tyre-fitting shops now possess sophisticated checking equipment. The following is provided as a guide, should the owner decide to carry out a DIY check.

Front wheel toe setting

The front wheel toe setting is checked by measuring the distance between the front and rear inside edges of the roadwheel rims. Proprietary toe measurement gauges are available from motor accessory shops. Adjustment is made by screwing the balljoints onto/off their track rods, to alter the effective length of the track rod assemblies.

For accurate checking, the vehicle must be at the kerb weight, ie unladen and with a full tank of fuel.

Before starting work, check first that the tyre sizes and types are as specified, then check the tyre pressures and tread wear, the roadwheel run-out, the condition of the hub bearings, the steering wheel free play, and the condition of the front suspension components (see "Weekly checks" and Chapter 1). Correct any faults found.

Park the vehicle on level ground, check that the front roadwheels are in the straight-ahead position, then rock the rear and front ends to settle the suspension. Release the handbrake, and roll the vehicle backwards 1 metre, then forwards again, to relieve any stresses in the steering and suspension components.

Measure the distance between the front edges of the wheel rims and the rear edges of the rims. Subtract the front measurement from the rear measurement, and check that the result is within the specified range.

If adjustment is necessary, apply the handbrake, then jack up the front of the vehicle and support it securely on axle stands. Turn the steering wheel onto full-left lock, and record the number of exposed threads on the right-hand track rod end. Now turn the steering onto full-right lock, and record the number of threads on the left-hand side. If

there are the same number of threads visible on both sides, then subsequent adjustment should be made equally on both sides. If there are more threads visible on one side than the other, it will be necessary to compensate for this during adjustment. **Note:** *It is most important that after adjustment, the same number of threads are visible on each track rod end.*

First clean the track rod threads; if they are corroded, apply penetrating fluid before starting adjustment. Release the rubber gaiter outer clips and peel back the gaiters; apply a smear of grease to the inside of the gaiters, so that both are free, and will not be twisted or strained as their respective track rods are rotated.

Use a straight-edge and a scriber or similar to mark the relationship of each track rod to its balljoint then, holding each balljoint in turn, slacken its locknut.

Alter the length of the track rods, bearing in mind the note made in paragraph 13. **Note:** *One complete rotation of the track rod equals approximately 6 mm of adjustment.* Screw them into or out of the balljoints, rotating the track rod using an open-ended spanner fitted to the flats provided on the track rod. Shortening the track rods (screwing them into their balljoints) will reduce toe-in/increase toe-out.

When the setting is correct, securely tighten the balljoint locknuts. Check that the balljoints are seated correctly in their sockets, and count the exposed threads to check the length of both track rods. If they are not the same, then the adjustment has not been made equally, and problems will be encountered with tyre scrubbing in turns; also, the steering wheel spokes will no longer be horizontal when the wheels are in the straight-ahead position.

If the track rod lengths are the same, lower the vehicle to the ground and re-check the toe setting; re-adjust if necessary. When the setting is correct, securely tighten the track rod balljoint locknuts. Ensure that the rubber gaiters are seated correctly, and are not twisted or strained, and secure them in position with the retaining clips.

Front suspension castor angle - early models

As mentioned earlier, specialist equipment is required to check the castor angle. For reference, the castor angle is adjusted by altering the effective length of the radius arms by slackening the front mounting nut and moving the locknut and adjuster nut (see Section 8). Once the arm length is correctly set, securely tighten the locknut and adjuster nut then tighten the front mounting nut to the specified torque.

Chapter 11
Bodywork and fittings

Contents

Bonnet - removal, refitting and adjustment 8
Bonnet lock - removal and refitting 10
Bonnet release cable - removal and refitting 9
Boot lid (Saloon models) - removal, refitting and adjustment 16
Boot lid lock components (Saloon models) - removal and refitting . 18
Central locking system components - removal and refitting 20
Centre console - removal and refitting 24
Door - removal, refitting and adjustment 12
Door inner trim panel - removal and refitting 13
Door latch, lock cylinder and handle components - removal and
    refitting 14
Door window glass and regulator - removal and refitting 15
Exterior mirror - removal and refitting 21
Facia and glovebox - removal and refitting 25

Front bumper - removal and refitting 6
General information 1
Maintenance - bodywork and underframe 2
Maintenance - upholstery and carpets 3
Major body damage - repair 5
Minor body damage - repair 4
Radiator grille - removal and refitting 11
Rear bumper - removal and refitting 7
Seats and seat belts - removal and refitting 23
Sunroof - general information 22
Tailgate and support strut (Hatchback models) - removal, refitting
    and adjustment 17
Tailgate lock and handle components (Hatchback models) -
    removal and refitting 19

Degrees of difficulty

Easy, suitable for novice with little experience		Fairly easy, suitable for beginner with some experience		Fairly difficult, suitable for competent DIY mechanic		Difficult, suitable for experienced DIY mechanic		Very difficult, suitable for expert DIY or professional	

Specifications

Torque wrench settings	Nm	lbf ft
Door hinge-to-body bolts	39	29
Door hinge-to-door bolts	20	15
Bootlid-to-hinge bolts	8	6
Bootlid hinge-to-body	8	6
Tailgate-to-hinge bolts	32	24
Tailgate hinge-to-body	32	24
Bonnet hinge-to-body bolts	12	9
Bonnet hinge-to-bonnet	25	19
Bonnet latch to body	8	6
Front seat mounting nut	30	22
Front seat mounting bolt	45	33
Seat belt mounting	43	32

1 General information

The bodyshell is composed of pressed-steel sections which are welded together, although some use of structural adhesives is made. The front wings are bolted on.

Anti-corrosion treatment consists of zinc phosphate etching and electro deposition, and in addition vulnerable areas such as the leading edge of the bonnet, windscreen pillars and the lower areas of the door panels are treated with stone chip primer.

Extensive use is made of plastic materials, mainly in the interior, but also in exterior components. The outer sections of the front and rear bumpers are injection-moulded from a strong, lightweight synthetic material. Plastic components such as wheelarch liners are fitted, to improve resistance to corrosion.

The windscreen and rear window are bonded in position and cannot be replaced by the home mechanic.

2 Maintenance - bodywork and underframe

The general condition of a vehicle's bodywork significantly affects its value. Maintenance is easy, but needs to be regular. Neglect, particularly after minor damage, can lead quickly to further deterioration and costly repair bills. It is important also to keep watch on those parts of the vehicle not immediately visible, for instance the underside, inside all the wheelarches, and the lower part of the engine compartment.

The basic maintenance routine for the bodywork is washing - preferably with a lot of water, from a hose. This will remove all the loose solids which may have stuck to the vehicle. It is important to flush these off in such a way as to prevent grit from scratching the finish. The wheelarches and underframe need washing in the same way, to remove any accumulated mud which will retain moisture and tend to encourage rust. Strangely enough, the best time to clean the underframe and wheelarches is in wet weather, when the mud is thoroughly wet and soft. In very wet weather, the underframe is usually cleaned of large accumulations automatically, and this is a good time for inspection.

Periodically, except on vehicles with a wax-based underbody protective coating, it is a good idea to have the whole of the underframe of the vehicle steam-cleaned, engine compartment included, so that a thorough inspection can be carried out to see what minor repairs and renovations are necessary. Steam-cleaning is available at many garages, and is necessary for the removal of the accumulation of oily grime, which sometimes is allowed to become thick in certain areas. If steam-cleaning facilities are not available, there are some excellent grease solvents available which can be brush-applied; the dirt can then be simply hosed off. Note that these methods should not be used on vehicles with wax-based underbody protective coating, or the coating will be removed. Such vehicles should be inspected annually, preferably just prior to Winter, when the underbody should be washed down, and any damage to the wax coating repaired using Undershield. Ideally, a completely fresh coat should be applied. It would also be worth considering the use of such wax-based protection for injection into door panels, sills, box sections, etc, as an additional safeguard against rust damage, where such protection is not provided by the vehicle manufacturer.

After washing paintwork, wipe off with a chamois leather to give an unspotted clear finish. A coat of clear protective wax polish will give added protection against chemical pollutants in the air. If the paintwork sheen has dulled or oxidised, use a cleaner/polisher combination to restore the brilliance of the shine. This requires a little effort, but such dulling is usually caused because regular washing has been neglected. Care needs to be taken with metallic paintwork, as special non-abrasive cleaner/polisher is required to avoid damage to the finish. Always check that the door and ventilator opening drain holes and pipes are completely clear, so that water can be drained out. Brightwork should be treated in the same way as paintwork. Windscreens and windows can be kept clear of the smeary film which often appears by the use of a proprietary glass cleaner. Never use any form of wax or other body or chromium polish on glass.

3 Maintenance - upholstery and carpets

Mats and carpets should be brushed or vacuum-cleaned regularly, to keep them free of grit. If they are badly stained, remove them from the vehicle for scrubbing or sponging, and make quite sure they are dry before refitting. Seats and interior trim panels can be kept clean by wiping with a damp cloth and a proprietary cleaner. If they do become stained (which can be more apparent on light-coloured upholstery), use a little liquid detergent and a soft nail brush to scour the grime out of the grain of the material. Do not forget to keep the headlining clean in the same way as the upholstery. When using liquid cleaners inside the vehicle, do not over-wet the surfaces being cleaned. Excessive damp could get into the seams and padded interior, causing stains, offensive odours or even rot. If the inside of the vehicle gets wet accidentally, it is worthwhile taking some trouble to dry it out properly, particularly where carpets are involved. *Do not leave oil or electric heaters inside the vehicle for this purpose.*

4 Minor body damage - repair

Repairs of minor scratches in bodywork

If the scratch is very superficial, and does not penetrate to the metal of the bodywork, repair is very simple. Lightly rub the area of the scratch with a paintwork renovator, or a very fine cutting paste to remove loose paint from the scratch, and to clear the surrounding bodywork of wax polish. Rinse the area with clean water.

Apply touch-up paint to the scratch using a fine paint brush; continue to apply fine layers of paint until the surface of the paint in the scratch is level with the surrounding paintwork. Allow the new paint at least two weeks to harden, then blend it into the surrounding paintwork by rubbing the scratch area with a paintwork renovator or a very fine cutting paste. Finally, apply a good wax polish.

Where the scratch has penetrated right through to the metal of the bodywork, causing the metal to rust, a different repair technique is required. Remove any loose rust from the bottom of the scratch with a penknife, then apply rust-inhibiting paint to prevent the formation of rust in the future. Using a rubber or nylon applicator, fill the scratch with bodystopper paste. If required, this paste can be mixed with cellulose thinners to provide a very thin paste which is ideal for filling narrow scratches. Before the stopper-paste in the scratch hardens, wrap a piece of smooth cotton rag around the top of a finger. Dip the finger in cellulose thinners, and quickly sweep it across the surface of the stopper-paste in the scratch; this will ensure that the surface of the stopper-paste is slightly hollowed. The scratch can now be painted over as described earlier in this Section.

Repairs of dents in bodywork

When deep denting of the vehicle's bodywork has taken place, the first task is to pull the dent out, until the affected bodywork almost attains its original shape. There is little point in trying to restore the original shape completely, as the metal in the damaged area will have stretched on impact, and cannot be reshaped fully to its original contour. It is better to bring the level of the dent up to a point which is about 3 mm below the level of the surrounding bodywork. In cases where the dent is very shallow anyway, it is not worth trying to pull it out at all. If the underside of the dent is accessible, it can be hammered out gently from behind, using a mallet with a wooden or plastic head. Whilst doing this, hold a suitable block of wood firmly against the outside of the panel, to absorb the impact from the hammer blows and thus prevent a large area of the bodywork from being "belled-out".

Should the dent be in a section of the bodywork which has a double skin, or some other factor making it inaccessible from behind, a different technique is called for. Drill several small holes through the metal inside the area - particularly in the deeper section. Then screw long self-tapping screws into the holes, just sufficiently for them to gain a good purchase in the metal. Now the dent can be pulled out by pulling on the protruding heads of the screws with a pair of pliers.

The next stage of the repair is the removal of the paint from the damaged area, and from an inch or so of the surrounding "sound" bodywork. This is accomplished most easily by using a wire brush or abrasive pad on a power drill, although it can be done just as effectively by hand, using sheets of abrasive paper. To complete the preparation for filling, score the surface of the bare metal with a screwdriver or the tang of a file, or alternatively, drill small holes in the affected area. This will provide a really good "key" for the filler paste.

To complete the repair, see the Section on filling and respraying.

Repairs of rust holes or gashes in bodywork

Remove all paint from the affected area, and from an inch or so of the surrounding "sound" bodywork, using an abrasive pad or a wire brush on a power drill. If these are not available, a few sheets of abrasive paper will do the job most effectively. With the paint removed, you will be able to judge the severity of the corrosion, and therefore decide whether to renew the whole panel (if this is possible) or to repair the affected area. New body panels are not as expensive as most people think, and it is often quicker and more satisfactory to fit a new panel than to attempt to repair large areas of corrosion.

Remove all fittings from the affected area, except those which will act as a guide to the original shape of the damaged bodywork (eg headlight shells, etc). Then, using tin snips or a hacksaw blade, remove all loose metal and any other metal badly affected by corrosion. Hammer the edges of the hole inwards, in order to create a slight depression for the filler paste.

Wire-brush the affected area to remove the powdery rust from the surface of the remaining metal. Paint the affected area with rust-inhibiting paint; if the back of the rusted area is accessible, treat this also.

Before filling can take place, it will be necessary to block the hole in some way. This can be achieved by the use of aluminium or plastic mesh, or aluminium tape.

Aluminium or plastic mesh, or glass-fibre matting, is probably the best material to use for a large hole. Cut a piece to the approximate size and shape of the hole to be filled, then position it in the hole so that its edges are below the level of the surrounding bodywork. It can be retained in position by several blobs of filler paste around its periphery.

Aluminium tape should be used for small or very narrow holes. Pull a piece off the roll, trim it to the approximate size and shape required, then pull off the backing paper (if used) and stick the tape over the hole; it can be overlapped if the thickness of one piece is insufficient. Burnish down the edges of the tape with the handle of a screwdriver or similar, to ensure that the tape is securely attached to the metal underneath.

Bodywork repairs - filling and respraying

Before using this Section, see the Sections on dents, scratches, rust holes and gash repairs.

Many types of bodyfiller are available, but generally speaking, those proprietary kits which contain a tin of filler paste and a tube of resin hardener are best for this type of repair, or a proprietary ready mixed filler, which can be used directly from the tube. A wide, flexible plastic or nylon applicator will be found invaluable for imparting a smooth and well-contoured finish to the surface of the filler.

Mix up a little filler on a clean piece of card or board - measure the hardener carefully (follow the maker's instructions on the pack), otherwise the filler will set too rapidly or too slowly. Alternatively, a ready mixed filler can be used straight from the tube without mixing, but daylight is required to cure it. Using the applicator, apply the filler paste to the prepared area; draw the applicator across the surface of the filler to achieve the correct contour and to level the surface. As soon as a contour that approximates to the correct one is achieved, stop working the paste - if you carry on too long, the paste will become sticky and begin to "pick-up" on the applicator. Continue to add thin layers of filler paste at 20-minute intervals, until the level of the filler is just proud of the surrounding bodywork.

Once the filler has hardened, the excess can be removed using a metal plane or file. From then on, progressively-finer grades of abrasive paper should be used, starting with a 40-grade production paper, and finishing with a 400-grade wet-and-dry paper. Always wrap the abrasive paper around a flat rubber, cork, or wooden block - otherwise the surface of the filler will not be completely flat. During the smoothing of the filler surface, the wet-and-dry paper should be periodically rinsed in water. This will ensure that a very smooth finish is imparted to the filler at the final stage.

At this stage, the "dent" should be surrounded by a ring of bare metal, which in turn should be encircled by the finely "feathered" edge of the good paintwork. Rinse the repair area with clean water, until all of the dust produced by the rubbing-down operation has gone.

Spray the whole area with a light coat of primer - this will show up any imperfections in the surface of the filler. Repair these imperfections with fresh filler paste or bodystopper, and once more smooth the surface with abrasive paper. If bodystopper is used, it can be mixed with cellulose thinners, to form a really thin paste which is ideal for filling small holes. Repeat this spray-and-repair procedure until you are satisfied that the surface of the filler, and the feathered edge of the paintwork, are perfect. Clean the repair area with clean water, and allow to dry fully.

The repair area is now ready for final spraying. Paint spraying must be carried out in a warm, dry, windless and dust-free atmosphere. This condition can be created artificially if you have access to a large indoor working area, but if you are forced to work in the open, you will have to pick your day very carefully. If you are working indoors, dousing the floor in the work area with water will help to settle the dust which would otherwise be in the atmosphere. If the repair area is confined to one body panel, mask off the surrounding panels; this will help to minimise the effects of a slight mis-match in paint colours. Bodywork fittings (eg chrome strips, door handles etc) will also need to be masked off. Use genuine masking tape, and several thicknesses of newspaper, for the masking operations.

Before commencing to spray, agitate the aerosol can thoroughly, then spray a test area (an old tin, or similar) until the technique is mastered. Cover the repair area with a thick coat of primer; the thickness should be built up using several thin layers of paint, rather than one thick one. Using 400-grade wet-and-dry paper, rub down the surface of the primer until it is really smooth. While doing this, the work area should be thoroughly doused with water, and the wet-and-dry paper periodically rinsed in water. Allow to dry before spraying on more paint.

Spray on the top coat, again building up the thickness by using several thin layers of paint. Start spraying in the centre of the repair area, and then, using a circular motion, work outwards until the whole repair area and about 2 inches of the surrounding original paintwork is covered. Remove all masking material 10 to 15 minutes after spraying on the final coat of paint.

Allow the new paint at least two weeks to harden, then, using a paintwork renovator or a very fine cutting paste, blend the edges of the paint into the existing paintwork. Finally, apply wax polish.

Plastic components

With the use of more and more plastic body components by the vehicle manufacturers (eg bumpers. spoilers, and in some cases major body panels), rectification of more serious damage to such items has become a matter of either entrusting repair work to a specialist in this field, or renewing complete components. Repair of such damage by the DIY owner is not really feasible, owing to the cost of the equipment and materials required for effecting such repairs. The basic technique involves making a groove along the line of the crack in the plastic, using a rotary burr in a power drill. The damaged part is then welded back together, using a hot air gun to heat up and fuse a plastic filler rod into the groove. Any excess plastic is then removed, and the area rubbed down to a smooth finish. It is important that a filler rod of the correct plastic is used, as body components can be made of a variety of different types (eg polycarbonate, ABS, polypropylene).

Damage of a less serious nature (abrasions, minor cracks etc) can be repaired by the DIY owner using a two-part epoxy filler repair material, or a ready mixed filler which can be used directly from the tube. Once mixed in equal proportions (or applied directly from the tube in the case of the ready mixed filler), this is used in similar fashion to the bodywork filler used on metal panels. The filler is usually cured in twenty to thirty minutes, ready for sanding and painting.

If the owner is renewing a complete component himself, or if he has repaired it with epoxy filler, he will be left with the problem of finding a suitable paint for finishing which is compatible with the type of plastic used. At one time, the use of a universal paint was not possible, owing to the complex range of plastics encountered in body component applications. Standard paints, generally speaking, will not bond to plastic or rubber satisfactorily, but a proprietary brand of paint, to match any plastic or rubber finish, can be obtained from dealers. However, it is now possible to obtain a plastic body parts finishing kit which consists of a pre-primer treatment, a primer and coloured top coat. Full instructions are normally supplied with a kit, but basically, the method of use is to first apply the pre-primer to the component concerned, and allow it to dry for up to 30 minutes. Then the primer is applied, and left to dry for about an hour before finally applying the special-coloured top coat. The result is a correctly-coloured component, where the paint will flex with the plastic or rubber; a property that standard paint does not normally posses.

6.9 Front bumper upper mounting screws/clips

6.10a Remove the screws . . .

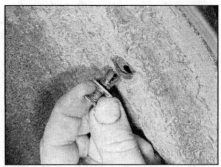

6.10b . . . and pull out the clips securing the wheelarch liner under the wing

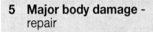

5 Major body damage - repair

Where serious damage has occurred, or large areas need renewal due to neglect, it means that complete new panels will need welding-in, and this is best left to professionals. If the damage is due to impact, it will also be necessary to check completely the alignment of the bodyshell, and this can only be carried out accurately by a Hyundai dealer using special jigs. If the alignment of the bodyshell is not corrected, the cars handling may be seriously affected. In addition, excessive stress may be imposed on the steering, suspension, tyres or transmission, causing abnormal wear or even complete failure.

6 Front bumper - removal and refitting

Removal

Early models

1 Apply the handbrake lever, then jack up the front of the vehicle and support on axle stands (see "*Jacking and Vehicle Support*").
2 Remove the radiator grille (see Section 11).
3 Unscrew and remove the front lower mounting bolts.
4 Unscrew and remove the side mounting bolts and the front of the wheelarches.

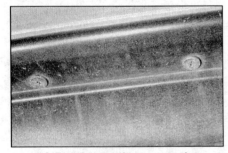

7.9 Rear bumper lower mounting screws/clips

5 Unscrew and remove the bolts securing the mounting brackets to the front valance, then withdraw the front bumper from the body.

Later models

6 Apply the handbrake lever, then jack up the front of the vehicle and support on axle stands (see "*Jacking and Vehicle Support*").
7 Remove the radiator grille (see Section 11).
8 Remove the headlight units (see Chapter 12).
9 Unscrew and remove the upper mounting screws/clips **(see illustration)**.
10 Working under the front right-hand wheelarch, remove the retaining clips and pull back the liner for access to the washer reservoir. Remove the reservoir with reference to Chapter 12 **(see illustrations)**.
11 Unscrew and remove the bolts securing the engine compartment lower splash guard to the front bumper.
12 Unscrew and remove the mounting bracket bolts and withdraw the front bumper from the vehicle.

Refitting

13 Refitting is a reversal of removal.

7 Rear bumper - removal and refitting

Removal

Early models

1 Chock the front wheels, then jack up the rear of the vehicle and support on axle stands (see "*Jacking and Vehicle Support*").
2 Remove the plugs from the rear floor panel, then unscrew the mounting bolts securing the bumper mounting brackets to the rear floor.
3 Unscrew and remove the side mounting bolts.
4 Unbolt and remove the rear mudguards.
5 Withdraw the rear bumper from the vehicle.

Later models

6 Chock the front wheels, then jack up the rear of the vehicle and support on axle stands (see "*Jacking and Vehicle Support*").
7 Unscrew the bolts and remove the mudguards, then unscrew the clips and release the wheelarch liners from the bumper.

8 Unscrew and remove the rear mounting bolts noting that the towing eye bracket is secured with the right-hand bolts.
9 Open the bootlid/tailgate then unscrew and remove the upper mounting screws/clips. Where necessary, unscrew and remove the lower mounting screws/clips **(see illustration)**.
10 Withdraw the rear bumper from the vehicle. Where necessary, disconnect the wiring for the rear foglights.

Refitting

11 Refitting is a reversal of removal.

8 Bonnet - removal, refitting and adjustment

Note: *On early models the bonnet is hinged at the front, but on later models it is hinged at the rear.*

Removal

⚠️ **Warning: It is essential that the help of an assistant is enlisted during this operation.**

1 Support the bonnet in its open position.
2 On early models use a screwdriver to release the clip securing the stay rod to the body.
3 Mark the relationship between the hinges and the edge of the bonnet using a soft pencil or a marker pen. Slacken and unscrew the hinge-to-bonnet bolts - have an assistant support the bonnet whilst the last bolts are removed **(see illustration)**.

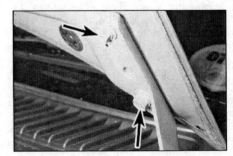

8.3 Bonnet mounting bolts

9.5a Remove the screws . . .

9.5b . . . and detach the bonnet release cable from the facia lower trim

4 With the help of your assistant, lift off the bonnet and set it down on its edge, using a dust sheet to protect the paintwork.

5 If required, remove the bonnet hinges by marking their position then unscrewing the mounting bolts. On early models the radiator grille must be removed first (see Section 11).

Refitting

6 Refit the bonnet by reversing the removal process, using the markings made during removal to achieve the correct alignment. Note that the bolt mounting holes are slotted to allow adjustment if required. On comp-letion, tighten the bolts to the specified torque.

Adjustment

7 Check that the bonnet shuts and releases satisfactorily and that its closing edge aligns with the surrounding bodywork. Check that it is positioned centrally between the front wings.

8 To adjust the position of the bonnet within the bodywork, loosen the bonnet-to-hinge mounting bolts and move the bonnet as necessary. Tighten the bolts on completion.

9 To adjust the closing edge of the bonnet turn the rubber buffers as required. If the bonnet striker is not aligned with the lock, loosen the lock mounting bolts and reposition the lock, then tighten the bolts.

9 Bonnet release cable - removal and refitting

Removal

1 Secure the bonnet in the fully open position.

2 On later models, remove the radiator grille as described in Section 11.

3 Disconnect the bonnet release cable from the lock by moving the lever so that the cable is slack.

4 Work along the exposed length of the release cable in the engine bay and release the cable from its securing clips.

5 Inside the vehicle, unscrew and remove the screws securing the release cable end fitting to the facia lower trim. On later models the trim may be removed first if necessary **(see illustrations)**.

6 Release the cable from the remaining clips under the facia, then carefully pull the entire cable, together with the bulkhead grommet, into the passenger compartment.

Refitting

7 Refitting is a reversal of removal. Finally check that the bonnet release operates correctly.

10 Bonnet lock - removal and refitting

Latch

Removal

1 Open and support the bonnet for access to the lock which is located on the bulkhead on early models and on the engine compartment front crossmember on later models. On later models improved access may be gained by removing the radiator grille as described in Section 11.

2 Use a marker pen to mark the position of the latch, then unscrew and remove the mounting bolts, noting the location of the earth cables (early models) or cable support (later models) **(see illustrations)**.

3 Move the release lever and disconnect the inner cable, then disconnect the outer cable from the latch. Withdraw the latch from the vehicle.

Refitting

4 Refitting is a reversal of removal. Use the alignment markings made during removal to aid accurate refitting. On completion check that the bonnet striker enters the latch centrally. If necessary, loosen the mounting bolts and reposition the latch, then retighten the bolts to the specified torque.

Striker

Removal

5 Where the striker is bolted to the bonnet, unscrew the mounting bolts and remove the striker. On some models the striker is integral with the bonnet.

Refitting

6 Refitting is a reversal of removal.

10.2a Bonnet latch on later models

10.2b Bonnet latch mounting bolts on early models - note the location of the earth cables

11.2a Remove the upper mounting screws . . .

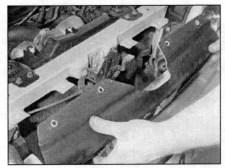

11.2b . . . and withdraw the radiator grille from the front of the vehicle

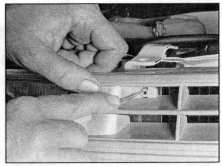

11.2c On some early models, release the clips with a small screwdriver

11 Radiator grille - removal and refitting

Removal

1 Open the bonnet and secure it in the fully open position using the stay.
2 On early models unscrew the six mounting screws and withdraw the grille - note that on some early models it is necessary to release the clips using a small screwdriver. On later models, unscrew the upper mounting screws then withdraw the grille (see illustrations).

Refitting

3 Refitting is a reversal of removal.

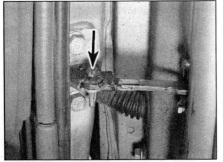

12.5 Front door check strap pin

12 Door - removal, refitting and adjustment

Note: *This procedure is applicable both to the front and rear doors.*

Removal

1 Disconnect the battery negative lead.
Caution: If the radio/cassette in your vehicle is equipped with an anti-theft system, make sure you have the correct activation code before disconnecting the battery.
2 Refer to Section 13 and remove the door inner trim panel.
3 Unplug all electrical wiring from the connectors inside the door space, labelling each one to aid correct refitting later.

12.6a Rear door upper hinge . . .

4 Prise the wiring harness grommet from the leading edge of the door, then draw the wiring harness out through the exposed hole.
5 Remove the check strap pin by tapping it upward using a suitable drift, and separate the door check strap from the door pillar (see illustration).
6 Have an assistant support the door, then unscrew the door hinge bolts, and lift the door from the vehicle. Either the hinge bolts on the door or pillar may be removed (see illustrations).

Refitting

7 Refitting is a reversal of removal. On completion, tighten the hinge bolts to the specified torque.

Adjustment

8 Close the door carefully (in case the alignment is incorrect) and check the fit of the door with the surrounding panels.
9 If adjustment is required, loosen the hinge-to-body securing bolts (the bolt holes are elongated to allow for adjustment) and move the hinges as required to achieve satisfactory alignment. Tighten the hinge bolts to the specified torque on completion.
10 Check the operation of the door lock. If necessary, slacken the securing bolts, and adjust the position of the lock striker on the body pillar to achieve satisfactory alignment. Tighten the bolts securely on completion (see illustrations).

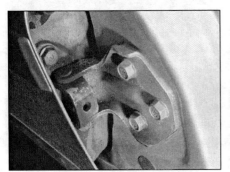

12.6b . . . and lower hinge

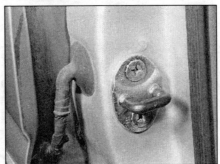

12.10a Front door striker

12.10b Rear door striker

13.3a Prise out the plastic cover . . .

13.3b . . . remove the screw . . .

13.3c . . . and withdraw the bezel over the handle

13 Door inner trim panel -
removal and refitting

Removal

1 Disconnect the battery negative lead.
Caution: If the radio/cassette in your vehicle is equipped with an anti-theft system, make sure you have the correct activation code before disconnecting the battery.
2 On models with manual windows, note the position of the winder handle with the window fully closed. Insert a flat-bladed screwdriver between the door trim panel and the window winder handle. Release the clip using the tip of the screwdriver then pull the winder handle from its shaft. Another method of releasing the clip is to use a length of cloth, working it back and forth behind the handle.
3 Prise the plastic cover from the interior door handle bezel, then remove the screw and withdraw the bezel over the handle **(see illustrations)**.
4 On early models remove the screws and withdraw the armrest and map pocket.
5 On later models, prise out the plastic covers and unscrew the trim panel mounting screws located below the armrest **(see illustrations)**.

6 Remove the locking knob **(see illustration)**.
7 Using a suitable forked tool inserted between the door and the trim panel, release the press-stud clips located around the edge of the panel and unhook the top of the panel releasing it from the locking knob rod **(see illustration)**.
8 If work is to be carried out on the door internal components, it will be necessary to remove the plastic sealing sheet. Start at one corner of the sheet and carefully peel it away, if necessary using a sharp blade to split the sealant bead **(see illustration)**.
9 Store the detached sealing sheet such that it cannot become contaminated with dust; this will allow it to be re-used later.

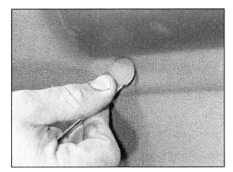

13.5a Prise out the plastic covers . . .

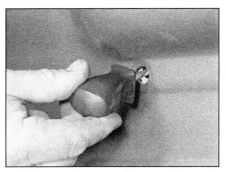

13.5b . . . and remove the screws located below the armrest

13.6 Removing the locking knob

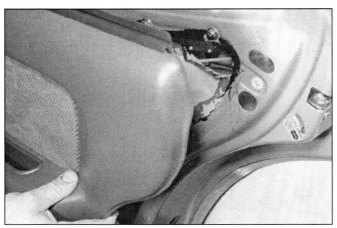

13.7 Removing the inner trim panel from the door

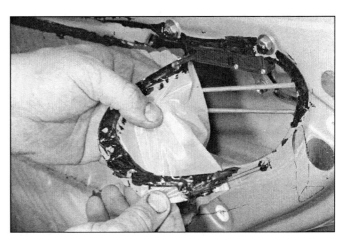

13.8 Removing the plastic sealing sheet from the door

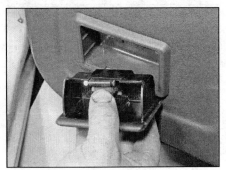

13.10a Remove the ashtray . . .

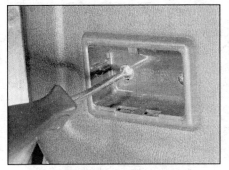

13.10b . . . unscrew the screws . . .

13.10c . . . and remove the casing

10 On later models, remove the ashtray; unscrew the screws and withdraw the casing. Note it is not necessary to remove the trim panel to carry out this work **(see illustrations)**.

Refitting

11 Refitting is a reversal of removal. Make sure that the sealing sheet is adequately sealed around its edges. It should be possible to use the original sealant, but if necessary, new sealant can be obtained from a Hyundai dealer.

14 Door latch, lock cylinder and handle components - removal and refitting

1 Ensure that the door window glass is fully raised, then disconnect the battery negative cable and position it away from the terminal.

Caution: If the radio/cassette in your vehicle is equipped with an anti-theft system, make sure you have the correct activation code before disconnecting the battery.
2 Refer to Section 13 and remove the door inner trim panel and sealing sheet.

Door exterior handle

Removal

3 Remove the tape from the mounting bolt and access holes, then use a screwdriver to prise the operating rod from the lever on the exterior handle **(see illustration)**.
4 On the front doors, use a screwdriver to release the plastic retainer then disconnect the operating rod from the private lock cylinder **(see illustration)**.
5 Unscrew and remove the mounting bolts, then carefully remove the handle assembly from the outside of the door. Take care not to

damage the paintwork, and if necessary protect it with masking tape **(see illustrations)**.
Refitting
6 Refitting is a reversal of removal.

Door interior handle

Removal

7 Mark the position of the handle, then remove the two screws that secure the handle assembly to the door **(see illustration)**.
8 Detach the link rod from the operating lever on the side of the lock mechanism.
9 Release the link rod from the support, then withdraw the handle from the door **(see illustration)**.
Refitting
10 Refitting is a reversal of removal. If necessary the position of the handle may be adjusted within the elongated screw holes.

14.3 Use a screwdriver to prise the operating rod from the lever on the exterior handle

14.4 Plastic retainer securing the operating rod to the private lock cylinder

14.5a Unscrew the mounting bolts . . .

14.5b . . . and withdraw the exterior handle from the rear door . . .

14.5c . . . and front door

14.7 Removing the interior door handle

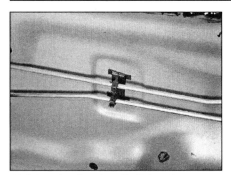

14.9 Interior door handle link rod supports

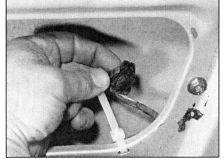

14.11 Unplug the wiring for the central locking motor

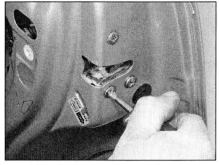

14.13a Removing the rear door lock mounting screws

Lock mechanism

Removal

Note: *The front lock is removed together with the central locking unit, then separated on the bench.*

11 If removing the front door lock, unplug the wiring for the central locking motor **(see illustration)**.

12 Disconnect the relevant operating rods from the lock using a screwdriver inserted through the apertures in the door panel. The exterior handle rod must be prised from its socket, however the remaining rods are disconnected by releasing the plastic retainers then removing the rod from the lock.

13 At the trailing edge of the door, remove the three screws that secure the lock mechanism to the door **(see illustrations)**.

14 On the front door, unscrew the central locking unit mounting bolt **(see illustration)**.

15 Withdraw the lock mechanism from the door space **(see illustrations)**.

16 On the front door, unscrew the bolts and separate the central locking unit from the lock **(see illustration)**.

Refitting

17 Refitting is a reversal of removal.

Lock cylinder

Removal

18 On early models, disconnect the operating rod from the lock cylinder, then use pliers to slide the retaining clip off and remove the lock cylinder from the door.

19 On later models, remove the exterior door handle as described earlier in this Section, then extract the clip and remove the operating lever. Prise the retaining clip from the handle casing and withdraw the lock cylinder.

14.13b Removing the front door lock mounting screws

Refitting

20 Refitting is a reversal of removal.

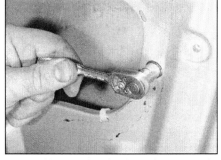

14.14 Unscrewing the front door central locking unit mounting bolt

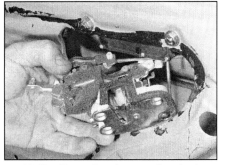

14.15a Removing the rear door lock mechanism

14.15b The rear door lock mechanism

14.15c Removing the front door lock mechanism

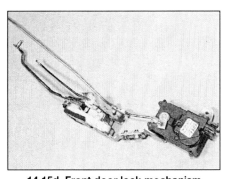

14.15d Front door lock mechanism together with the central locking unit

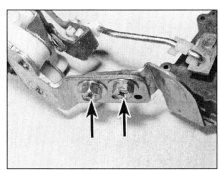

14.16 Bolts securing the front door lock to the central locking unit

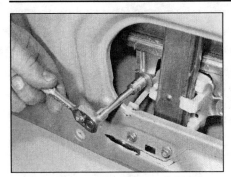

15.2a Unscrew the bolts securing the window channel bracket to the regulator

15.2b After removing the bolts the window will remain on the support tabs (arrowed)

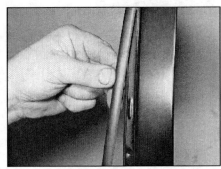

15.3a Unclip the plastic moulding . . .

15 Door window glass and regulator - removal and refitting

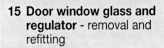

Door window glass

Removal

1 Lower the window so that the lower channel bracket-to-regulator bolts are visible in the door aperture. To do this on models with power windows, temporarily switch on the ignition and operate the power window switch. On models with manual windows temporarily refit the regulator handle.
2 Unscrew and remove the window channel bracket mounting bolts. Note that the bracket incorporates tabs which allow it to rest on top

of the regulator bracket and prevent the window from dropping to the bottom of the door. However, the window must be supported later when it is released from the side channels **(see illustrations)**.
3 Carefully unclip the exterior plastic moulding from the rear of the window aperture, then pull out the window rear rubber guide from the channel. Support the window while doing this **(see illustrations)**. The upper part of the rubber guide can remain in the door upper channel.
4 Lift the window then tilt it forwards and withdraw from the door while manipulating it past the weatherstrips **(see illustrations)**. The rear door fixed glass may be removed by unscrewing the division channel upper and lower screws, removing the channel, then withdrawing the glass forwards from the door.

Refitting

5 Refitting is a reversal of removal, but note the following:
  a) Ensure that the weather strip is fully entered in its channel.
  b) Check the operation of the window regulator mechanism before refitting the door inner trim panel.
  c) Refit the door inner trim panel with reference to Section 13.

Door window regulator

Removal

6 Detach the window glass from the regulator mechanism as described earlier in this Section, then manually raise the window to the top of its travel and retain in this position using strong adhesive tape (eg parcel tape).

15.3b . . . then ease out the rubber guide . . .

15.3c . . . and pull it up from the channel

15.4a Removing the rear door window . . .

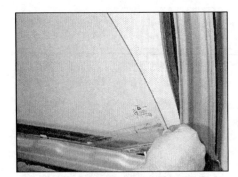

15.4b . . . and front door window

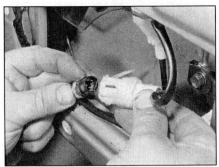

15.7a Disconnecting the rear door power window wiring . . .

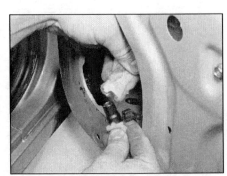

15.7b . . . and front door power window wiring

15.8a Rear door lower regulator mounting bolt

15.8b Front door lower regulator mounting bolts

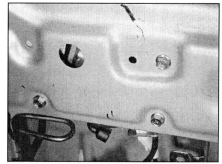

15.8c Rear door upper mounting bolts

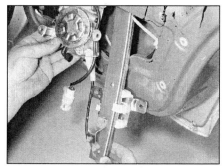

15.8d Removing the rear door regulator

15.8e Rear door regulator-to-cable bracket and mounting screws

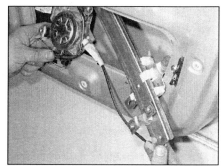

15.8f Removing the front door regulator

7 On models with power windows, disconnect the wiring **(see illustrations)**.
8 Unscrew the mounting bolts and withdraw the regulator assembly from inside the door - on manual windows mark the position of the mounting bolts to ensure correct refitting. The location of the mounting bolts varies between front and rear doors, and manual and power windows. On the power window rear door there is a single lower mounting bolt, but on the front door there are two bolts **(see illustrations)**.
9 On power windows, if the regulator motor is faulty it may be renewed separate to the cable assembly by unscrewing the mounting screws.

Refitting
10 Refitting is a reversal of removal, but check the operation of the window regulator before refitting the door inner trim panel.

16 Boot lid (Saloon models) - removal, refitting and adjustment

Removal
1 Open the boot lid, then where applicable remove the plastic covers and disconnect the wiring for the boot lid opener.
2 Using a pencil or felt-tipped pen, mark the outline of each hinge arm relative to the boot lid, to use as a guide on refitting.

3 Unscrew the bolts securing the hinge arms to the boot lid, then lift the boot lid from the vehicle - take care not to scratch the bodywork as the boot lid is removed **(see illustration)**.

Refitting
4 With the aid of an assistant, offer up the boot lid, and loosely fit the retaining bolts. Align the hinge arms with the marks made on removal, then tighten the retaining bolts securely.
5 Check and adjust the alignment of the boot lid as follows.

Adjustment
6 Close the boot lid carefully, in case the alignment is incorrect (which may cause scratching on the lid or the body as the boot lid is closed), and check for alignment with the adjacent panels. If necessary, slacken the hinge arm bolts and re-align the boot lid to suit. Once the boot lid is correctly aligned, tighten the hinge bolts to the specified torque.
7 With the boot lid correctly aligned, check that the boot lid fastens and releases in a satisfactory manner and that the striker (on the rear panel) enters the latch centrally. If adjustment is necessary, loosen the mounting bolts and reposition the striker as required, then re-tighten the bolts. On early models the lock position can also be adjusted.
8 Check that the boot lid is supported in the closed position by the rubber buffers, and if necessary screw them in or out as required.

15.8g Front door regulator-to-cable bracket and mounting screws

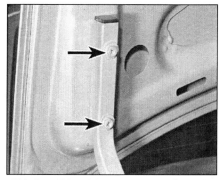

16.3 Boot lid-to-hinge arm mounting bolts

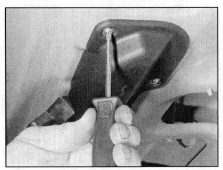

18.1a Remove the screws . . .

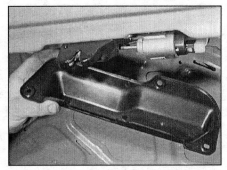

18.1b . . . and withdraw the cover from the boot lid lock

18.4 Boot lid lock and opener

17 Tailgate and support strut (Hatchback models) - removal, refitting and adjustment

Support strut

Removal

1 Open the tailgate and support it using a suitable prop.
2 Unscrew the bolts/studs securing the strut to the tailgate and body and withdraw it from the vehicle. Note which way up the strut is fitted (ie the piston rod is uppermost).

Refitting

3 Refitting is a reversal of removal.

Tailgate

Removal

4 Open the tailgate and support it using a suitable prop. Make sure that all electrical components are switched off.
5 Inside the rear of the vehicle, release the rear of the headlining for access to the tailgate hinges.
6 Disconnect the tailgate wiring at the connector.
7 Disconnect the tubing from the tailgate washer jet at the connector.
8 Remove the support strut as described in paragraph 2.

9 Mark the position of the hinges on the roof panel and tailgate using a pencil or marker pen.
10 With the aid of an assistant, unscrew the hinge mounting bolts/nuts then withdraw the tailgate from the rear of the vehicle.

Refitting

11 Refitting is a reversal of removal. If necessary, adjust the tailgate as follows.

Adjustment

12 Close the tailgate carefully, in case the alignment is incorrect, which may cause scratching on the tailgate or the body as the tailgate is closed), and check for alignment with the adjacent panels. If necessary, slacken the hinge bolts/nuts and re-align the tailgate to suit. Once the tailgate is correctly aligned, tighten the hinge bolts/nuts to the specified torque.
13 With the tailgate correctly aligned, check that the tailgate fastens and releases in a satisfactory manner and that the striker enters the latch centrally. If adjustment is necessary, loosen the mounting bolts and reposition the striker as required, then re-tighten the bolts. On early models the lock position can also be adjusted. **Note:** *On early models the striker is located on the rear panel and the lock is located on the tailgate, however on later models the striker is located on the tailgate and the lock is located on the rear panel.*
14 Check that the tailgate is supported in the closed position by the rubber buffers, and if necessary screw them in or out as required.

18 Boot lid lock components (Saloon models) - removal and refitting

Boot lid lock

Removal

1 With the boot lid open, remove the screws and withdraw the plastic cover from the lock **(see illustrations)**.
2 Disconnect the private lock operating rod at the private lock. To do this, release the plastic retainer and remove the rod.
3 On early models disconnect the opener operating rod from the lock. On later models disconnect the wiring from the opener mounted on the lock baseplate.
4 Unscrew the mounting bolts and withdraw the lock from the boot lid. On later models disconnect the operating rod then unbolt the opener from the lock baseplate **(see illustration)**.

Refitting

5 Refitting is a reversal of removal.

Boot lid private lock

Removal

6 With the boot lid open, release the plastic retainer and disconnect the operating rod from the private lock lever.
7 Using pliers, pull out the retaining clip, then withdraw the private lock from the boot lid **(see illustration)**.

Refitting

8 Refitting is a reversal of removal.

Boot lid lock striker

Removal

9 With the boot lid open, prise out the clips and remove the plastic trim from the rear panel **(see illustration)**.
10 Prise out the clips and pull back the carpet from the rear panel **(see illustration)**.
11 Undo the screw and remove the luggage compartment illumination light switch from the striker **(see illustration)**. There is no need to disconnect the wiring.

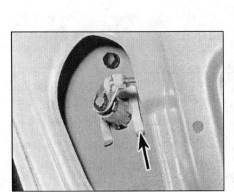

18.7 Boot lid private lock retaining clip

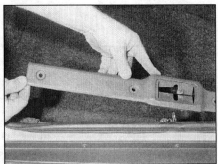

18.9 Removing the rear panel plastic trim

12 Using a pencil or marker pen, mark the position of the striker on the rear panel.
13 Unscrew the mounting bolts and withdraw the striker from the vehicle (**see illustration**).

Refitting

14 Refitting is a reversal of removal, but if necessary adjust the striker position as described in Section 16.

Boot lid opener (early models)

Note: *On later models the procedure is described in paragraphs 1 to 5 of this Section. The following paragraphs describe the procedure for early models.*

Removal

15 Where necessary remove the trim from inside the boot lid.
16 Disconnect the opener operating rod from the lock.
17 Mark the position of the opener, then unbolt it from the boot lid and disconnect the wiring plug.

Refitting

18 Refitting is a reversal of removal.

---

19 Tailgate lock and handle components (Hatchback models) - removal and refitting

Lock mechanism (early models - on tailgate)

Removal

1 Open the tailgate, then remove the clips and screws and remove the trim panel.
2 Disconnect the opener and private lock operating rods by releasing the plastic retainers.
3 Mark the position of the lock using a pencil or marker pen, then unbolt it from the tailgate.

Refitting

4 Refitting is a reversal of removal, but check and if necessary adjust the lock and striker as described in Section 17.

Tailgate private lock (early models - on tailgate)

Removal

5 Open the tailgate, then remove the clips and screws and remove the trim panel.
6 Disconnect the operating rod from the private lock.
7 Using pliers, pull out the retaining clip, then withdraw the private lock from the tailgate.

Refitting

8 Refitting is a reversal of removal.

Tailgate opener (early models - on tailgate)

Removal

9 Open the tailgate, then remove the clips and screws and remove the trim panel.

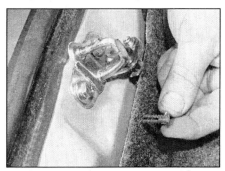

18.10 Prise out the clips and pull back the carpet

10 Disconnect the operating rod and wiring plug from the opener.
11 Unbolt the opener from the tailgate.

Refitting

12 Refitting is a reversal of removal.

Tailgate lock striker (early models - on rear panel)

Removal

13 With the tailgate open, remove the trim from the rear of the luggage compartment as necessary.
14 Mark the position of the striker using a pencil or marker pen, then unscrew the bolts and remove the striker.

Refitting

15 Refitting is a reversal of removal, but check and if necessary adjust the position of the striker with reference to Section 17.

Lock mechanism (later models - on rear panel)

Removal

16 With the tailgate open, prise out the clips and remove the plastic trim and carpet from the rear of the luggage compartment.
17 Disconnect the private lock operating rod from the lock.
18 Mark the position of the lock using a pencil or marker pen, then unscrew the bolts and withdraw the lock together with the opener. Disconnect the opener wiring plug.
19 Disconnect the operating rod and unbolt the opener from the lock baseplate.

18.13 Boot lid lock striker

18.11 Removing the luggage compartment illumination light switch

Refitting

20 Refitting is a reversal of removal.

Tailgate private lock (later models - on rear panel)

Removal

21 With the tailgate open, prise out the clips and remove the plastic trim and carpet from the rear of the luggage compartment.
22 Disconnect the operating rod from the private lock.
23 Using pliers, pull out the retaining clip, then withdraw the private lock from the rear panel.

Refitting

24 Refitting is a reversal of removal.

Tailgate opener (later models - on rear panel)

Removal and refitting

25 The procedure is described in paragraphs 16 to 20.

Tailgate lock striker (later models - on tailgate)

Removal

26 With the tailgate open, mark the position of the striker using a pencil or marker pen.
27 Unscrew the mounting bolts and remove the striker.

Refitting

28 Refitting is a reversal of removal.

---

20 Central locking system components - removal and refitting

Front door actuator

Removal and refitting

1 The front door actuator is removed together with the front door lock, then separated on the bench. Refer to Section 14.

Rear door actuator

Removal

2 Remove the rear door inner trim panel and plastic sealing strip as described in Section 13.

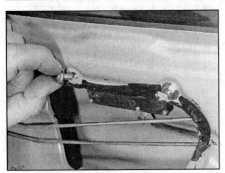

20.4a Removing the central locking rear door actuator mounting bolts

3 Disconnect the actuator operating rod from the door lock by releasing the plastic retainer.
4 Unscrew the mounting bolts and withdraw the actuator from the door, then disconnect the wiring plug **(see illustrations)**.

Refitting

5 Refitting is a reversal of removal

21 Exterior mirror -
removal and refitting

Removal

Early models

1 Using a screwdriver, prise the cover from the adjusting lever **(see illustration)**.
2 Undo the screw and remove the lever, then

20.4b Removing the central locking rear door actuator

lift off the mirror trim cover **(see illustration)**.
3 Support the mirror from the outside, then unscrew the mounting screws and withdraw the mirror from the door.

Later models

4 Carefully pull off the adjusting knob **(see illustration)**.
5 For improved access to the lower mirror mounting screws, remove the door inner trim panel as described in Section 13.
6 Prise out the window corner trim piece **(see illustration)**.
7 Remove the three securing bolts, and detach the mirror assembly from the outer surface of the door **(see illustrations)**.

Refitting

8 Refitting is a reversal of removal, but tighten the mirror securing screws securely.

22 Sunroof -
general information

Due to the complexity of the sunroof mechanism, considerable expertise is needed to repair, replace or adjust the sunroof components successfully. Removal of the sunroof first requires the headlining to be removed, which is a complex and tedious operation, and not a task to be undertaken lightly. Therefore, any problems with the sunroof should be referred to a Hyundai dealer.

23 Seats and seat belts -
removal and refitting

Front seats

Removal

1 Adjust the seat fully rearwards for access to the front mounting bolts.
2 Remove the plastic cover (later models) by pulling them forwards, then unscrew and remove the front mounting bolts/nuts **(see illustrations)**.
3 Adjust the seat fully forwards for access to the rear mounting bolts.
4 Unscrew and remove the rear mounting bolts.

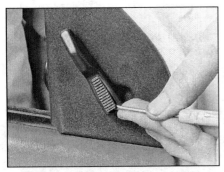

21.1 On early models prise out the cover . . .

21.2 . . . and remove the screw from the lever

21.4 Pull off the adjusting knob . . .

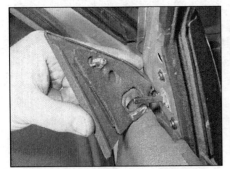

21.6 . . . and remove the corner trim piece . . .

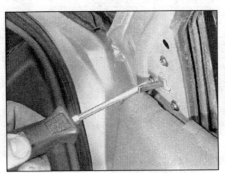

21.7a . . . then remove the bolts . . .

21.7b . . . and detach the exterior mirror from the outer surface of the door

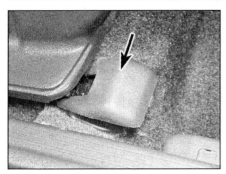

23.2a Remove the plastic cover . . .

23.2b . . . for access to the front seat mounting bolts/nuts

23.12 Rear seat side mounting bracket and bolts

5 Lift the seat from inside the vehicle.

Refitting

6 Refitting is a reversal of removal, but tighten the bolts/nuts to the specified torque.

Rear seat cushion

Removal

7 On early models, unscrew the two mounting bolts securing the front of the cushion to the floor.
8 Lift the front edge of the cushion and remove the seat from inside the vehicle.

Refitting

9 Refitting is a reversal of removal.

Rear seat back rests

Removal

10 Remove the rear seat cushion.

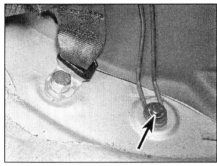

23.13 Rear seat side cushion mounting bolt - also showing rear seat belt lower anchor

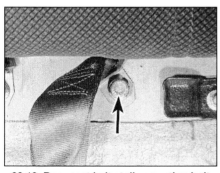

23.19 Rear seat belt stalk mounting bolt

11 On Hatchback models, fold the back rest forwards and unclip the carpet from its rear face. Unscrew and remove the side bracket mounting bolts, then slide the back rest off the centre mounting bracket. If necessary, unbolt and remove the centre mounting bracket.
12 On Saloon models, unscrew the side mounting bolts and lift the back rest from inside the vehicle (see illustration).
13 Where fitted, the side cushions may be removed by unscrewing the mounting bolts (see illustration).

Refitting

14 Refitting is a reversal of removal.

Seat belts

Front seat belt removal

15 To remove a front seat belt, first remove the front and rear door scuff trim and the trim from the centre pillar.
16 Prise off the plastic cover then unscrew the bolt from the upper anchor point.
17 Unscrew the bolt from the lower (floor) anchor point.
18 Unscrew the mounting bolt and remove the reel from the base of the pillar.
19 To remove the centre stalk, prise up the plastic cover then unscrew and remove the mounting bolt (see illustration).

Rear seat belt removal

20 Remove the rear seat cushion.
21 The stalks and centre lap belt are bolted to the rear floor. Unscrew and remove the mounting bolts.

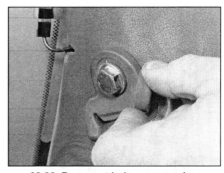

23.22 Rear seat belt upper anchor

22 To remove the shoulder straps, prise off the plastic cover then unscrew the bolt from the upper anchor point (see illustration).
23 Unscrew and remove the bolt from the lower anchor point.
24 In the luggage compartment, unscrew the mounting bolt and remove the reel from the side panel (see illustration).

Refitting

25 Refitting is a reversal of removal, but tighten the mounting bolts to the specified torque.

24 Centre console - removal and refitting

Removal

1 Disconnect the battery negative lead.
Caution: If the radio/cassette in your vehicle is equipped with an anti-theft system, make sure you have the correct activation code before disconnecting the battery.

Early models

2 Remove the screws from the sides of the front supplementary console.
3 Withdraw the supplementary console from the facia and disconnect the wiring for the digital clock.
4 Unscrew and remove the screws from the sides of the main console. Move the front seats forwards if necessary for access to the screws.

23.24 Rear seat belt reel and mounting bolt

24.8a Centre console rear mounting screw removal (later models)

24.8b Front location pegs on the rear console

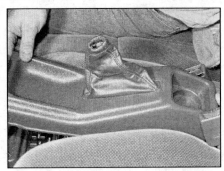

24.8c Removing the rear console

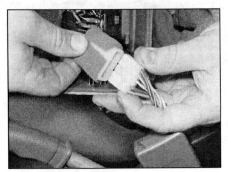

24.8d Disconnecting the wiring for the rear power window switch

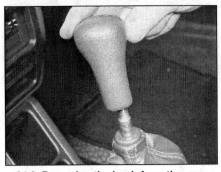

24.9 Removing the knob from the gear lever

24.10a Remove the front console rear mounting screw . . .

5 Lift the console from the floor. Where necessary, disconnect the wiring from the power window switch.
6 If required, remove the knob or handle from the top of the gear lever then unbolt the gaiter from the floor.

Later models

7 Adjust the front seats fully forwards.
8 Unscrew and remove the rear console mounting screws, then withdraw the rear console from the front location pegs, lift it over the handbrake lever, and where necessary disconnect the wiring from the rear power window switch (see illustrations).
9 Remove the knob or handle from the top of the gear lever (see illustration).
10 Remove the front console side and rear mounting screws, then lift the front console from the floor and disconnect the wiring from the power window switch (see illustrations).

Refitting

11 Refitting is a reversal of removal, but ensure that the wiring plugs are correctly reconnected.

25 Facia and glovebox - removal and refitting

Removal

1 Disconnect the battery negative lead.
Caution: If the radio/cassette in your vehicle is equipped with an anti-theft system, make sure you have the correct activation code before disconnecting the battery.

Early models

2 Remove the steering wheel as described in Chapter 10.

3 Unscrew the mounting screws and withdraw the steering column shrouds.
4 Open the glovebox, then unscrew the mounting screws and withdraw it from the facia.
5 Remove the small trim panel from below the steering column (see illustration).
6 Prise out the covers then remove the screws and withdraw the cover from the facia lower panel.
7 Remove the screws and detach the bonnet release handle from the facia lower panel.
8 Remove the choke cable knob and headlamp levelling knob.
9 Remove the screws and withdraw the driver side facia lower panel. Disconnect the wiring.
10 Remove the cigar lighter and the ashtray.
11 Remove the screws and withdraw the passenger side facia lower panel. Disconnect the wiring.

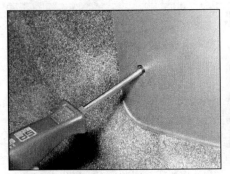

24.10b . . . and front mounting screws . . .

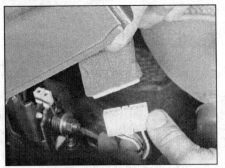

24.10c . . . then disconnect the wiring from the front power window switch

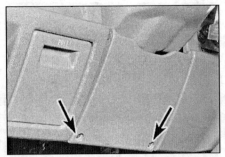

25.5 Location of the screws securing the small trim panel beneath the steering column

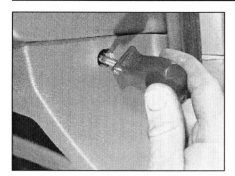

25.23a To remove the driver side lower facia panel, remove the side screw . . .

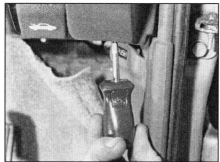

25.23b . . . lower screws . . .

25.23c . . . and upper screw . . .

25.23d . . . then withdraw the panel . . .

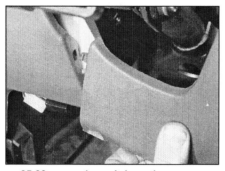

25.23e . . . release it from the peg . . .

25.23f . . . and disconnect the wiring

12 Beneath the facia, disconnect the wiring at the main loom.
13 Remove the instrument panel as described in Chapter 12.
14 Remove the radio/cassette unit as described in Chapter 12.

25.24a Unscrew the upper mounting screws . . .

15 Disconnect the control cables from the heater unit beneath the centre of the facia.
16 Unscrew the facia mounting screws beneath the centre of the facia.
17 Prise out the covers from the facia upper mounting screws, then unscrew and remove the screws.
18 Unscrew the remaining mounting screws.
19 With the help of an assistant, carefully remove the facia panel from inside the vehicle.

Later models

20 Remove the steering wheel as described in Chapter 10.
21 Unscrew the mounting screws and withdraw the steering column shrouds.
22 Remove the instrument panel as described in Chapter 12.
23 Remove the screws and withdraw the driver side lower facia panel from the main

facia panel. Note that the lower inner end of the panel locates with a peg. Disconnect the wiring from the instrument panel illumination rheostat **(see illustrations)**. If necessary, remove the bonnet release knob from the panel by removing the two screws.
24 Prise out the dummy switch covers from the centre panel. Unscrew the mounting screws and remove the centre panel from the facia. Disconnect the wiring. The radio/cassette may remain in the centre panel or alternatively it may be removed first with reference to Chapter 12 **(see illustrations)**.
25 Open the glovebox, then unscrew the mounting screws and withdraw the glovebox from the facia **(see illustrations)**.
26 Unscrew the screws and remove the passenger side lower facia panel.
27 Remove the loudspeakers from the top of the facia panel with reference to Chapter 12.

25.24b . . . and lower mounting screws . . .

25.24c . . . and remove the centre panel from the facia

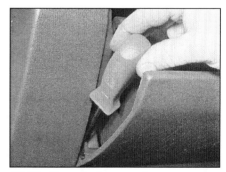

25.25a Unscrew the mounting screws . . .

25.25b . . . and remove the glovebox

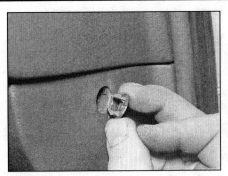

25.28a Prise out the plastic covers for access to the facia side upper mounting bolts

25.28b Facia side lower mounting bolt

28 Carefully prise out the plastic covers, then unscrew the mounting bolts and withdraw the facia panel from the bulkhead with the help of an assistant (see illustrations).

Refitting

29 Refitting is a reversal of removal. Make sure all the wiring connectors are fitted correctly, and check the function of all the switches after reconnecting the battery.

Chapter 12
Body electrical systems

Contents

Bulbs (exterior lights) - renewal 5
Bulbs (interior lights) - renewal 6
"Dim-dip" lighting system (UK models only) - general information . . 18
Electrical fault-finding - general information 2
Exterior light units - removal and refitting 7
Fuses and relays - general information 3
General information and precautions 1
Headlight beam alignment 8
Horn - removal and refitting 10
Instrument panel - removal and refitting 9

Loudspeakers - removal and refitting 17
Radio/cassette player and aerial - removal and refitting 16
Speedometer drive cable - removal and refitting 11
Switches, clock and cigar lighter - removal and refitting 4
Tailgate wiper motor - removal and refitting 14
Windscreen/tailgate washer system components - removal and
   refitting 15
Windscreen wiper motor and linkage - removal and refitting 13
Wiper arm - removal and refitting 12

Degrees of difficulty

Easy, suitable for novice with little experience	Fairly easy, suitable for beginner with some experience	Fairly difficult, suitable for competent DIY mechanic	Difficult, suitable for experienced DIY mechanic	Very difficult, suitable for expert DIY or professional 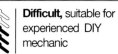

Specifications

Bulb ratings

	Watts
Headlights	60/55
Front direction indicator light	21
Front direction indicator repeater light	5
Front sidelight	5
Stop/tail light	21/5
Reversing light	21
Rear direction indicator light	21
Rear foglight	21
Rear number plate light	8
Load space light	5
High-mounted stop light	17
Overhead console light	10
Courtesy light	10
Instrument panel illumination lights	1.2
Low fuel and high beam warning lights	3.0

Torque wrench settings

	Nm	lbf ft
Windscreen wiper motor securing nuts	9	7
Windscreen wiper linkage bolts	5	4
Front wiper arm spindle nuts	5	4
Tailgate wiper arm spindle nut	5	4
Tailgate wiper motor mounting bolt	9	7
Headlight	4	3
Rear light cluster	3	2

1 General information and precautions

General information

The body electrical system consists of all lights, wash/wipe equipment, interior electrical equipment, and associated switches and wiring.

The electrical system is of the 12-volt negative earth type. Power to the system is provided by a 12-volt battery, which is charged by the alternator when the engine is running (see Chapter 5).

The engine electrical system (battery, alternator, starter motor, ignition system, etc) is covered in Chapter 5.

Precautions

 Warning: Before carrying out any work on the electrical system, read through the precautions given in "Safety first!" at the beginning of this manual, and in Chapter 5.
Caution: If the radio/cassette player fitted to the vehicle has an anti-theft security code, ensure that you have a copy of the code written down before disconnecting the battery.

Prior to working on any component in the electrical system, the battery negative lead should first be disconnected, to prevent the possibility of electrical short-circuits and/or fires.

2 Electrical fault-finding - general information

Note: *Refer to the precautions given in "Safety first!" and in Section 1 of this Chapter before starting work. The following tests relate to testing of the main electrical circuits, and should not be used to test delicate electronic circuits, particularly where an electronic control module is used.*

General

A typical electrical circuit consists of an electrical component, any switches, relays, motors, fuses, fusible links or circuit breakers related to that component, and the wiring and connectors which link the component to both the battery and the chassis. To help to pinpoint a problem in an electrical circuit, wiring diagrams are included at the end of this Chapter.

Before attempting to diagnose an electrical fault, first study the appropriate wiring diagram, to obtain a more complete understanding of the components included in the particular circuit concerned. The possible sources of a fault can be narrowed down by noting whether other components related to the circuit are operating properly. If several components or circuits fail at one time, the problem is likely to be related to a shared fuse or earth connection.

Electrical problems usually stem from simple causes, such as loose or corroded connections, a faulty earth connection, a blown fuse, a melted fusible link, or a faulty relay (refer to Section 3 for details of testing relays). Visually inspect the condition of all fuses, wires and connections in a problem circuit before testing the components. Use the wiring diagrams to determine which terminal connections will need to be checked, in order to pinpoint the trouble-spot.

The basic tools required for electrical fault-finding include a circuit tester or voltmeter (a 12-volt bulb with a set of test leads can also be used for certain tests); a self-powered test light (sometimes known as a continuity tester); an ohmmeter (to measure resistance); a battery and set of test leads; and a jumper wire, preferably with a circuit breaker or fuse incorporated, which can be used to bypass suspect wires or electrical components. Before attempting to locate a problem with test instruments, use the wiring diagram to determine where to make the connections.

To find the source of an intermittent wiring fault (usually due to a poor or dirty connection, or damaged wiring insulation), a "wiggle" test can be performed on the wiring. This involves wiggling the wiring by hand, to see if the fault occurs as the wiring is moved. It should be possible to narrow down the source of the fault to a particular section of wiring. This method of testing can be used in conjunction with any of the tests described in the following sub-Sections.

Apart from problems due to poor connections, two basic types of fault can occur in an electrical circuit - open-circuit, or short-circuit.

Open-circuit faults are caused by a break somewhere in the circuit, which prevents current from flowing. An open-circuit fault will prevent a component from working, but will not cause the relevant circuit fuse to blow.

Short-circuit faults are caused by a "short" somewhere in the circuit, which allows the current flowing in the circuit to "escape" along an alternative route, usually to earth. Short-circuit faults are normally caused by a breakdown in wiring insulation, which allows a feed wire to touch either another wire, or an earthed component such as the bodyshell. A short-circuit fault will normally cause the relevant circuit fuse to blow.

Finding an open-circuit

To check for an open-circuit, connect one lead of a circuit tester or voltmeter to either the negative battery terminal or a known good earth.

Connect the other lead to a connector in the circuit being tested, preferably nearest to the battery or fuse.

Switch on the circuit, bearing in mind that some circuits are live only when the ignition switch is moved to a particular position.

If voltage is present (indicated either by the tester bulb lighting or a voltmeter reading, as applicable), this means that the section of the circuit between the relevant connector and the battery is problem-free.

Continue to check the remainder of the circuit in the same fashion.

When a point is reached at which no voltage is present, the problem must lie between that point and the previous test point with voltage. Most problems can be traced to a broken, corroded or loose connection.

Finding a short-circuit

To check for a short-circuit, first disconnect the load(s) from the circuit (loads are the components which draw current from a circuit, such as bulbs, motors, heating elements, etc).

Remove the relevant fuse from the circuit, and connect a circuit tester or voltmeter to the fuse connections.

Switch on the circuit, bearing in mind that some circuits are live only when the ignition switch is moved to a particular position.

If voltage is present (indicated either by the tester bulb lighting or a voltmeter reading, as applicable), this means that there is a short-circuit.

If no voltage is present, but the fuse still blows with the load(s) connected, this indicates an internal fault in the load(s).

Finding an earth fault

The battery negative terminal is connected to "earth" - the metal of the engine/transmission and the car body - and most systems are wired so that they only receive a positive feed, the current returning via the metal of the car body. This means that the component mounting and the body form part of that circuit. Loose or corroded mountings can therefore cause a range of electrical faults, ranging from total failure of a circuit, to a puzzling partial fault. In particular, lights may shine dimly (especially when another circuit sharing the same earth point is in operation), motors (eg wiper motors or the radiator cooling fan motor) may run slowly, and the operation of one circuit may have an apparently-unrelated effect on another. Note that on many vehicles, earth straps are used between certain components, such as the engine/transmission and the body, usually where there is no metal-to-metal contact between components, due to flexible rubber mountings, etc.

To check whether a component is properly earthed, disconnect the battery, and connect one lead of an ohmmeter to a known good earth point. Connect the other lead to the wire or earth connection being tested. The resistance reading should be zero; if not, check the connection as follows.

If an earth connection is thought to be faulty, dismantle the connection, and clean back to bare metal both the bodyshell and the wire terminal or the component earth connection mating surface. Be careful to remove all traces

3.2a Fusebox located in the left-hand side of the engine compartment on later models

3.2b Fusible link box located next to the battery on later models

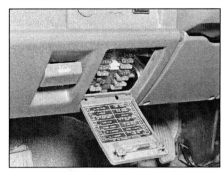

3.3 Main fuses on early models

of dirt and corrosion, then use a knife to trim away any paint, so that a clean metal-to-metal joint is made. On reassembly, tighten the joint fasteners securely; if a wire terminal is being refitted, use serrated washers between the terminal and the bodyshell, to ensure a clean and secure connection. When the connection is remade, prevent the onset of corrosion in the future by applying a coat of petroleum jelly or silicone-based grease, or by spraying on (at regular intervals) a proprietary ignition sealer, or a water-dispersant lubricant.

3 Fuses and relays - general information

Fuses

1 Fuses are designed to break a circuit when a predetermined current is reached, in order to protect the components and wiring which could be damaged by excessive current flow. Any excessive current flow will be due to a fault in the circuit, usually a short-circuit (see Section 2).

2 On early models the main fusebox is located behind a pull-down cover on the passenger side of the facia. On later models it is located behind a cover in the driver's footwell. Further fuses are located in the left-hand side of the engine compartment on later models. Fusible links are provided next to the battery (see illustrations).

3 To gain access to the main fuses, pull down the cover (early models) (see illustration) or depress the button and release the cover (later models).

4 A blown fuse can be recognised from its melted or broken wire (see illustration).

5 To remove a fuse, first ensure that the relevant circuit is switched off.

6 Pull the fuse squarely from its socket (see illustration).

7 Spare fuses are fitted in dummy sockets in the main fusebox.

8 Before renewing a blown fuse, trace and rectify the cause, and always use a new fuse of the correct rating (fuse ratings are specified on the inside of the fusebox cover). Never substitute a fuse of a higher rating, or make temporary repairs using wire or metal foil; more serious damage, or even fire, could result.

9 Note that the fuses are colour-coded as shown in the following table. Refer to the wiring diagrams for details of the fuse ratings used and the circuits protected.

Colour	Rating
Orange	5A
Red	10A
Blue	15A
Yellow	20A
Clear or White	25A
Green	30A

10 The radio/cassette player fuse is located in the rear of the unit, and can be accessed after removing the radio/cassette player - refer to Section 16 for greater detail (see illustration).

Relays (and control units)

11 Relays are electrical switches, operated indirectly by an electromagnetic solenoid. The internal components are encapsulated in a single case, with the electrical terminals at the bottom of the case. They are used in preference to normal switches for the following reasons:

a) A relay can be used to switch a heavy load current remotely, allowing the use of lighter-gauge wiring and contacts in the switching circuit.

b) A relay can be activated by more than one control input, whereas a mechanically controlled switch can only act on a single input.

c) A relay can be manufactured to include a time delay function - for example, an intermittent wiper relay, or a direction indicator flasher unit.

12 The relays are located beneath the facia adjacent to the fusebox, in the left-hand side of the engine compartment, or behind the instrument panel. Some additional relays may be fitted, depending on model and specification. These are generally mounted adjacent to the component being controlled.

13 The direction indicator/hazard warning flasher unit is mounted beneath the facia.

14 If a circuit or system controlled by a relay develops a fault, and the relay is suspect, activate the system by operating the appropriate switch. If the relay is functioning, it should be possible to hear or feel it "click" as it is energised, by listening to it carefully or resting

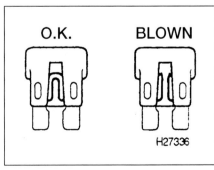

3.4 A blown fuse can be recognised from its melted or broken wire

3.6 Removing a fuse on later models

3.10 Radio/cassette fuse in the rear of the unit

3.15 Removing a relay on a later model

3.16a The TACU unit is located beneath the passenger front seat on later models

3.16b Removing the TACU unit

a finger tip on the relay case. If this is so, the fault may lie with the components or wiring of the system. If the relay cannot be felt or heard to energise, then either the relay is not receiving a switching current, or the relay itself is faulty. Testing is by substitution of an identical unit that is known to be operating correctly. Exercise caution, though - while some relays are identical in appearance and in operation, others look similar but perform different functions. Check that you have the correct type of relay for the circuit you are dealing with.

15 To remove a relay, first ensure that the relevant circuit is switched off - the relay can then be pulled out from its socket as required **(see illustration)**.

16 On later models the time and alarm functions for various circuits are operated by a separate control unit known as the TACU (Time And Control Unit). The circuits involved include the variable intermittent wiper, the heated rear

window, seat belt warning and door ajar warning. The TACU unit is located beneath the passenger seat **(see illustrations)**.

---

4 Switches, clock and cigar lighter - removal and refitting

Steering column-mounted stalk (combination) switch

Removal

1 Disconnect the battery negative lead.
Caution: If the radio/cassette in your vehicle is equipped with an anti-theft system, make sure you have the correct activation code before disconnecting the battery.
2 Remove the steering wheel as described in Chapter 10.

3 On early models, remove the small trim panel from under the steering column as described in Chapter 11.
4 Unscrew the screws and remove the upper and lower shrouds from the steering column **(see illustrations)**.
5 Disconnect the switch wiring at the connector beneath the facia **(see illustration)**. Remove the plastic tie(s) from the upper end of the wiring.
6 Unscrew and remove the four mounting screws, then carefully withdraw the switch assembly from the top of the steering column **(see illustrations)**. To provide sufficient room to remove the wiring connector, adjust the steering column height to its lowest position.
7 Individual parts of the switch assembly may be renewed separately, if necessary, by removing the crosshead screws **(see illustrations)**.

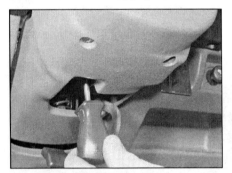

4.4a Remove the screws . . .

4.4b . . . then remove the upper steering column shroud . . .

4.4c . . . followed by the lower shroud

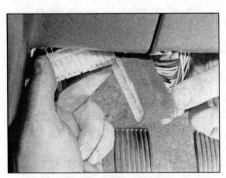

4.5 Disconnecting the wiring from the combination switch

4.6a Unscrew the screws . . .

4.6b . . . and withdraw the combination switch from the top of the steering column

4.7a Wiper switch mounting screws

4.7b Lighting switch mounting screws

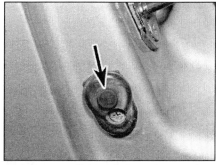
4.15 Courtesy light switch on the rear door

Refitting
8 Refitting is a reversal of removal.

Brake light switch
9 Refer to the information given in Chapter 9.

Facia-mounted switches

Removal
10 Make sure that the circuit is switched off.
11 On early models, carefully prise the switch from the facia with a screwdriver, then disconnect the wiring.
12 On later models, withdraw the centre switch panel from the facia with reference to Section 16. Disconnect the wiring from the rear of the switch, then carefully depress the tabs and push the switch out from the switch panel.

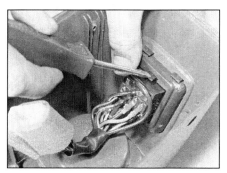
4.17a Depress the tabs . . .

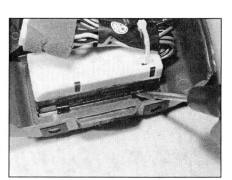
4.18a Depress the tabs . . .

Refitting
13 Refitting is a reversal of removal.

Door-mounted courtesy light switches

Removal
14 Open the door to expose the switch.
15 Remove the crosshead screw and withdraw the switch from the bodywork. Disconnect the wiring connector as it becomes accessible **(see illustration)**.

 TOOL TiP *Tape the wiring to the door pillar, or tie a length of string to the wiring, to retrieve it if it falls back inside the bodywork.*

Refitting
16 Refitting is a reversal of removal.

4.17b . . . and remove the electric window switch from the rear console

4.18b . . . and remove the electric window switch from the front console

Electric window switches

Removal
17 To remove the rear electric window switch (later models only), remove the rear centre console as described in Chapter 11. Invert the console, then use a screwdriver to depress the tabs and release the switch **(see illustrations)**.
18 To remove the front electric window switch, remove the front console as described in Chapter 11. Invert the console, then use a screwdriver to depress the tabs and release the switch **(see illustrations)**.

Refitting
19 Refitting is a reversal of removal.

Instrument panel rheostat

Removal
20 Remove the lower facia panel from below the steering column as described in Chapter 11.
21 Pull off the knob, then disconnect the wiring and push the rheostat from the panel **(see illustration)**.

Refitting
22 Refitting is a reversal of removal.

Boot lid opener switch

Removal
23 Remove the lower facia panel from below the steering column as described in Chapter 11.
24 Disconnect the wiring from the opener switch, then use a screwdriver to depress the tabs and push the switch from the panel **(see illustration)**.

4.21 Removing the instrument panel rheostat from the lower facia panel

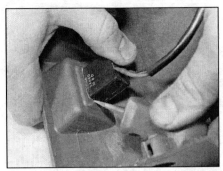

4.24 Removing the boot lid opener switch

4.26 Prising the digital clock from the facia

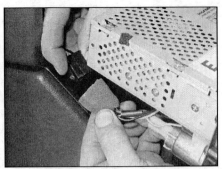

4.29a Disconnect the wiring . . .

Refitting

25 Refitting is a reversal of removal.

Clock

Removal

26 Using a wide-bladed tool, carefully prise the clock from the facia. To prevent damage, place some card on the facia to lever against (see illustration).
27 Disconnect the wiring.

Refitting

28 Refitting is a reversal of removal.

Cigar lighter

Removal

29 Remove the facia centre surround panel, then disconnect the wiring and unscrew the retaining ring. Withdraw the cigar lighter from the panel (see illustrations).

Refitting

30 Refitting is a reversal of removal.

---

5 Bulbs (exterior lights) - renewal

General

1 Whenever a bulb is renewed, note the following points:
   a) Ensure that the relevant electrical circuit is isolated before removing a bulb. If in

doubt, disconnect the battery negative lead before starting work.
   b) Remember that, if the circuit has just been in use, the bulb may be very hot.
   c) Always check the bulb contacts and holder, ensuring that there is clean metal-to-metal contact between the bulb and its live contact(s) and earth. Clean off any corrosion or dirt before fitting a new bulb.
   d) Wherever bayonet-type bulbs are fitted, ensure that the socket contacts bear firmly against the bulb contacts.
   e) Always ensure that the new bulb is of the correct rating (see Specifications), and that it is completely clean before fitting it; this applies particularly to headlight/foglamp bulbs (see following paragraphs).
   f) Pay attention to the orientation when fitting multi-filament bulbs (e.g. combined tail/brake light bulbs) - incorrect fitting will cause the filaments to illuminate in the wrong sequence.

Headlight

2 Open the bonnet. Ensure that the headlights and sidelights are turned off at the switch.
3 Remove the plastic cover from the rear of the headlight (see illustration).
4 Carefully pull the wiring plug from the headlight bulb terminals (see illustration).
5 Squeeze together the spring clip and release it from the bulb, then withdraw the bulb from the headlight (see illustration).
6 When handling the new bulb, use a tissue or clean cloth, to avoid touching the glass

4.29b . . . and unscrew the retaining ring to remove the cigar lighter

with the fingers; moisture and grease from the skin can cause blackening and rapid failure of this type of bulb. If the glass is accidentally touched, wipe it clean using methylated spirit. Avoid knocking or shaking the bulb as this may weaken or even break the internal filament.
7 Install the new bulb, using a reversal of the removal procedure, ensuring that its locating tabs are correctly located in the light unit cut-outs.
8 Secure the bulb in position with the retaining clip, refit the wiring plug, and secure the plastic cover.

Sidelights

9 Open the bonnet. Ensure that the headlights and sidelights are turned off at the switch.
10 Twist the plastic cover from the rear of the headlight.

5.3 Remove the plastic cover . . .

5.4 . . . then disconnect the wiring . . .

5.5 . . . and remove the headlight bulb

5.11 Remove the sidelight bulbholder from the rear of the headlight . . .

5.12 . . . and remove the bulb

5.14 Removing a front direction indicator bulb from its bulbholder

11 Twist and remove the sidelight bulbholder from the headlight (see illustration).
12 Depress and twist the bayonet type bulb from the bulbholder (see illustration).
13 Fit the new bulb, using a reversal of the removal procedure.

Front direction indicator

14 With the bonnet open, reach down behind the front direction indicator light unit and twist the bulbholder anticlockwise to remove it. On some models where access is difficult, remove the front direction indicator light unit first (see illustration).
15 Fit the new bulb, using a reversal of the removal procedure.

Direction indicator side repeater

16 On early models, turn the repeater anticlockwise and remove it from the front wing. On later models, using a small screwdriver

carefully depress the plastic tab at the rear of the light unit and withdraw the repeater light unit from the front wing; to prevent damage to the paintwork, place some card on the paintwork (see illustrations).
17 Twist the bulbholder and remove it from the light unit (see illustration).
18 Pull out the wedge-type bulb from the bulbholder (see illustration).
19 Fit the new bulb, using a reversal of the removal procedure.

Rear light cluster

20 Open the boot lid or tailgate. On early models depress the tabs and withdraw the bulbholder from the light unit. On later models, pull down the cover for access to the rear of the light cluster, then twist the appropriate bulbholder from the cluster (see illustration).
21 Depress and twist the bulb from the bulbholder.

22 Fit the new bulb, using a reversal of the removal procedure.

Rear number plate light

23 On early models, unscrew the lens retaining screws and lift off the lens. Depress and twist the bulb to remove it.
24 On later models, unscrew the lens retaining screws and lift off the lens. Separate the bulbholder from the lens, then depress and twist the bulb to remove it (see illustrations).
25 Fit the new bulb, using a reversal of the removal procedure.

High level stop lamp (spoiler mounted)

26 Unscrew the screws and remove the lens from the high level stop lamp (see illustration).
27 Remove the bulbholder, then depress and twist the bulb to remove it.

5.16a Carefully insert a small screwdriver and depress the plastic tab . . .

5.16b . . . then withdraw the side repeater . . .

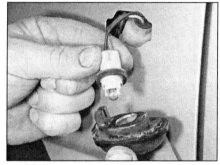

5.17 . . . remove the bulbholder . . .

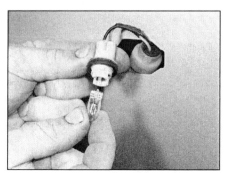

5.18 . . . and pull out the wedge-type bulb

5.20 Removing a rear light cluster bulb

5.24a On later models, remove the rear number plate light lens retaining screws . . .

5.24b ... separate the bulbholder ...

5.24c ... then remove the bulb

5.26 Removing the high level stop lamp lens

28 Fit the new bulb, using a reversal of the removal procedure.

High level stop lamp (rear window mounted)

29 Remove the screws and withdraw the cover from the lamp unit.
30 Remove the bulbholder, then depress and twist the bulb to remove it.
31 Fit the new bulb, using a reversal of the removal procedure.

Rear fog lamp (later models)

32 Remove the screws and withdraw the lens from the rear fog lamp mounted in the rear bumper.
33 Remove the bulbholder, then depress and twist the bulb to remove it.
34 Fit the new bulb, using a reversal of the removal procedure.

6 Bulbs (interior lights) - renewal

General

1 Whenever a bulb is renewed, note the following points:
a) *Always ensure that the relevant electrical circuit is switched off, before removing a bulb. If in doubt, disconnect the battery negative lead before starting work.*
b) *Remember that, if the light has just been in use, the bulb may be extremely hot.*
c) *Always check the bulb contacts and holder, ensuring that there is clean metal-to-metal contact between the bulb and its live contact(s) and earth. Clean off any corrosion or dirt before fitting a new bulb.*

d) *Wherever bayonet-type bulbs are fitted, ensure that the live contact(s) bear firmly against the bulb contact.*
e) *Always ensure that the new bulb is of the correct rating (see Specifications), and that it is completely clean before fitting it.*

Courtesy light

2 Carefully prise the lens from the light unit using a flat bladed screwdriver (see illustration).
3 Remove the festoon-type bulb from the spring loaded contacts (see illustration).
4 Fit the new bulb using a reversal of the removal procedure.

Luggage compartment illumination

5 With the boot lid or tailgate open, carefully prise the lens from the light unit using a flat bladed screwdriver (see illustration).
6 Remove the festoon-type bulb from the spring loaded contacts.
7 Fit the new bulb using a reversal of the removal procedure.

Instrument panel illumination

8 Remove the instrument panel as described in Section 9.
9 Twist the appropriate bulbholder from the rear of the instrument panel (see illustration).
10 Fit the new bulb using a reversal of the removal procedure.

Heater control panel illumination

11 Remove the heater control panel as described in Chapter 3.

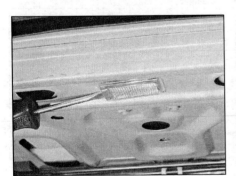

6.2 Prise off the lens ...

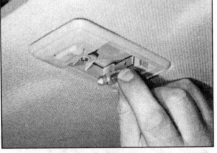

6.3 ... and remove the festoon-type bulb from the courtesy light

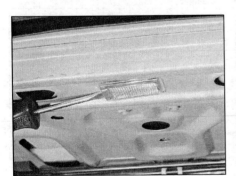

6.5 Removing the lens from the luggage compartment illumination light

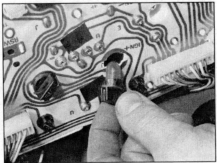

6.9 Instrument panel illumination bulb removal

6.12 Removing a heater control panel illumination bulb

7.4a Headlight outer mounting bolts

7.4b Headlight inner mounting bolts

7.4c Headlight upper mounting bolt

12 Twist the bulbholder to remove it from the rear of the control panel (see illustration).
13 Pull out the wedge-type bulb from the bulbholder.
14 Fit the new bulb using a reversal of the removal procedure.

7 Exterior light units - removal and refitting

Caution: Disconnect the battery negative lead before starting work. Refer to the caution in Section 1 if a security-coded radio/cassette player is fitted.

Headlight

Removal

1 Refer to Chapter 11 and remove the radiator grille.
2 Remove the adjacent direction indicator light unit as described later in this Section.
3 Disconnect all wiring from the rear of the light unit at the connectors. Label each carefully to aid correct refitting later.
4 Unscrew and remove the side mounting nuts (early models) or side and upper mounting bolts (later models) and withdraw the headlight unit from the front of the vehicle (see illustrations).
5 On later models unbolt the trim from the bottom of the headlight.

Refitting

6 Refitting is a reversal of removal but tighten the mounting nuts/bolts to the specified torque. On completion, check and if necessary adjust the headlight beam alignment as described in Chapter 1, but have the alignment checked at the earliest opportunity.

Front direction indicator light

Removal

7 On early models, loosen the retaining knob from inside the engine compartment, then withdraw the indicator light unit from its location slot and disconnect the wiring.
8 On later models, reach in behind the headlight unit and unhook the spring retaining the indicator light unit. Withdraw the unit

7.4d Removing the headlight

forwards from the location points, then twist and remove the bulbholder (see illustrations).

Refitting

9 Refitting is a reversal of removal.

Front direction indicator side repeater light

10 The procedure is described as part of the bulb renewal procedure in Section 5.

Rear light cluster

Removal

11 With the boot lid or tailgate open, prise out the plastic retainers and withdraw the trim in the area of the rear light cluster (see illustration).
12 Disconnect the wiring from the rear of the rear light cluster.

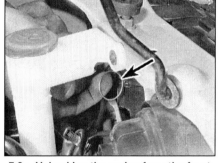

7.8a Unhooking the spring from the front direction indicator light

7.8b Release the front direction indicator light from the location points . . .

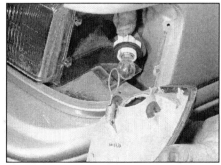

7.8c . . . then remove the bulbholder

7.11 Prising out the trim retainers for access to the rear light cluster

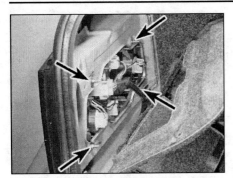

7.13 Rear light cluster mounting nuts

13 Unscrew the mounting nuts and withdraw the cluster unit from the rear of the vehicle **(see illustration)**.

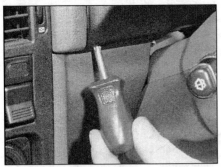

9.4a Remove the instrument panel lower mounting screws . . .

Refitting

14 Refitting is a reversal of removal, but tighten the mounting nuts to the specified torque.

8 Headlight beam alignment -
general information

Accurate adjustment of the headlight beam is only possible using optical beam-setting equipment, and this work should therefore be carried out by a Hyundai dealer or service station with the necessary facilities. In an emergency, however, the following procedure will provide an acceptable light pattern.

Position the car on a level surface with tyres correctly inflated, approximately 10 metres in front of, and at right-angles to, a wall or garage door.

Draw a horizontal line on the wall or door at headlamp centre height. Draw a vertical line corresponding to the centre line of the car, then measure off a point either side of this, on the horizontal line, corresponding with the headlamp centres.

Switch on the main beam and check that the areas of maximum illumination coincide with the headlamp centre marks on the wall. If not, turn the adjustment knobs on the rear of the headlight unit to adjust the beam horizontally and vertically. On models with a headlight leveller, make sure that it is set at its basic setting before making the adjustment.

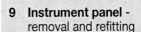

9 Instrument panel -
removal and refitting

Removal

1 Disconnect the battery negative lead.
Caution: If the radio/cassette in your vehicle is equipped with an anti-theft system, make sure you have the correct activation code before disconnecting the battery.
2 Remove the steering wheel as described in Chapter 10.
3 Remove the steering column shrouds.
4 Unscrew the screws and remove the instrument panel surround **(see illustrations)**.
5 Unscrew the mounting screws and withdraw the instrument panel from the facia. Disconnect the wiring, and on early models only disconnect the speedometer cable end fitting. **Note:** *On later models the cable end fitting remains in the facia as the instrument panel is withdrawn* **(see illustrations)**.

Refitting

6 Refitting is a reversal of removal, noting the following points:
a) *When reconnecting the speedometer cable on early models, make sure that it is pressed firmly onto the speedometer.*
b) *Refit the steering wheel with reference to Chapter 10.*

9.4b . . . and upper mounting screws . . .

9.4c . . . and withdraw the surround

9.5a Instrument panel mounting screw locations

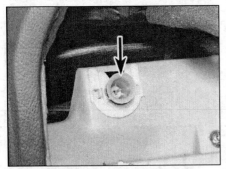

9.5b Speedometer cable end fitting behind the instrument panel on later models

9.5c Removing the instrument panel on later models

9.5d Squeeze the end fitting to disconnect the cable from the instrument panel on early models

10.3 Horn and mounting bracket

10 Horn -
removal and refitting

Removal

1 Remove the radiator grille as described in Chapter 11. Where necessary, also remove the headlight unit.
2 Disconnect the wiring from the horn.
3 Unscrew the mounting bolt, and withdraw the horn complete with the mounting bracket **(see illustration)**.

Refitting

4 Refitting is a reversal of removal.

11 Speedometer drive cable -
removal and refitting

Removal

1 Remove the instrument panel as described in Section 9. Where applicable, unclip the cable from the facia.
2 Apply the handbrake then jack up the front of the vehicle and support on axle stands (see *"Jacking and Vehicle Support"*).
3 Unscrew the knurled ring and disconnect the cable from the transmission.
4 Release the cable from the support brackets in the engine compartment and withdraw it through the bulkhead.

13.2a Remove the screws . . .

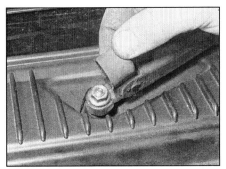

12.3 Lift up the wiper arm spindle nut cover for access to the retaining nut

Refitting

5 Refitting is a reversal of removal, but make sure that the bulkhead grommet is securely seated. Refit the instrument panel with reference to Section 9.

12 Wiper arm -
removal and refitting

Removal

1 Operate the wiper motor, then switch it off so that the wiper arm returns to the at-rest/parked position.
2 Stick a length of masking tape on the glass below the edge of the wiper blade, to use as an alignment aid on refitting.
3 Where applicable, lift up the wiper arm spindle nut cover, then unscrew and remove the spindle nut **(see illustration)**.
4 Lift the wiper blade off the surface of the glass, then counteract the tension of the hinge spring by pressing against the centre of the hinge. Lift the wiper arm squarely from the spindle **(see illustration)**. If necessary, the arm can be carefully levered off the spindle using a suitable flat-bladed screwdriver.
5 If both windscreen wiper arms are removed, note their locations, as different arms are fitted to the driver's and passenger's sides on certain models.

Refitting

6 Ensure that the wiper arm and spindle splines are clean and dry.

13.2b . . . and clips . . .

12.4 Removing a wiper arm from its spindle

7 When refitting a windscreen or tailgate wiper arm, refit the arm to the spindle, aligning the wiper blade with the tape fitted before removal. If both windscreen wiper arms have been removed, ensure that the arms are refitted to their correct positions as noted before removal.
8 Refit the spindle nut, tighten it securely, and if applicable, clip the nut cover back into position.
9 Operate the wipers and check that the swept area is satisfactory. If the tip of the blade wipes beyond the edge of the windscreen, the arm should be removed from the spindle and repositioned.
10 Switch off the wipers and check that both wiper blades are level when at rest. If they are not, they may snag each other during operation and jam. Rectify this by adjusting the position of the wiper arms on their spindles, as described in the previous paragraph.

13 Windscreen wiper motor and
linkage - removal and refitting

Removal

1 Disconnect the battery negative lead.
Caution: If the radio/cassette in your vehicle is equipped with an anti-theft system, make sure you have the correct activation code before disconnecting the battery.
2 Remove the wiper arms (see Section 12) and the cowl top cover retaining screws/clips, then detach the cover for access to the motor and disconnect the washer hoses from the jets **(see illustrations)**.

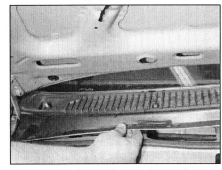

13.2c . . . then withdraw the cowl top cover . . .

13.2d ... and disconnect the hoses from the washer jets

3 Detach the wiper arm spindle link from the motor.

4 Disconnect the wiring, then unscrew the mounting bolts and withdraw the motor from the bulkhead **(see illustrations)**.

5 Remove the rubber covers, then unscrew the linkage mounting bolts and withdraw the linkage **(see illustration)**.

Refitting

6 Refitting is a reversal of removal.

14 Tailgate wiper motor - removal and refitting

Removal

1 Disconnect the battery negative lead.
Caution: If the radio/cassette in your vehicle is equipped with an anti-theft system, make sure you have the correct activation code before disconnecting the battery.

2 Remove the rear wiper arm as described in Section 12.

3 Remove the sealing cap and washer, then unscrew the nut and remove the grommet and spacer.

4 Open the tailgate, then unbolt and remove the trim panel for access to the wiper motor.

5 Disconnect the wiring, then unscrew the mounting bolts and withdraw the wiper motor from the tailgate.

Refitting

6 Refitting is a reversal of removal. Refit the wiper arm with reference to Section 12.

15.2 On later models use a pair of pliers to release the jet from the cowl top cover

13.4a Use a screwdriver to release the wiring connector from the bracket ...

13.4c Unscrewing the windscreen wiper motor mounting bolts

15 Windscreen/tailgate washer system components - removal and refitting

Removal

1 On carburettor models the washer fluid reservoir is located in the right-hand side of the engine compartment. On fuel-injection models the reservoir is located beneath the left-hand front wing. The fluid hoses to the windscreen washer jets, are clipped to the sides of the engine compartment. On Hatchback models the fluid hose to the rear washer runs along the left-hand side of the vehicle on fuel-injection models; on carburettor models it runs along the right-hand side of the vehicle.

2 To remove a windscreen washer jet, first remove the cowl top cover with reference to Section 13. On early models unscrew the nut and remove the jet from the cowl. On later models, use a pair of pliers to release the jet from the cowl **(see illustration)**.

3 To remove a tailgate washer jet, open the tailgate and disconnect the hose, then unscrew the nut and remove the jet from the tailgate.

4 To remove the reservoir on fuel-injection models, first remove the front bumper. Unscrew the mounting screws and withdraw the reservoir, then disconnect the wiring and hoses.

5 With the reservoir removed, the pump motor may be removed by carefully pulling it from the rubber grommet. Remove the grommet from the reservoir.

Refitting

6 Refitting is a reversal of removal.

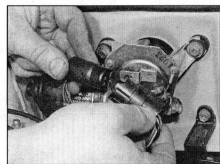

13.4b ... then separate the connector

13.5 Removing the rubber covers from the wiper spindles

16 Radio/cassette player and aerial - removal and refitting

Removal - radio/cassette

1 Disconnect the battery negative lead.
Caution: If the radio/cassette in your vehicle is equipped with an anti-theft system, make sure you have the correct activation code before disconnecting the battery.

Early models

2 Carefully pull the knobs from the radio, then unscrew the nuts and withdraw the surround from the radio.

3 Unscrew the mounting screws and withdraw the radio from the facia mounting box. Disconnect the wiring and aerial.

Later models

4 On later models, remove the ashtray, then unscrew the surround lower mounting screws.

16.5 Prise out the outer switch covers for access to the surround mounting screws

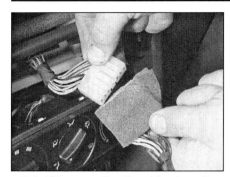

16.6a Disconnecting the wiring from the surround components

16.6b Disconnecting the radio/cassette wiring

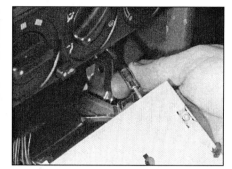

16.6c Disconnecting the aerial from the radio/cassette

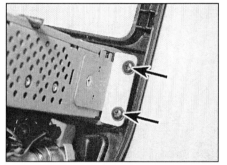

16.7 Radio/cassette side mounting screws

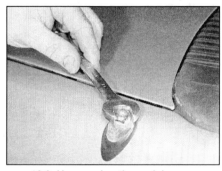

16.9 Unscrewing the aerial upper mounting nut

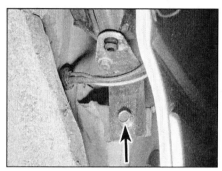

16.10 Aerial lower mounting bolt and bracket

5 Prise out the outer switch covers from the surround **(see illustration)**, then unscrew the surround upper mounting screws.

6 Withdraw the surround from the facia and disconnect the wiring and aerial, noting the location of each connector **(see illustrations)**.

7 Unscrew the side screws and remove the radio from the surround **(see illustration)**.

Removal - aerial

8 Undo the screws and pull back the wheelarch liner from beneath the left-hand front wing.

9 Unscrew the nut from the top of the aerial **(see illustration)**.

10 Unscrew the lower mounting bolt, then remove the bracket and lower the aerial **(see illustration)**.

11 Disconnect the inner end of the aerial from the radio/cassette with reference to

17.4 Front facia-mounted speaker on later models

paragraphs 1 to 7, then feed it through the bulkhead and withdraw it from under the left-hand front wing.

Refitting

12 Refitting is a reversal of removal.

17 Loudspeakers -
removal and refitting

Removal

Early models

1 To remove the front door-mounted speaker, first remove the door inner trim panel as described in Chapter 11.

2 Disconnect the wiring and unscrew the mounting screws, then withdraw the speaker from the front door.

3 To remove the rear-mounted speaker, disconnect the wiring and unscrew the mounting screws, then withdraw the speaker from the rear luggage compartment.

Later models

4 To remove the front facia-mounted speaker, carefully prise the grille from the facia then unscrew the speaker mounting screws **(see illustration)**.

5 Lift the speaker from the facia and disconnect the wiring.

Refitting

6 Refitting is a reversal of removal.

18 "Dim-dip" lighting system (UK models only) -
general information

1 To comply with UK regulations, a "dim-dip" lighting system is fitted to all UK models. The system operates through a dim-dip relay, and a resistor unit. The dim-dip relay is located next to the battery on the right-hand side of the engine compartment **(see illustration)**.

2 The dim-dip relay is supplied with current from the sidelight circuit, and is energised by a feed from the ignition switch. When energised, the unit allows battery voltage to pass through the resistor unit to the headlight dipped-beam circuits; this illuminates the headlights with approximately one-sixth of their normal power, so that the vehicle cannot be driven using sidelights alone.

18.1 On later models the dim-dip relay is located next to the battery

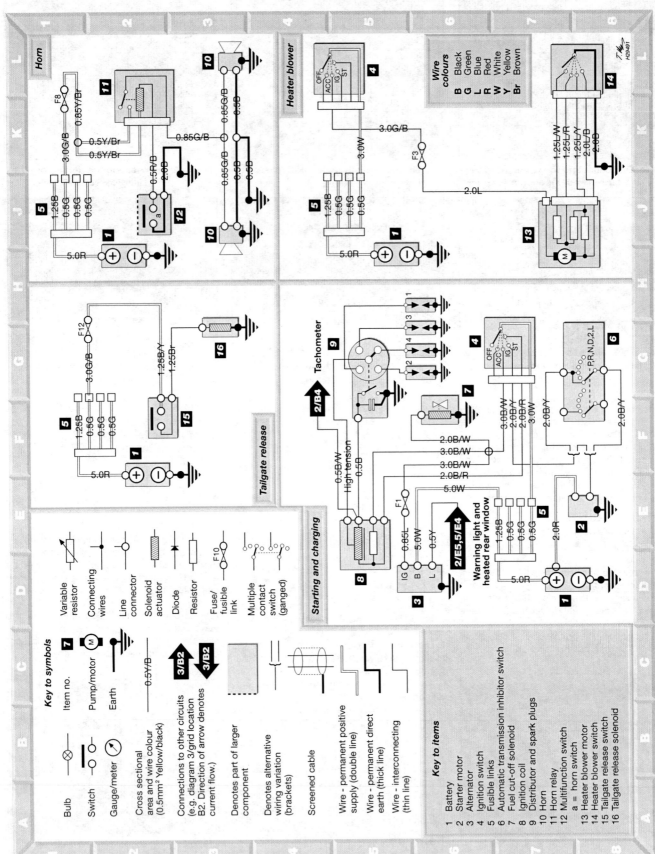

Diagram 1 : Information for wiring diagrams, typical starting/charging, horn, heater blower, and tailgate release

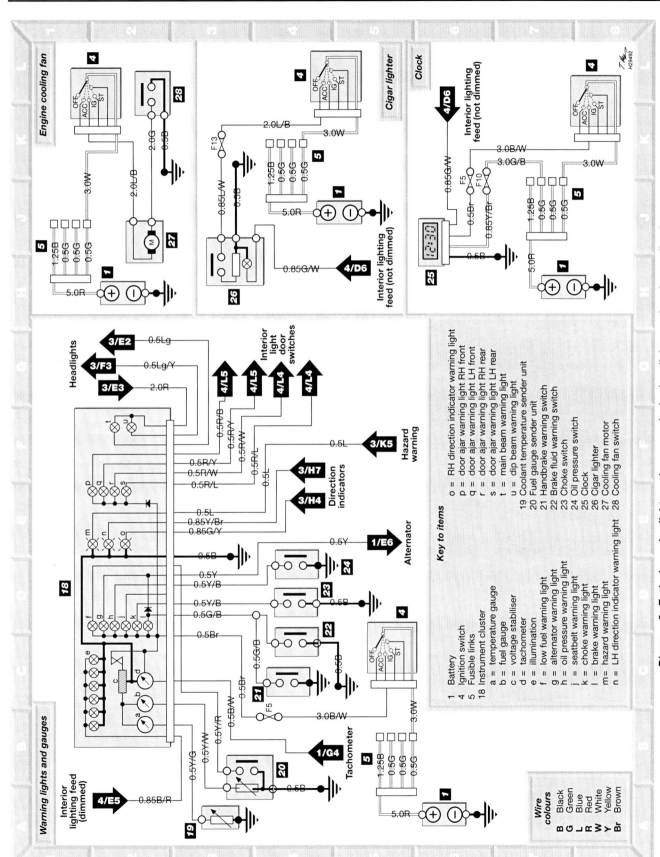

Diagram 2 : Typical warning lights and gauges, clock, cigar lighter and engine cooling fan

Engine cooling fan

Cigar lighter

Clock

Interior lighting feed (not dimmed)

Interior lighting feed (not dimmed)

Headlights

3/E2   0.5Lg
3/F3   0.5Lg/Y
3/E3   2.0R

Interior light door switches

4/L5   0.5R/B
4/L5   0.5R/Y
4/L4   0.5R/W
4/L4   0.5R/L

3/K5   0.5L   Hazard warning

3/H7   0.5R/Y / 0.5R/W / 0.5R/L
3/H4   Direction indicators

0.5L
0.85Y/Br
0.85G/Y

1/E6   0.5Y   Alternator

0.5Y
0.5Y/B
0.5Y/B
0.5G/B
0.5Br

1/G4   Tachometer

4/E5   0.85B/R   Interior lighting feed (dimmed)

Warning lights and gauges

Key to items

1 Battery
4 Ignition switch
5 Fusible links
18 Instrument cluster
    a = temperature gauge
    b = fuel gauge
    c = voltage stabiliser
    d = tachometer
    e = illumination
    f = low fuel warning light
    g = alternator warning light
    h = oil pressure warning light
    j = seatbelt warning light
    k = choke warning light
    l = brake warning light
    m= hazard warning light
    n = LH direction indicator warning light

o = RH direction indicator warning light
p = door ajar warning light RH front
q = door ajar warning light LH front
r = door ajar warning light RH rear
s = door ajar warning light LH rear
t = main beam warning light
u = dip beam warning light
19 Coolant temperature sender unit
20 Fuel gauge sender unit
21 Handbrake warning switch
22 Brake fluid warning switch
23 Choke switch
24 Oil pressure switch
25 Clock
26 Cigar lighter
27 Cooling fan motor
28 Cooling fan switch

Wire colours

B   Black
G   Green
L   Blue
R   Red
W   White
Y   Yellow
Br Brown

H29492

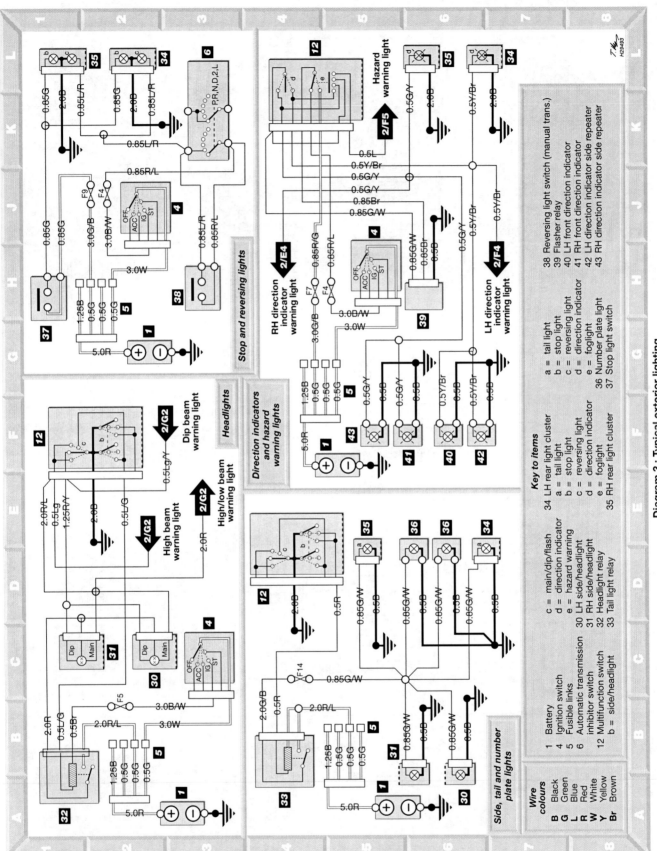

Diagram 3 : Typical exterior lighting

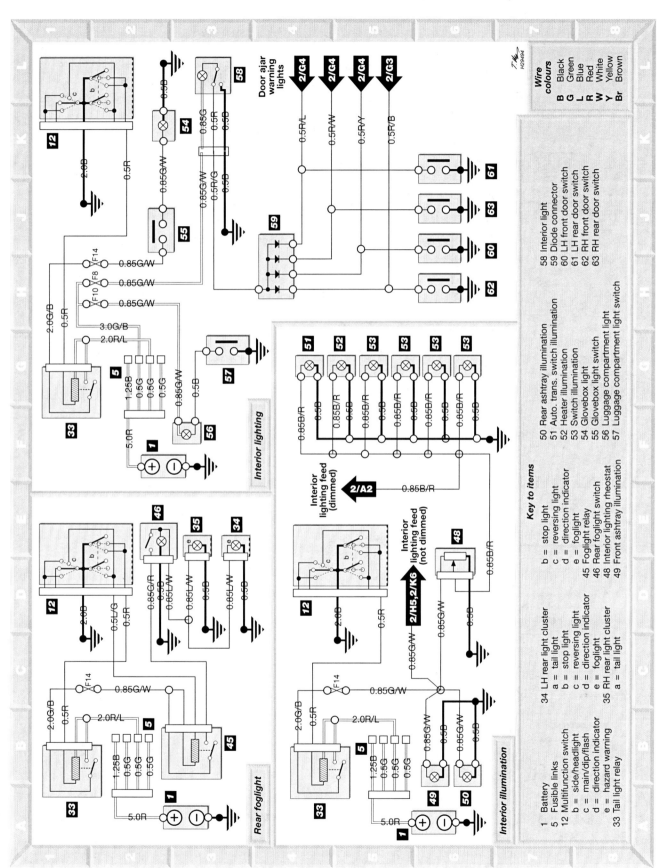

Diagram 4 : Typical rear foglight and interior lighting/illumination

Wire colours

B Black
G Green
L Blue
R Red
W White
Y Yellow
Br Brown

Key to items

1 Battery
5 Fusible links
12 Multifunction switch
  b = side/headlight
  c = main/dip/flash
  d = direction indicator
  e = hazard warning
33 Tail light relay
34 LH rear light cluster
  a = tail light
  b = stop light
  c = reversing light
  d = direction indicator
  e = foglight
35 RH rear light cluster
  a = tail light
  b = stop light
  c = reversing light
  d = direction indicator
  e = foglight
45 Foglight relay
46 Rear foglight switch
48 Interior lighting rheostat
49 Front ashtray illumination
50 Rear ashtray illumination
51 Auto. trans. switch illumination
52 Heater illumination
53 Switch illumination
54 Glovebox light
55 Glovebox light switch
56 Luggage compartment light
57 Luggage compartment light switch
58 Interior light
59 Diode connector
60 LH front door switch
61 LH rear door switch
62 RH front door switch
63 RH rear door switch

Door ajar warning lights

Interior lighting

Rear foglight

Interior illumination

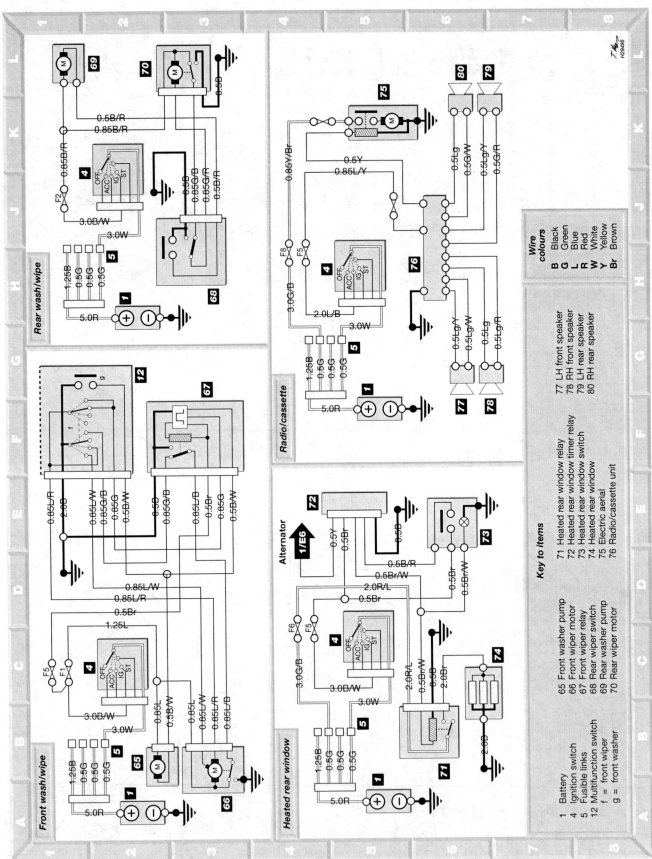

Diagram 5 : Typical wash/wipe, heated rear window, and radio/cassette

Wire colours

B	Black
G	Green
L	Blue
R	Red
W	White
Y	Yellow
Br	Brown

Key to items

1	Battery
4	Ignition switch
5	Fusible links
12	Multifunction switch
	f = front wiper
	g = front washer
65	Front washer pump
66	Front wiper motor
67	Front wiper relay
68	Rear wiper switch
69	Rear washer pump
70	Rear wiper motor
71	Heated rear window relay
72	Heated rear window timer relay
73	Heated rear window switch
74	Heated rear window
75	Electric aerial
76	Radio/cassette unit
77	LH front speaker
78	RH front speaker
79	LH rear speaker
80	RH rear speaker

Rear wash/wipe

Radio/cassette

Front wash/wipe

Heated rear window

Alternator

Dimensions and Weights	**REF•1**	Tools and Working Facilities	**REF•6**
Conversion Factors	**REF•2**	MOT Test Checks	**REF•8**
Buying Spare Parts	**REF•3**	Fault Finding	**REF•12**
Vehicle Identification	**REF•3**	Glossary of Technical Terms	**REF•19**
General Repair Procedures	**REF•4**	Index	**REF•24**
Jacking and Vehicle Support	**REF•5**		

Dimensions and Weights

Note: *All figures are approximate, and may vary according to model. Refer to manufacturer's data for exact figures.*

Dimensions

Overall length:
  Early (pre 1991) models:
    Saloon .... 4160 mm
    Hatchback .... 3985 mm
  Later (1991 on) models:
    Saloon .... 4282 mm
    Hatchback .... 4104 mm
Overall width:
  Early (pre 1991) models .... 1595 mm
  Later (1991 on) models .... 1607 mm
Overall height (unladen):
  Early (pre 1991) models .... 1375 mm
  Later (1991 on) models:
    Saloon .... 1361 mm
    Hatchback .... 1385 mm
Wheelbase:
  Early (pre 1991) models .... 2380 mm
  Later (1991 on) models .... 2383 mm

Weights

Kerb weight (approximate)*:
  Early (pre 1991) models .... 850 to 885 kg (depending on model)
  Later (1991 on) models .... 914 kg to 1014 kg (depending on model)
Automatic transmission models add 50 kg
Maximum gross vehicle weight:
  Early (pre 1991) models .... 1360 kg
  Later (1991 on) models .... 1450 kg
Maximum towing weight:
  Braked trailer .... 1000 kg
  Unbraked trailer .... 700 kg
Maximum trailer nose weight:
  Braked trailer .... 100 kg
  Unbraked trailer .... 70 kg

Conversion factors

Length (distance)

Inches (in)	x 25.4	= Millimetres (mm)	x 0.0394	= Inches (in)
Feet (ft)	x 0.305	= Metres (m)	x 3.281	= Feet (ft)
Miles	x 1.609	= Kilometres (km)	x 0.621	= Miles

Volume (capacity)

Cubic inches (cu in; in³)	x 16.387	= Cubic centimetres (cc; cm³)	x 0.061	= Cubic inches (cu in; in³)
Imperial pints (Imp pt)	x 0.568	= Litres (l)	x 1.76	= Imperial pints (Imp pt)
Imperial quarts (Imp qt)	x 1.137	= Litres (l)	x 0.88	= Imperial quarts (Imp qt)
Imperial quarts (Imp qt)	x 1.201	= US quarts (US qt)	x 0.833	= Imperial quarts (Imp qt)
US quarts (US qt)	x 0.946	= Litres (l)	x 1.057	= US quarts (US qt)
Imperial gallons (Imp gal)	x 4.546	= Litres (l)	x 0.22	= Imperial gallons (Imp gal)
Imperial gallons (Imp gal)	x 1.201	= US gallons (US gal)	x 0.833	= Imperial gallons (Imp gal)
US gallons (US gal)	x 3.785	= Litres (l)	x 0.264	= US gallons (US gal)

Mass (weight)

Ounces (oz)	x 28.35	= Grams (g)	x 0.035	= Ounces (oz)
Pounds (lb)	x 0.454	= Kilograms (kg)	x 2.205	= Pounds (lb)

Force

Ounces-force (ozf; oz)	x 0.278	= Newtons (N)	x 3.6	= Ounces-force (ozf; oz)
Pounds-force (lbf; lb)	x 4.448	= Newtons (N)	x 0.225	= Pounds-force (lbf; lb)
Newtons (N)	x 0.1	= Kilograms-force (kgf; kg)	x 9.81	= Newtons (N)

Pressure

Pounds-force per square inch (psi; lbf/in²; lb/in²)	x 0.070	= Kilograms-force per square centimetre (kgf/cm²; kg/cm²)	x 14.223	= Pounds-force per square inch (psi; lbf/in²; lb/in²)
Pounds-force per square inch (psi; lbf/in²; lb/in²)	x 0.068	= Atmospheres (atm)	x 14.696	= Pounds-force per square inch (psi; lbf/in²; lb/in²)
Pounds-force per square inch (psi; lbf/in²; lb/in²)	x 0.069	= Bars	x 14.5	= Pounds-force per square inch (psi; lbf/in²; lb/in²)
Pounds-force per square inch (psi; lbf/in²; lb/in²)	x 6.895	= Kilopascals (kPa)	x 0.145	= Pounds-force per square inch (psi; lbf/in²; lb/in²)
Kilopascals (kPa)	x 0.01	= Kilograms-force per square centimetre (kgf/cm²; kg/cm²)	x 98.1	= Kilopascals (kPa)
Millibar (mbar)	x 100	= Pascals (Pa)	x 0.01	= Millibar (mbar)
Millibar (mbar)	x 0.0145	= Pounds-force per square inch (psi; lbf/in²; lb/in²)	x 68.947	= Millibar (mbar)
Millibar (mbar)	x 0.75	= Millimetres of mercury (mmHg)	x 1.333	= Millibar (mbar)
Millibar (mbar)	x 0.401	= Inches of water (inH₂O)	x 2.491	= Millibar (mbar)
Millimetres of mercury (mmHg)	x 0.535	= Inches of water (inH₂O)	x 1.868	= Millimetres of mercury (mmHg)
Inches of water (inH₂O)	x 0.036	= Pounds-force per square inch (psi; lbf/in²; lb/in²)	x 27.68	= Inches of water (inH₂O)

Torque (moment of force)

Pounds-force inches (lbf in; lb in)	x 1.152	= Kilograms-force centimetre (kgf cm; kg cm)	x 0.868	= Pounds-force inches (lbf in; lb in)
Pounds-force inches (lbf in; lb in)	x 0.113	= Newton metres (Nm)	x 8.85	= Pounds-force inches (lbf in; lb in)
Pounds-force inches (lbf in; lb in)	x 0.083	= Pounds-force feet (lbf ft; lb ft)	x 12	= Pounds-force inches (lbf in; lb in)
Pounds-force feet (lbf ft; lb ft)	x 0.138	= Kilograms-force metres (kgf m; kg m)	x 7.233	= Pounds-force feet (lbf ft; lb ft)
Pounds-force feet (lbf ft; lb ft)	x 1.356	= Newton metres (Nm)	x 0.738	= Pounds-force feet (lbf ft; lb ft)
Newton metres (Nm)	x 0.102	= Kilograms-force metres (kgf m; kg m)	x 9.804	= Newton metres (Nm)

Power

Horsepower (hp)	x 745.7	= Watts (W)	x 0.0013	= Horsepower (hp)

Velocity (speed)

Miles per hour (miles/hr; mph)	x 1.609	= Kilometres per hour (km/hr; kph)	x 0.621	= Miles per hour (miles/hr; mph)

Fuel consumption*

Miles per gallon (mpg)	x 0.354	= Kilometres per litre (km/l)	x 2.825	= Miles per gallon (mpg)

Temperature

Degrees Fahrenheit = (°C x 1.8) + 32   Degrees Celsius (Degrees Centigrade; °C) = (°F - 32) x 0.56

It is common practice to convert from miles per gallon (mpg) to litres/100 kilometres (l/100km), where mpg x l/100 km = 282

Buying spare parts REF•3

Spare parts are available from many sources, including maker's appointed garages, accessory shops, and motor factors. To be sure of obtaining the correct parts, it will sometimes be necessary to quote the vehicle identification number. If possible, it can also be useful to take the old parts along for positive identification. Items such as starter motors and alternators may be available under a service exchange scheme - any parts returned should be clean.

Our advice regarding spare parts is as follows.

Officially appointed garages

This is the best source of parts which are peculiar to your car, and which are not otherwise generally available (eg, badges, interior trim, certain body panels, etc). It is also the only place at which you should buy parts if the vehicle is still under warranty.

Accessory shops

These are very good places to buy materials and components needed for the maintenance of your car (oil, air and fuel filters, light bulbs, drivebelts, greases, brake pads, touch-up paint, etc). Components of this nature sold by a reputable shop are usually of the same standard as those used by the car manufacturer.

Besides components, these shops also sell tools and general accessories, usually have convenient opening hours, charge lower prices, and can often be found close to home. Some accessory shops have parts counters where components needed for almost any repair job can be purchased or ordered.

Motor factors

Good factors will stock all the more important components which wear out comparatively quickly, and can sometimes supply individual components needed for the overhaul of a larger assembly (eg, brake seals and hydraulic parts, bearing shells, pistons, valves). They may also handle work such as cylinder block reboring, crankshaft regrinding, etc.

Tyre and exhaust specialists

These outlets may be independent, or members of a local or national chain. They frequently offer competitive prices when compared with a main dealer or local garage, but it will pay to obtain several quotes before making a decision. When researching prices, also ask what "extras" may be added - for instance fitting a new valve and balancing the wheel are both commonly charged on top of the price of a new tyre.

Other sources

Beware of parts or materials obtained from market stalls, car boot sales or similar outlets. Such items are not invariably sub-standard, but there is little chance of compensation if they do prove unsatisfactory. in the case of safety-critical components such as brake pads, there is the risk not only of financial loss, but also of an accident causing injury or death.

Second-hand components or assemblies obtained from a car breaker can be a good buy in some circumstances, but this sort of purchase is best made by the experienced DIY mechanic.

Vehicle Identification

Modifications are a continuing and unpublicised process in vehicle manufacture, quite apart from major model changes. Spare parts manuals and lists are compiled upon a numerical basis, the individual vehicle identification numbers being essential to correct identification of the component concerned.

When ordering spare parts, always give as much information as possible. Quote the car model, year of manufacture and registration, chassis and engine numbers as appropriate.

The *Vehicle Identification Number (VIN)* is stamped onto the right-hand side of the engine compartment bulkhead and is visible once the bonnet has been opened. The vehicle identification plate is situated next to the number **(see illustration)**.

The *engine number* can be found on the front of the cylinder block, at its left-hand end **(see illustration)**.

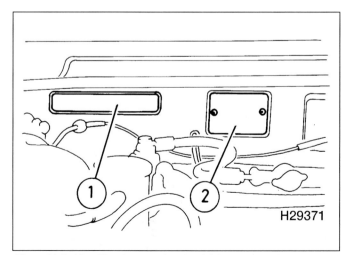

The vehicle identification number (VIN) (1) and identification plate (2) are mounted onto the engine compartment bulkhead

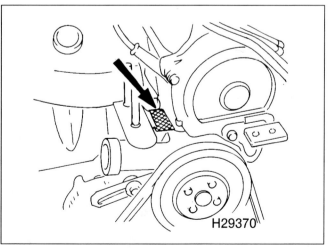

The engine number (arrowed) is stamped onto the front left-hand face of the cylinder block

Whenever servicing, repair or overhaul work is carried out on the car or its components, observe the following procedures and instructions. This will assist in carrying out the operation efficiently and to a professional standard of workmanship.

Joint mating faces and gaskets

When separating components at their mating faces, never insert screwdrivers or similar implements into the joint between the faces in order to prise them apart. This can cause severe damage which results in oil leaks, coolant leaks, etc upon reassembly. Separation is usually achieved by tapping along the joint with a soft-faced hammer in order to break the seal. However, note that this method may not be suitable where dowels are used for component location.

Where a gasket is used between the mating faces of two components, a new one must be fitted on reassembly; fit it dry unless otherwise stated in the repair procedure. Make sure that the mating faces are clean and dry, with all traces of old gasket removed. When cleaning a joint face, use a tool which is unlikely to score or damage the face, and remove any burrs or nicks with an oilstone or fine file.

Make sure that tapped holes are cleaned with a pipe cleaner, and keep them free of jointing compound, if this is being used, unless specifically instructed otherwise.

Ensure that all orifices, channels or pipes are clear, and blow through them, preferably using compressed air.

Oil seals

Oil seals can be removed by levering them out with a wide flat-bladed screwdriver or similar implement. Alternatively, a number of self-tapping screws may be screwed into the seal, and these used as a purchase for pliers or some similar device in order to pull the seal free.

Whenever an oil seal is removed from its working location, either individually or as part of an assembly, it should be renewed.

The very fine sealing lip of the seal is easily damaged, and will not seal if the surface it contacts is not completely clean and free from scratches, nicks or grooves. If the original sealing surface of the component cannot be restored, and the manufacturer has not made provision for slight relocation of the seal relative to the sealing surface, the component should be renewed.

Protect the lips of the seal from any surface which may damage them in the course of fitting. Use tape or a conical sleeve where possible. Lubricate the seal lips with oil before fitting and, on dual-lipped seals, fill the space between the lips with grease.

Unless otherwise stated, oil seals must be fitted with their sealing lips toward the lubricant to be sealed.

Use a tubular drift or block of wood of the appropriate size to install the seal and, if the seal housing is shouldered, drive the seal down to the shoulder. If the seal housing is unshouldered, the seal should be fitted with its face flush with the housing top face (unless otherwise instructed).

Screw threads and fastenings

Seized nuts, bolts and screws are quite a common occurrence where corrosion has set in, and the use of penetrating oil or releasing fluid will often overcome this problem if the offending item is soaked for a while before attempting to release it. The use of an impact driver may also provide a means of releasing such stubborn fastening devices, when used in conjunction with the appropriate screwdriver bit or socket. If none of these methods works, it may be necessary to resort to the careful application of heat, or the use of a hacksaw or nut splitter device.

Studs are usually removed by locking two nuts together on the threaded part, and then using a spanner on the lower nut to unscrew the stud. Studs or bolts which have broken off below the surface of the component in which they are mounted can sometimes be removed using a stud extractor. Always ensure that a blind tapped hole is completely free from oil, grease, water or other fluid before installing the bolt or stud. Failure to do this could cause the housing to crack due to the hydraulic action of the bolt or stud as it is screwed in.

When tightening a castellated nut to accept a split pin, tighten the nut to the specified torque, where applicable, and then tighten further to the next split pin hole. Never slacken the nut to align the split pin hole, unless stated in the repair procedure.

When checking or retightening a nut or bolt to a specified torque setting, slacken the nut or bolt by a quarter of a turn, and then retighten to the specified setting. However, this should not be attempted where angular tightening has been used.

For some screw fastenings, notably cylinder head bolts or nuts, torque wrench settings are no longer specified for the latter stages of tightening, "angle-tightening" being called up instead. Typically, a fairly low torque wrench setting will be applied to the bolts/nuts in the correct sequence, followed by one or more stages of tightening through specified angles.

Locknuts, locktabs and washers

Any fastening which will rotate against a component or housing during tightening should always have a washer between it and the relevant component or housing.

Spring or split washers should always be renewed when they are used to lock a critical component such as a big-end bearing retaining bolt or nut. Locktabs which are folded over to retain a nut or bolt should always be renewed.

Self-locking nuts can be re-used in non-critical areas, providing resistance can be felt when the locking portion passes over the bolt or stud thread. However, it should be noted that self-locking stiffnuts tend to lose their effectiveness after long periods of use, and should then be renewed as a matter of course.

Split pins must always be replaced with new ones of the correct size for the hole.

When thread-locking compound is found on the threads of a fastener which is to be re-used, it should be cleaned off with a wire brush and solvent, and fresh compound applied on reassembly.

Special tools

Some repair procedures in this manual entail the use of special tools such as a press, two or three-legged pullers, spring compressors, etc. Wherever possible, suitable readily-available alternatives to the manufacturer's special tools are described, and are shown in use. In some instances, where no alternative is possible, it has been necessary to resort to the use of a manufacturer's tool, and this has been done for reasons of safety as well as the efficient completion of the repair operation. Unless you are highly-skilled and have a thorough understanding of the procedures described, never attempt to bypass the use of any special tool when the procedure described specifies its use. Not only is there a very great risk of personal injury, but expensive damage could be caused to the components involved.

Environmental considerations

When disposing of used engine oil, brake fluid, antifreeze, etc, give due consideration to any detrimental environmental effects. Do not, for instance, pour any of the above liquids down drains into the general sewage system, or onto the ground to soak away. Many local council refuse tips provide a facility for waste oil disposal, as do some garages. If none of these facilities are available, consult your local Environmental Health Department, or the National Rivers Authority, for further advice.

With the universal tightening-up of legislation regarding the emission of environmentally-harmful substances from motor vehicles, most vehicles have tamperproof devices fitted to the main adjustment points of the fuel system. These devices are primarily designed to prevent unqualified persons from adjusting the fuel/air mixture, with the chance of a consequent increase in toxic emissions. If such devices are found during servicing or overhaul, they should, wherever possible, be renewed or refitted in accordance with the manufacturer's requirements or current legislation.

OIL CARE · FOLLOW THE CODE

OIL BANK LINE
0800 66 33 66

Note: It is antisocial and illegal to dump oil down the drain. To find the location of your local oil recycling bank, call this number free.

The jack supplied with the vehicle tool kit should only be used for changing the roadwheels - see *"Wheel changing"* at the front of this manual. When carrying out any other kind of work, raise the vehicle using a hydraulic (or "trolley") jack, and always supplement the jack with axle stands positioned under the vehicle jacking points.

Early (pre 1991) models

To raise the front of the vehicle, position the jack head underneath the centre of the front suspension crossmember. Lift the vehicle to the required height and support it on axle stands positioned underneath the front support points of the underbody box section members which run parallel along the vehicle underbody (see illustration).

To raise the rear of the vehicle, position the jack head underneath the centre of the underbody box section which is situated to the rear of the fuel tank. Lift the vehicle to the required height and support it on axle stands positioned underneath the rear support points of the underbody box section members which run parallel along the vehicle underbody.

Later (1991-on) models

To raise the front of the vehicle, position the jack head underneath the towing eye which is situated towards the front of the engine/transmission centre member. Lift the vehicle to the required height and support it on axle stands positioned underneath the vehicle jacking points on the sills (see illustration).

To raise the rear of the vehicle, position the jack head underneath the centre of the underbody box section which is situated to the rear of the fuel tank. Lift the vehicle to the required height and support it on axle stands positioned underneath the vehicle jacking points on the sills.

All models

The jack supplied with the vehicle locates with the jacking points on the sills. Ensure that the jack head is correctly engaged before attempting to raise the vehicle.

Never work under, around, or near a raised vehicle, unless it is adequately supported in at least two places.

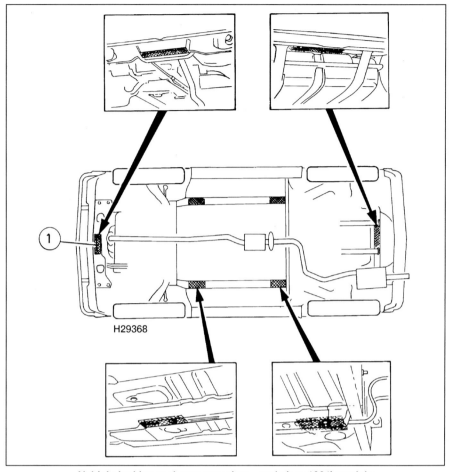

H29368

Vehicle jacking and support points - early (pre 1991) models

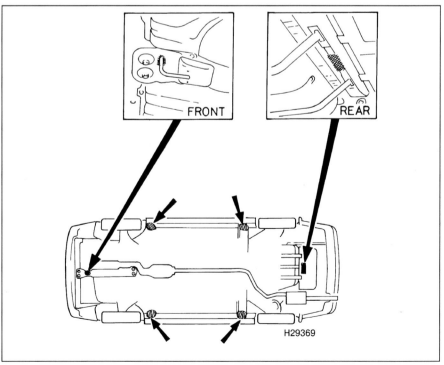

FRONT REAR

H29369

Vehicle jacking and support points - later (1991-on) models

Introduction

A selection of good tools is a fundamental requirement for anyone contemplating the maintenance and repair of a motor vehicle. For the owner who does not possess any, their purchase will prove a considerable expense, offsetting some of the savings made by doing-it-yourself. However, provided that the tools purchased meet the relevant national safety standards and are of good quality, they will last for many years and prove an extremely worthwhile investment.

To help the average owner to decide which tools are needed to carry out the various tasks detailed in this manual, we have compiled three lists of tools under the following headings: *Maintenance and minor repair, Repair and overhaul*, and *Special*. Newcomers to practical mechanics should start off with the *Maintenance and minor repair* tool kit, and confine themselves to the simpler jobs around the vehicle. Then, as confidence and experience grow, more difficult tasks can be undertaken, with extra tools being purchased as, and when, they are needed. In this way, a *Maintenance and minor repair* tool kit can be built up into a *Repair and overhaul* tool kit over a considerable period of time, without any major cash outlays. The experienced do-it-yourselfer will have a tool kit good enough for most repair and overhaul procedures, and will add tools from the *Special* category when it is felt that the expense is justified by the amount of use to which these tools will be put.

Maintenance and minor repair tool kit

The tools given in this list should be considered as a minimum requirement if routine maintenance, servicing and minor repair operations are to be undertaken. We recommend the purchase of combination spanners (ring one end, open-ended the other); although more expensive than open-ended ones, they do give the advantages of both types of spanner.

☐ Combination spanners:
  Metric - 8 to 19 mm inclusive
☐ Adjustable spanner - 35 mm jaw (approx.)
☐ Spark plug spanner (with rubber insert) - petrol models
☐ Spark plug gap adjustment tool - petrol models
☐ Set of feeler gauges
☐ Brake bleed nipple spanner
☐ Screwdrivers:
  Flat blade - 100 mm long x 6 mm dia
  Cross blade - 100 mm long x 6 mm dia
☐ Combination pliers
☐ Hacksaw (junior)
☐ Tyre pump
☐ Tyre pressure gauge
☐ Oil can
☐ Oil filter removal tool
☐ Fine emery cloth
☐ Wire brush (small)
☐ Funnel (medium size)

Repair and overhaul tool kit

These tools are virtually essential for anyone undertaking any major repairs to a motor vehicle, and are additional to those given in the *Maintenance and minor repair* list. Included in this list is a comprehensive set of sockets. Although these are expensive, they will be found invaluable as they are so versatile - particularly if various drives are included in the set. We recommend the half-inch square-drive type, as this can be used with most proprietary torque wrenches.

The tools in this list will sometimes need to be supplemented by tools from the *Special* list:

☐ Sockets (or box spanners) to cover range in previous list (including Torx sockets)
☐ Reversible ratchet drive (for use with sockets)
☐ Extension piece, 250 mm (for use with sockets)
☐ Universal joint (for use with sockets)
☐ Torque wrench (for use with sockets)
☐ Self-locking grips
☐ Ball pein hammer
☐ Soft-faced mallet (plastic/aluminium or rubber)
☐ Screwdrivers:
  Flat blade - long & sturdy, short (chubby), and narrow (electrician's) types
  Cross blade – Long & sturdy, and short (chubby) types
☐ Pliers:
  Long-nosed
  Side cutters (electrician's)
  Circlip (internal and external)
☐ Cold chisel - 25 mm
☐ Scriber
☐ Scraper
☐ Centre-punch
☐ Pin punch
☐ Hacksaw
☐ Brake hose clamp
☐ Brake/clutch bleeding kit
☐ Selection of twist drills
☐ Steel rule/straight-edge
☐ Allen keys (inc. splined/Torx type)
☐ Selection of files
☐ Wire brush
☐ Axle stands
☐ Jack (strong trolley or hydraulic type)
☐ Light with extension lead

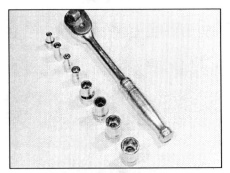
Sockets and reversible ratchet drive

Valve spring compressor

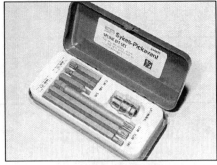
Spline bit set

Piston ring compressor

Clutch plate alignment set

Special tools

The tools in this list are those which are not used regularly, are expensive to buy, or which need to be used in accordance with their manufacturers' instructions. Unless relatively difficult mechanical jobs are undertaken frequently, it will not be economic to buy many of these tools. Where this is the case, you could consider clubbing together with friends (or joining a motorists' club) to make a joint purchase, or borrowing the tools against a deposit from a local garage or tool hire specialist. It is worth noting that many of the larger DIY superstores now carry a large range of special tools for hire at modest rates.

The following list contains only those tools and instruments freely available to the public, and not those special tools produced by the vehicle manufacturer specifically for its dealer network. You will find occasional references to these manufacturers' special tools in the text of this manual. Generally, an alternative method of doing the job without the vehicle manufacturers' special tool is given. However, sometimes there is no alternative to using them. Where this is the case and the relevant tool cannot be bought or borrowed, you will have to entrust the work to a dealer.

☐ Valve spring compressor
☐ Valve grinding tool
☐ Piston ring compressor
☐ Piston ring removal/installation tool
☐ Cylinder bore hone
☐ Balljoint separator
☐ Coil spring compressors (where applicable)
☐ Two/three-legged hub and bearing puller
☐ Impact screwdriver
☐ Micrometer and/or vernier calipers
☐ Dial gauge
☐ Stroboscopic timing light
☐ Dwell angle meter/tachometer
☐ Universal electrical multi-meter
☐ Cylinder compression gauge
☐ Hand-operated vacuum pump and gauge
☐ Clutch plate alignment set
☐ Brake shoe steady spring cup removal tool
☐ Bush and bearing removal/installation set
☐ Stud extractors
☐ Tap and die set
☐ Lifting tackle
☐ Trolley jack

Buying tools

Reputable motor accessory shops and superstores often offer excellent quality tools at discount prices, so it pays to shop around.

Remember, you don't have to buy the most expensive items on the shelf, but it is always advisable to steer clear of the very cheap tools. Beware of 'bargains' offered on market stalls or at car boot sales. There are plenty of good tools around at reasonable prices, but always aim to purchase items which meet the relevant national safety standards. If in doubt, ask the proprietor or manager of the shop for advice before making a purchase.

Care and maintenance of tools

Having purchased a reasonable tool kit, it is necessary to keep the tools in a clean and serviceable condition. After use, always wipe off any dirt, grease and metal particles using a clean, dry cloth, before putting the tools away. Never leave them lying around after they have been used. A simple tool rack on the garage or workshop wall for items such as screwdrivers and pliers is a good idea. Store all normal spanners and sockets in a metal box. Any measuring instruments, gauges, meters, etc, must be carefully stored where they cannot be damaged or become rusty.

Take a little care when tools are used. Hammer heads inevitably become marked, and screwdrivers lose the keen edge on their blades from time to time. A little timely attention with emery cloth or a file will soon restore items like this to a good finish.

Working facilities

Not to be forgotten when discussing tools is the workshop itself. If anything more than routine maintenance is to be carried out, a suitable working area becomes essential.

It is appreciated that many an owner-mechanic is forced by circumstances to remove an engine or similar item without the benefit of a garage or workshop. Having done this, any repairs should always be done under the cover of a roof.

Wherever possible, any dismantling should be done on a clean, flat workbench or table at a suitable working height.

Any workbench needs a vice; one with a jaw opening of 100 mm is suitable for most jobs. As mentioned previously, some clean dry storage space is also required for tools, as well as for any lubricants, cleaning fluids, touch-up paints etc, which become necessary.

Another item which may be required, and which has a much more general usage, is an electric drill with a chuck capacity of at least 8 mm. This, together with a good range of twist drills, is virtually essential for fitting accessories.

Last, but not least, always keep a supply of old newspapers and clean, lint-free rags available, and try to keep any working area as clean as possible.

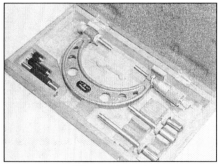
Micrometer set

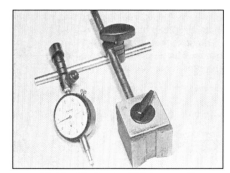
Dial test indicator ("dial gauge")

Stroboscopic timing light

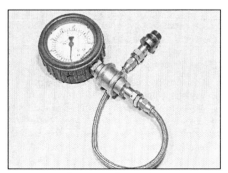
Compression tester

Stud extractor set

This is a guide to getting your vehicle through the MOT test. Obviously it will not be possible to examine the vehicle to the same standard as the professional MOT tester. However, working through the following checks will enable you to identify any problem areas before submitting the vehicle for the test.

Where a testable component is in borderline condition, the tester has discretion in deciding whether to pass or fail it. The basis of such discretion is whether the tester would be happy for a close relative or friend to use the vehicle with the component in that condition. If the vehicle presented is clean and evidently well cared for, the tester may be more inclined to pass a borderline component than if the vehicle is scruffy and apparently neglected.

It has only been possible to summarise the test requirements here, based on the regulations in force at the time of printing. Test standards are becoming increasingly stringent, although there are some exemptions for older vehicles. For full details obtain a copy of the Haynes publication Pass the MOT! (available from stockists of Haynes manuals).

An assistant will be needed to help carry out some of these checks.

The checks have been sub-divided into four categories, as follows:

1 Checks carried out **FROM THE DRIVER'S SEAT**

2 Checks carried out **WITH THE VEHICLE ON THE GROUND**

3 Checks carried out **WITH THE VEHICLE RAISED AND THE WHEELS FREE TO TURN**

4 Checks carried out on **YOUR VEHICLE'S EXHAUST EMISSION SYSTEM**

---

1 Checks carried out **FROM THE DRIVER'S SEAT**

Handbrake

☐ Test the operation of the handbrake. Excessive travel (too many clicks) indicates incorrect brake or cable adjustment.

☐ Check that the handbrake cannot be released by tapping the lever sideways. Check the security of the lever mountings.

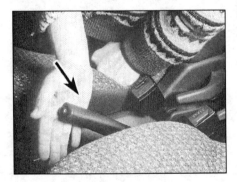

Footbrake

☐ Depress the brake pedal and check that it does not creep down to the floor, indicating a master cylinder fault. Release the pedal, wait a few seconds, then depress it again. If the pedal travels nearly to the floor before firm resistance is felt, brake adjustment or repair is necessary. If the pedal feels spongy, there is air in the hydraulic system which must be removed by bleeding.

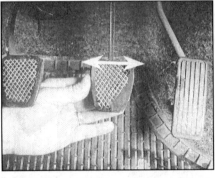

☐ Check that the brake pedal is secure and in good condition. Check also for signs of fluid leaks on the pedal, floor or carpets, which would indicate failed seals in the brake master cylinder.

☐ Check the servo unit (when applicable) by operating the brake pedal several times, then keeping the pedal depressed and starting the engine. As the engine starts, the pedal will move down slightly. If not, the vacuum hose or the servo itself may be faulty.

Steering wheel and column

☐ Examine the steering wheel for fractures or looseness of the hub, spokes or rim.

☐ Move the steering wheel from side to side and then up and down. Check that the steering wheel is not loose on the column, indicating wear or a loose retaining nut. Continue moving the steering wheel as before, but also turn it slightly from left to right.

☐ Check that the steering wheel is not loose on the column, and that there is no abnormal

movement of the steering wheel, indicating wear in the column support bearings or couplings.

Windscreen and mirrors

☐ The windscreen must be free of cracks or other significant damage within the driver's field of view. (Small stone chips are acceptable.) Rear view mirrors must be secure, intact, and capable of being adjusted.

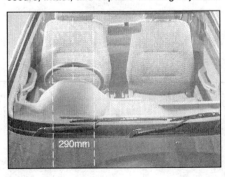

290mm

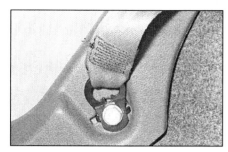

Seat belts and seats

Note: *The following checks are applicable to all seat belts, front and rear.*

☐ Examine the webbing of all the belts (including rear belts if fitted) for cuts, serious fraying or deterioration. Fasten and unfasten each belt to check the buckles. If applicable, check the retracting mechanism. Check the security of all seat belt mountings accessible from inside the vehicle.

☐ The front seats themselves must be securely attached and the backrests must lock in the upright position.

Doors

☐ Both front doors must be able to be opened and closed from outside and inside, and must latch securely when closed.

2 Checks carried out WITH THE VEHICLE ON THE GROUND

Vehicle identification

☐ Number plates must be in good condition, secure and legible, with letters and numbers correctly spaced – spacing at (A) should be twice that at (B).

☐ The VIN plate and/or homologation plate must be legible.

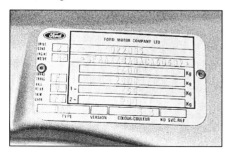

Electrical equipment

☐ Switch on the ignition and check the operation of the horn.

☐ Check the windscreen washers and wipers, examining the wiper blades; renew damaged or perished blades. Also check the operation of the stop-lights.

☐ Check the operation of the sidelights and number plate lights. The lenses and reflectors must be secure, clean and undamaged.

☐ Check the operation and alignment of the headlights. The headlight reflectors must not be tarnished and the lenses must be undamaged.

☐ Switch on the ignition and check the operation of the direction indicators (including the instrument panel tell-tale) and the hazard warning lights. Operation of the sidelights and stop-lights must not affect the indicators - if it does, the cause is usually a bad earth at the rear light cluster.

☐ Check the operation of the rear foglight(s), including the warning light on the instrument panel or in the switch.

Footbrake

☐ Examine the master cylinder, brake pipes and servo unit for leaks, loose mountings, corrosion or other damage.

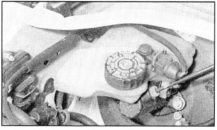

☐ The fluid reservoir must be secure and the fluid level must be between the upper (A) and lower (B) markings.

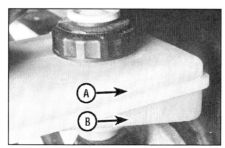

☐ Inspect both front brake flexible hoses for cracks or deterioration of the rubber. Turn the steering from lock to lock, and ensure that the hoses do not contact the wheel, tyre, or any part of the steering or suspension mechanism. With the brake pedal firmly depressed, check the hoses for bulges or leaks under pressure.

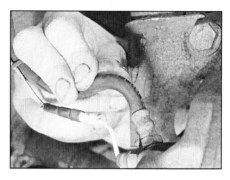

Steering and suspension

☐ Have your assistant turn the steering wheel from side to side slightly, up to the point where the steering gear just begins to transmit this movement to the roadwheels. Check for excessive free play between the steering wheel and the steering gear, indicating wear or insecurity of the steering column joints, the column-to-steering gear coupling, or the steering gear itself.

☐ Have your assistant turn the steering wheel more vigorously in each direction, so that the roadwheels just begin to turn. As this is done, examine all the steering joints, linkages, fittings and attachments. Renew any component that shows signs of wear or damage. On vehicles with power steering, check the security and condition of the steering pump, drivebelt and hoses.

☐ Check that the vehicle is standing level, and at approximately the correct ride height.

Shock absorbers

☐ Depress each corner of the vehicle in turn, then release it. The vehicle should rise and then settle in its normal position. If the vehicle continues to rise and fall, the shock absorber is defective. A shock absorber which has seized will also cause the vehicle to fail.

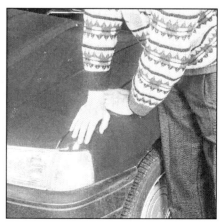

Exhaust system

☐ Start the engine. With your assistant holding a rag over the tailpipe, check the entire system for leaks. Repair or renew leaking sections.

3 Checks carried out
WITH THE VEHICLE RAISED AND THE WHEELS FREE TO TURN

Jack up the front and rear of the vehicle, and securely support it on axle stands. Position the stands clear of the suspension assemblies. Ensure that the wheels are clear of the ground and that the steering can be turned from lock to lock.

Steering mechanism

☐ Have your assistant turn the steering from lock to lock. Check that the steering turns smoothly, and that no part of the steering mechanism, including a wheel or tyre, fouls any brake hose or pipe or any part of the body structure.
☐ Examine the steering rack rubber gaiters for damage or insecurity of the retaining clips. If power steering is fitted, check for signs of damage or leakage of the fluid hoses, pipes or connections. Also check for excessive stiffness or binding of the steering, a missing split pin or locking device, or severe corrosion of the body structure within 30 cm of any steering component attachment point.

Front and rear suspension and wheel bearings

☐ Starting at the front right-hand side, grasp the roadwheel at the 3 o'clock and 9 o'clock positions and shake it vigorously. Check for free play or insecurity at the wheel bearings, suspension balljoints, or suspension mountings, pivots and attachments.
☐ Now grasp the wheel at the 12 o'clock and 6 o'clock positions and repeat the previous inspection. Spin the wheel, and check for roughness or tightness of the front wheel bearing.

☐ If excess free play is suspected at a component pivot point, this can be confirmed by using a large screwdriver or similar tool and levering between the mounting and the component attachment. This will confirm whether the wear is in the pivot bush, its retaining bolt, or in the mounting itself (the bolt holes can often become elongated).

☐ Carry out all the above checks at the other front wheel, and then at both rear wheels.

Springs and shock absorbers

☐ Examine the suspension struts (when applicable) for serious fluid leakage, corrosion, or damage to the casing. Also check the security of the mounting points.
☐ If coil springs are fitted, check that the spring ends locate in their seats, and that the spring is not corroded, cracked or broken.
☐ If leaf springs are fitted, check that all leaves are intact, that the axle is securely attached to each spring, and that there is no deterioration of the spring eye mountings, bushes, and shackles.

☐ The same general checks apply to vehicles fitted with other suspension types, such as torsion bars, hydraulic displacer units, etc. Ensure that all mountings and attachments are secure, that there are no signs of excessive wear, corrosion or damage, and (on hydraulic types) that there are no fluid leaks or damaged pipes.
☐ Inspect the shock absorbers for signs of serious fluid leakage. Check for wear of the mounting bushes or attachments, or damage to the body of the unit.

Driveshafts (fwd vehicles only)

☐ Rotate each front wheel in turn and inspect the constant velocity joint gaiters for splits or damage. Also check that each driveshaft is straight and undamaged.

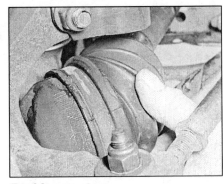

Braking system

☐ If possible without dismantling, check brake pad wear and disc condition. Ensure that the friction lining material has not worn excessively, (A) and that the discs are not fractured, pitted, scored or badly worn (B).

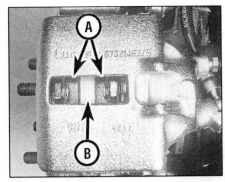

☐ Examine all the rigid brake pipes underneath the vehicle, and the flexible hose(s) at the rear. Look for corrosion, chafing or insecurity of the pipes, and for signs of bulging under pressure, chafing, splits or deterioration of the flexible hoses.
☐ Look for signs of fluid leaks at the brake calipers or on the brake backplates. Repair or renew leaking components.
☐ Slowly spin each wheel, while your assistant depresses and releases the footbrake. Ensure that each brake is operating and does not bind when the pedal is released.

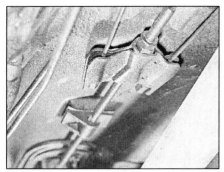

☐ Examine the handbrake mechanism, checking for frayed or broken cables, excessive corrosion, or wear or insecurity of the linkage. Check that the mechanism works on each relevant wheel, and releases fully, without binding.

☐ It is not possible to test brake efficiency without special equipment, but a road test can be carried out later to check that the vehicle pulls up in a straight line.

Fuel and exhaust systems

☐ Inspect the fuel tank (including the filler cap), fuel pipes, hoses and unions. All components must be secure and free from leaks.

☐ Examine the exhaust system over its entire length, checking for any damaged, broken or missing mountings, security of the retaining clamps and rust or corrosion.

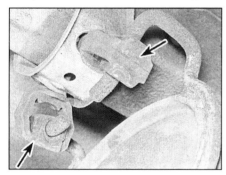

Wheels and tyres

☐ Examine the sidewalls and tread area of each tyre in turn. Check for cuts, tears, lumps, bulges, separation of the tread, and exposure of the ply or cord due to wear or damage. Check that the tyre bead is correctly seated on the wheel rim, that the valve is sound and

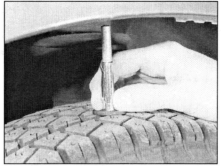

properly seated, and that the wheel is not distorted or damaged.

☐ Check that the tyres are of the correct size for the vehicle, that they are of the same size and type on each axle, and that the pressures are correct.

☐ Check the tyre tread depth. The legal minimum at the time of writing is 1.6 mm over at least three-quarters of the tread width. Abnormal tread wear may indicate incorrect front wheel alignment.

Body corrosion

☐ Check the condition of the entire vehicle structure for signs of corrosion in load-bearing areas. (These include chassis box sections, side sills, cross-members, pillars, and all suspension, steering, braking system and seat belt mountings and anchorages.) Any corrosion which has seriously reduced the thickness of a load-bearing area is likely to cause the vehicle to fail. In this case professional repairs are likely to be needed.

☐ Damage or corrosion which causes sharp or otherwise dangerous edges to be exposed will also cause the vehicle to fail.

4 Checks carried out on YOUR VEHICLE'S EXHAUST EMISSION SYSTEM

Petrol models

☐ Have the engine at normal operating temperature, and make sure that it is in good tune (ignition system in good order, air filter element clean, etc).

☐ Before any measurements are carried out, raise the engine speed to around 2500 rpm, and hold it at this speed for 20 seconds. Allow

the engine speed to return to idle, and watch for smoke emissions from the exhaust tailpipe. If the idle speed is obviously much too high, or if dense blue or clearly-visible black smoke comes from the tailpipe for more than 5 seconds, the vehicle will fail. As a rule of thumb, blue smoke signifies oil being burnt (engine wear) while black smoke signifies unburnt fuel (dirty air cleaner element, or other carburettor or fuel system fault).

☐ An exhaust gas analyser capable of measuring carbon monoxide (CO) and hydrocarbons (HC) is now needed. If such an instrument cannot be hired or borrowed, a local garage may agree to perform the check for a small fee.

CO emissions (mixture)

☐ At the time of writing, the maximum CO level at idle is 3.5% for vehicles first used after August 1986 and 4.5% for older vehicles. From January 1996 a much tighter limit (around 0.5%) applies to catalyst-equipped vehicles first used from August 1992. If the CO level cannot be reduced far enough to pass the test (and the fuel and ignition systems are otherwise in good condition) then the carburettor is badly worn, or there is some problem in the fuel injection system or catalytic converter (as applicable).

HC emissions

☐ With the CO emissions within limits, HC emissions must be no more than 1200 ppm (parts per million). If the vehicle fails this test at idle, it can be re-tested at around 2000 rpm; if the HC level is then 1200 ppm or less, this counts as a pass.

☐ Excessive HC emissions can be caused by oil being burnt, but they are more likely to be due to unburnt fuel.

Diesel models

☐ The only emission test applicable to Diesel engines is the measuring of exhaust smoke density. The test involves accelerating the engine several times to its maximum unloaded speed.

Note: *It is of the utmost importance that the engine timing belt is in good condition before the test is carried out.*

☐ Excessive smoke can be caused by a dirty air cleaner element. Otherwise, professional advice may be needed to find the cause.

Engine

- ☐ Engine fails to rotate when attempting to start
- ☐ Engine rotates, but will not start
- ☐ Engine difficult to start when cold
- ☐ Engine difficult to start when hot
- ☐ Starter motor noisy or excessively-rough in engagement
- ☐ Engine starts, but stops immediately
- ☐ Engine idles erratically
- ☐ Engine misfires at idle speed
- ☐ Engine misfires throughout the driving speed range
- ☐ Engine hesitates on acceleration
- ☐ Engine stalls
- ☐ Engine lacks power
- ☐ Engine backfires
- ☐ Oil pressure warning light illuminated with engine running
- ☐ Engine runs-on after switching off
- ☐ Engine noises

Cooling system

- ☐ Overheating
- ☐ Overcooling
- ☐ External coolant leakage
- ☐ Internal coolant leakage
- ☐ Corrosion

Fuel and exhaust systems

- ☐ Excessive fuel consumption
- ☐ Fuel leakage and/or fuel odour
- ☐ Excessive noise or fumes from exhaust system

Clutch

- ☐ Pedal travels to floor - no pressure or very little resistance
- ☐ Clutch fails to disengage (unable to select gears).
- ☐ Clutch slips (engine speed increases, with no increase in vehicle speed).
- ☐ Judder as clutch is engaged
- ☐ Noise when depressing or releasing clutch pedal

Manual transmission

- ☐ Noisy in neutral with engine running
- ☐ Noisy in one particular gear
- ☐ Difficulty engaging gears
- ☐ Jumps out of gear
- ☐ Vibration
- ☐ Lubricant leaks

Automatic transmission

- ☐ Fluid leakage
- ☐ Transmission fluid brown, or has burned smell
- ☐ General gear selection problems
- ☐ Transmission will not downshift (kickdown) with accelerator pedal fully depressed
- ☐ Engine will not start in any gear, or starts in gears other than Park or Neutral
- ☐ Transmission slips, shifts roughly, is noisy, or has no drive in forward or reverse gears

Driveshafts

- ☐ Vibration when accelerating or decelerating
- ☐ Clicking or knocking noise on turns (at slow speed on full-lock)

Braking system

- ☐ Vehicle pulls to one side under braking
- ☐ Noise (grinding or high-pitched squeal) when brakes applied
- ☐ Excessive brake pedal travel
- ☐ Brake pedal feels spongy when depressed
- ☐ Excessive brake pedal effort required to stop vehicle
- ☐ Judder felt through brake pedal or steering wheel when braking
- ☐ Brakes binding
- ☐ Rear wheels locking under normal braking

Suspension and steering

- ☐ Vehicle pulls to one side
- ☐ Wheel wobble and vibration
- ☐ Excessive pitching and/or rolling around corners, or during braking
- ☐ Wandering or general instability
- ☐ Excessively-stiff steering
- ☐ Excessive play in steering
- ☐ Lack of power assistance
- ☐ Tyre wear excessive

Electrical system

- ☐ Battery will not hold a charge for more than a few days
- ☐ Ignition/no-charge warning light remains illuminated with engine running
- ☐ Ignition/no-charge warning light fails to come on
- ☐ Lights inoperative
- ☐ Instrument readings inaccurate or erratic
- ☐ Horn inoperative, or unsatisfactory in operation
- ☐ Windscreen wipers inoperative, or unsatisfactory in operation
- ☐ Windscreen washers inoperative, or unsatisfactory in operation
- ☐ Electric windows inoperative, or unsatisfactory in operation
- ☐ Central locking system inoperative, or unsatisfactory in operation

Introduction

The vehicle owner who does his or her own maintenance according to the recommended service schedules should not have to use this section of the manual very often. Modern component reliability is such that, provided those items subject to wear or deterioration are inspected or renewed at the specified intervals, sudden failure is comparatively rare. Faults do not usually just happen as a result of sudden failure, but develop over a period of time. Major mechanical failures in particular are usually preceded by characteristic symptoms over hundreds or even thousands of miles. Those components which do occasionally fail without warning are often small and easily carried in the vehicle.

With any fault-finding, the first step is to decide where to begin investigations. Sometimes this is obvious, but on other occasions, a little detective work will be necessary. The owner who makes half a dozen haphazard adjustments or replacements may be successful in curing a fault (or its symptoms), but will be none the wiser if the fault recurs, and ultimately may have spent more time and money than was necessary. A calm and logical approach will be found to be more satisfactory in the long run. Always take into account any warning signs or abnormalities that may have been noticed in the period preceding the fault -

power loss, high or low gauge readings, unusual smells, etc - and remember that failure of components such as fuses or spark plugs may only be pointers to some underlying fault.

The pages which follow provide an easy-reference guide to the more common problems which may occur during the operation of the vehicle. These problems and their possible causes are grouped under headings denoting various components or systems, such as Engine, Cooling system, etc. The Chapter and/or Section which deals with the problem is also shown in brackets. Whatever the fault, certain basic principles apply. These are as follows:

Verify the fault. This is simply a matter of being sure that you know what the symptoms are before starting work. This is particularly important if you are investigating a fault for someone else, who may not have described it very accurately.

Don't overlook the obvious. For example, if the vehicle won't start, is there fuel in the tank? (Don't take anyone else's word on this particular point, and don't trust the fuel gauge either!) If an electrical fault is indicated, look for loose or broken wires before digging out the test gear.

Cure the disease, not the symptom. Substituting a flat battery with a fully-charged one will get you off the hard shoulder, but if the underlying cause is not attended to, the new battery will go the same way. Similarly, changing oil-fouled spark plugs for a new set will get you moving again, but remember that the reason for the fouling (if it wasn't simply an incorrect grade of plug) will have to be established and corrected.

Don't take anything for granted. Particularly, don't forget that a "new" component may itself be defective (especially if it's been rattling around in the boot for months), and don't leave components out of a fault diagnosis sequence just because they are new or recently-fitted. When you do finally diagnose a difficult fault, you'll probably realise that all the evidence was there from the start.

Engine

Engine fails to rotate when attempting to start

☐ Battery terminal connections loose or corroded (see *"Weekly checks"*)
☐ Battery discharged or faulty (Chapter 5)
☐ Broken, loose or disconnected wiring in the starting circuit (Chapter 5)
☐ Defective starter solenoid or switch (Chapter 5)
☐ Defective starter motor (Chapter 5)
☐ Starter pinion or flywheel ring gear teeth loose or broken (Chapters 2 and 5)
☐ Engine earth strap broken or disconnected (Chapter 5)

Engine rotates, but will not start

☐ Fuel tank empty
☐ Battery discharged (engine rotates slowly) (Chapter 5)
☐ Battery terminal connections loose or corroded (see *"Weekly checks"*)
☐ Ignition components damp or damaged (Chapters 1 and 5)
☐ Broken, loose or disconnected wiring in the ignition circuit (Chapters 1 and 5)
☐ Worn, faulty or incorrectly-gapped spark plugs (Chapter 1)
☐ Fuel injection system/carburettor fault (Chapter 4)
☐ Major mechanical failure (eg camshaft drive) (Chapter 2)

Engine difficult to start when cold

☐ Battery discharged (Chapter 5)
☐ Battery terminal connections loose or corroded (see *"Weekly checks"*)
☐ Worn, faulty or incorrectly-gapped spark plugs (Chapter 1)
☐ Fuel injection system/carburettor fault (Chapter 4)
☐ Other ignition system fault (Chapters 1 and 5)
☐ Low cylinder compressions (Chapter 2)

Engine difficult to start when hot

☐ Air filter element dirty or clogged (Chapter 1)
☐ Fuel injection system/carburettor fault (Chapter 4)
☐ Low cylinder compressions (Chapter 2)

Starter motor noisy or excessively-rough in engagement

☐ Starter pinion or flywheel ring gear teeth loose or broken (Chapters 2 and 5)
☐ Starter motor mounting bolts loose or missing (Chapter 5)
☐ Starter motor internal components worn or damaged (Chapter 5)

Engine starts, but stops immediately

☐ Loose or faulty electrical connections in the ignition circuit (Chapters 1 and 5)
☐ Vacuum leak at the carburettor/throttle body or inlet manifold (Chapter 4)
☐ Blocked injector/carburettor jet or other fuel system fault (Chapter 4)

Engine idles erratically

☐ Air filter element clogged (Chapter 1)
☐ Vacuum leak at the carburettor/throttle body, inlet manifold or associated hoses (Chapter 4)
☐ Worn, faulty or incorrectly-gapped spark plugs (Chapter 1)
☐ Uneven or low cylinder compressions (Chapter 2)
☐ Camshaft lobes worn (Chapter 2)
☐ Timing belt incorrectly fitted (Chapter 2)
☐ Blocked injector/carburettor jet or other fuel system fault (Chapter 4)

Engine misfires at idle speed

☐ Worn, faulty or incorrectly-gapped spark plugs (Chapter 1)
☐ Faulty spark plug HT leads (Chapter 1)
☐ Vacuum leak at the carburettor/throttle body, inlet manifold or associated hoses (Chapter 4)
☐ Blocked injector/carburettor jet or other fuel system fault (Chapter 4)
☐ Distributor cap cracked or tracking internally (Chapter 1).
☐ Uneven or low cylinder compressions (Chapter 2)
☐ Disconnected, leaking, or perished crankcase ventilation hoses (Chapter 4)

Engine misfires throughout the driving speed range

☐ Fuel filter choked (Chapter 1)
☐ Fuel pump faulty, or delivery pressure low (Chapter 4)
☐ Fuel tank vent blocked, or fuel pipes restricted (Chapter 4)
☐ Vacuum leak at the carburettor/throttle body, inlet manifold or associated hoses (Chapter 4)
☐ Worn, faulty or incorrectly-gapped spark plugs(Chapter 1)
☐ Faulty spark plug HT leads (Chapter 1)
☐ Distributor cap cracked or tracking internally (Chapter 1)
☐ Faulty ignition coil (Chapter 5)
☐ Uneven or low cylinder compressions (Chapter 2)
☐ Blocked injector/carburettor jet or other fuel system fault (Chapter 4)

Engine hesitates on acceleration

☐ Worn, faulty or incorrectly-gapped spark plugs (Chapter 1)
☐ Vacuum leak at the carburettor/throttle body, inlet manifold or associated hoses (Chapter 4)
☐ Blocked injector/carburettor jet or other fuel system fault (Chapter 4)

Engine stalls

☐ Vacuum leak at the carburettor/throttle body, inlet manifold or associated hoses (Chapter 4)
☐ Fuel filter choked (Chapter 1)
☐ Fuel pump faulty, or delivery pressure low (Chapter 4)
☐ Fuel tank vent blocked, or fuel pipes restricted (Chapter 4)
☐ Blocked injector/carburettor jet or other fuel system fault (Chapter 4)

Engine (continued)

Engine lacks power

- ☐ Timing belt incorrectly fitted (Chapter 2)
- ☐ Fuel filter choked (Chapter 1)
- ☐ Fuel pump faulty, or delivery pressure low (Chapter 4)
- ☐ Uneven or low cylinder compressions (Chapter 2)
- ☐ Worn, faulty or incorrectly-gapped spark plugs (Chapter 1)
- ☐ Vacuum leak at the carburettor/throttle body, inlet manifold or associated hoses (Chapter 4)
- ☐ Blocked injector/carburettor jet or other fuel system fault (Chapter 4)
- ☐ Brakes binding (Chapters 1 and 9)
- ☐ Clutch slipping (Chapter 6)

Engine backfires

- ☐ Timing belt incorrectly fitted (Chapter 2)
- ☐ Vacuum leak at the carburettor/throttle body, inlet manifold or associated hoses (Chapter 4)
- ☐ Blocked injector/carburettor jet or other fuel system fault (Chapter 4)

Oil pressure warning light illuminated with engine running

- ☐ Low oil level, or incorrect oil grade (see *"Weekly checks"*)
- ☐ Faulty oil pressure sensor (Chapter 5)
- ☐ Worn engine bearings and/or oil pump (Chapter 2)
- ☐ High engine operating temperature (Chapter 3)
- ☐ Oil pressure relief valve defective (Chapter 2)
- ☐ Oil pick-up strainer clogged (Chapter 2)

Engine runs-on after switching off

- ☐ Excessive carbon build-up in engine (Chapter 2)
- ☐ High engine operating temperature (Chapter 3)
- ☐ Fuel injection system/carburettor fault (Chapter 4)

Engine noises

Pre-ignition (pinking) or knocking during acceleration or under load

- ☐ Ignition timing incorrect/ignition system fault (Chapters 1 and 5)
- ☐ Incorrect grade of spark plug (Chapter 1)
- ☐ Incorrect grade of fuel (Chapter 1)
- ☐ Vacuum leak at the carburettor/throttle body, inlet manifold or associated hoses (Chapter 4)
- ☐ Excessive carbon build-up in engine (Chapter 2)
- ☐ Blocked injector/carburettor jet or other fuel system fault (Chapter 4)

Whistling or wheezing noises

- ☐ Leaking inlet manifold or carburettor/throttle body gasket (Chapter 4)
- ☐ Leaking exhaust manifold gasket or pipe-to-manifold joint (Chapter 4)
- ☐ Leaking vacuum hose (Chapters 4, 5 and 9)
- ☐ Blowing cylinder head gasket (Chapter 2)

Tapping or rattling noises

- ☐ Worn valve gear or camshaft (Chapter 2)
- ☐ Ancillary component fault (coolant pump, alternator, etc) (Chapters 3, 5, etc)

Knocking or thumping noises

- ☐ Worn big-end bearings (regular heavy knocking, perhaps less under load) (Chapter 2)
- ☐ Worn main bearings (rumbling and knocking, perhaps worsening under load) (Chapter 2)
- ☐ Piston slap (most noticeable when cold) (Chapter 2)
- ☐ Ancillary component fault (coolant pump, alternator, etc) (Chapters 3, 5, etc)

Cooling system

Overheating

- ☐ Insufficient coolant in system (*"Weekly Checks"*)
- ☐ Thermostat faulty (Chapter 3)
- ☐ Radiator core blocked, or grille restricted (Chapter 3)
- ☐ Cooling fan faulty (Chapter 3)
- ☐ Inaccurate temperature gauge sender unit (Chapter 3)
- ☐ Airlock in cooling system (Chapter 3)
- ☐ Pressure cap faulty (Chapter 3)

Overcooling

- ☐ Thermostat faulty (Chapter 3)
- ☐ Inaccurate temperature gauge sender unit (Chapter 3)
- ☐ Cooling fan faulty (Chapter 3)

External coolant leakage

- ☐ Deteriorated or damaged hoses or hose clips (Chapter 1)
- ☐ Radiator core or heater matrix leaking (Chapter 3)
- ☐ Pressure cap faulty (Chapter 3)
- ☐ Coolant pump internal seal leaking (Chapter 3)
- ☐ Coolant pump-to-block seal leaking (Chapter 3)
- ☐ Boiling due to overheating (Chapter 3)
- ☐ Core plug leaking (Chapter 2)

Internal coolant leakage

- ☐ Leaking cylinder head gasket (Chapter 2)
- ☐ Cracked cylinder head or cylinder block (Chapter 2)

Corrosion

- ☐ Infrequent draining and flushing (Chapter 1)
- ☐ Incorrect coolant mixture or inappropriate coolant type (see *"Weekly checks"*)

Fuel and exhaust systems

Excessive fuel consumption

☐ Air filter element dirty or clogged (Chapter 1)
☐ Fuel injection system/carburettor fault (Chapter 4)
☐ Ignition timing incorrect/ignition system fault (Chapters 1 and 5)
☐ Tyres under-inflated (see "Weekly checks")

Fuel leakage and/or fuel odour

☐ Damaged or corroded fuel tank, pipes or connections (Chapter 4)

Excessive noise or fumes from exhaust system

☐ Leaking exhaust system or manifold joints (Chapters 1 and 4)
☐ Leaking, corroded or damaged silencers or pipe (Chapters 1 and 4)
☐ Broken mountings causing body or suspension contact (Chapter 1)

Clutch

Pedal travels to floor - no pressure or very little resistance

☐ Broken clutch cable - cable-operated clutch (Chapter 6)
☐ Faulty hydraulic release system - hydraulically-operated clutch (Chapter 6)
☐ Broken clutch release bearing or fork (Chapter 6)
☐ Broken diaphragm spring in clutch pressure plate (Chapter 6)

Clutch fails to disengage (unable to select gears)

☐ Faulty/incorrectly adjusted clutch cable - cable-operated clutch (Chapter 6)
☐ Faulty hydraulic release system - hydraulically-operated clutch (Chapter 6)
☐ Clutch disc sticking on gearbox input shaft splines (Chapter 6)
☐ Clutch disc sticking to flywheel or pressure plate (Chapter 6)
☐ Faulty pressure plate assembly (Chapter 6)
☐ Clutch release mechanism worn or incorrectly assembled (Chapter 6)

Clutch slips (engine speed increases, with no increase in vehicle speed)

☐ Faulty/incorrectly adjusted clutch cable - cable-operated clutch (Chapter 6)
☐ Faulty hydraulic release system - hydraulically-operated clutch (Chapter 6)
☐ Clutch disc linings excessively worn (Chapter 6)
☐ Clutch disc linings contaminated with oil or grease (Chapter 6)
☐ Faulty pressure plate or weak diaphragm spring (Chapter 6)

Judder as clutch is engaged

☐ Clutch disc linings contaminated with oil or grease (Chapter 6)
☐ Clutch disc linings excessively worn (Chapter 6)
☐ Faulty or distorted pressure plate or diaphragm spring (Chapter 6).
☐ Worn or loose engine or gearbox mountings (Chapter 2)
☐ Clutch disc hub or gearbox input shaft splines worn (Chapter 6)

Noise when depressing or releasing clutch pedal

☐ Worn clutch release bearing (Chapter 6)
☐ Worn or dry clutch pedal bushes (Chapter 6)
☐ Faulty pressure plate assembly (Chapter 6)
☐ Pressure plate diaphragm spring broken (Chapter 6)
☐ Broken clutch disc cushioning springs (Chapter 6)

Manual transmission

Noisy in neutral with engine running

☐ Input shaft bearings worn (noise apparent with clutch pedal released, but not when depressed) (Chapter 7A)*
☐ Clutch release bearing worn (noise apparent with clutch pedal depressed, possibly less when released) (Chapter 6)

Noisy in one particular gear

☐ Worn, damaged or chipped gear teeth (Chapter 7A)*

Difficulty engaging gears

☐ Clutch fault (Chapter 6)
☐ Worn or damaged gearchange linkage/cable (Chapter 7A)
☐ Incorrectly-adjusted gearchange linkage/cable (Chapter 7A)
☐ Worn synchroniser units (Chapter 7A)*

Jumps out of gear

☐ Worn or damaged gearchange linkage/cable (Chapter 7A)
☐ Incorrectly-adjusted gearchange linkage/cable (Chapter 7A)
☐ Worn synchroniser units (Chapter 7A)*
☐ Worn selector forks (Chapter 7A)*

Vibration

☐ Lack of oil (Chapter 1)
☐ Worn bearings (Chapter 7A)*

Lubricant leaks

☐ Leaking differential output oil seal (Chapter 7A)
☐ Leaking housing joint (Chapter 7A)*
☐ Leaking input shaft oil seal (Chapter 7A)*

Although the corrective action necessary to remedy the symptoms described is beyond the scope of the home mechanic, the above information should be helpful in isolating the cause of the condition, so that the owner can communicate clearly with a professional mechanic.

Automatic transmission

Note: *Due to the complexity of the automatic transmission, it is difficult for the home mechanic to properly diagnose and service this unit. For problems other than the following, the vehicle should be taken to a dealer service department or automatic transmission specialist. Do not be too hasty in removing the transmission if a fault is suspected, as most of the testing is carried out with the unit still fitted.*

Fluid leakage

☐ Automatic transmission fluid is usually dark in colour. Fluid leaks should not be confused with engine oil, which can easily be blown onto the transmission by airflow.

☐ To determine the source of a leak, first remove all built-up dirt and grime from the transmission housing and surrounding areas using a degreasing agent, or by steam-cleaning. Drive the vehicle at low speed, so airflow will not blow the leak far from its source. Raise and support the vehicle, and determine where the leak is coming from. The following are common areas of leakage:
a) *Oil pan (Chapter 1 and 7B)*
b) *Dipstick tube (Chapter 1 and 7B)*
c) *Transmission-to-fluid cooler unions (Chapter 7B)*

Transmission fluid brown, or has burned smell

☐ Transmission fluid level low (Chapter 1)

General gear selection problems

☐ Chapter 7B deals with checking the selector cable on automatic transmissions. The following are common problems which may be caused by a faulty cable:
a) *Engine starting in gears other than Park or Neutral.*
b) *Indicator panel indicating a gear other than the one actually being used.*
c) *Vehicle moves when in Park or Neutral.*
d) *Poor gear shift quality or erratic gear changes.*

Transmission will not downshift (kickdown) with accelerator pedal fully depressed

☐ Low transmission fluid level (Chapter 1)
☐ Incorrect selector cable adjustment (Chapter 7B)

Engine will not start in any gear, or starts in gears other than Park or Neutral

☐ Incorrect starter/inhibitor switch adjustment (Chapter 7B)
☐ Incorrect selector cable adjustment (Chapter 7B)

Transmission slips, shifts roughly, is noisy, or has no drive in forward or reverse gears

☐ There are many probable causes for the above problems, but the home mechanic should be concerned with only one possibility - fluid level. Before taking the vehicle to a dealer or transmission specialist, check the fluid level and condition of the fluid as described in Chapter 1. Correct the fluid level as necessary, or change the fluid if needed. If the problem persists, professional help will be necessary.

Driveshafts

Vibration when accelerating or decelerating

☐ Worn inner constant velocity joint (Chapter 8)
☐ Bent or distorted driveshaft (Chapter 8)

Clicking or knocking noise on turns (at slow speed on full-lock)

☐ Worn outer constant velocity joint (Chapter 8)
☐ Lack of constant velocity joint lubricant, possibly due to damaged gaiter (Chapter 8)

Braking system

Note: *Before assuming that a brake problem exists, make sure that the tyres are in good condition and correctly inflated, that the front wheel alignment is correct, and that the vehicle is not loaded with weight in an unequal manner.*

Vehicle pulls to one side under braking

☐ Worn, defective, damaged or contaminated brake pads/shoes on one side (Chapters 1 and 9)
☐ Seized or partially-seized brake caliper piston/wheel cylinder (Chapters 1 and 9)
☐ A mixture of brake pad/shoe lining materials fitted between sides (Chapters 1 and 9)
☐ Brake caliper/backplate mounting bolts loose (Chapter 9)
☐ Worn or damaged steering or suspension components (Chapters 1 and 10)

Noise (grinding or high-pitched squeal) when brakes applied

☐ Brake pad/shoe friction lining material worn down to metal backing (Chapters 1 and 9)
☐ Excessive corrosion of brake disc/drum (may be apparent after the vehicle has been standing for some time (Chapters 1 and 9)
☐ Foreign object (stone chipping, etc) trapped between brake disc and shield (Chapters 1 and 9)

Excessive brake pedal travel

☐ Faulty master cylinder (Chapter 9)
☐ Air in hydraulic system (Chapters 1 and 9)
☐ Faulty vacuum servo unit (Chapter 9)

Brake pedal feels spongy when depressed

☐ Air in hydraulic system (Chapters 1 and 9)
☐ Deteriorated flexible rubber brake hoses (Chapters 1 and 9)
☐ Master cylinder mounting nuts loose (Chapter 9)
☐ Faulty master cylinder (Chapter 9)

Excessive brake pedal effort required to stop vehicle

☐ Faulty vacuum servo unit (Chapter 9)
☐ Disconnected, damaged or insecure brake servo vacuum hose (Chapter 9)
☐ Primary or secondary hydraulic circuit failure (Chapter 9)
☐ Seized brake caliper/wheel cylinder piston (Chapter 9)
☐ Brake pads/shoes incorrectly fitted (Chapters 1 and 9)
☐ Incorrect grade of brake pads/shoes fitted (Chapters 1 and 9)
☐ Brake pad/shoe linings contaminated (Chapters 1 and 9)

Braking system (continued)

Judder felt through brake pedal or steering wheel when braking

- [ ] Excessive run-out or distortion of discs/drums (Chapters 1 and 9)
- [ ] Brake pad/shoe linings worn (Chapters 1 and 9)
- [ ] Brake caliper/backplate mounting bolts loose (Chapter 9)
- [ ] Wear in suspension or steering components or mountings (Chapters 1 and 10)

Brakes binding

- [ ] Seized brake caliper/wheel cylinder piston (Chapter 9)
- [ ] Incorrectly-adjusted handbrake mechanism (Chapter 9)
- [ ] Faulty master cylinder (Chapter 9)

Rear wheels locking under normal braking

- [ ] Rear brake pad/shoe linings contaminated (Chapters 1 and 9)
- [ ] Rear brake discs/drums warped (Chapters 1 and 9)

Suspension and steering

Note: *Before diagnosing suspension or steering faults, be sure that the trouble is not due to incorrect tyre pressures, mixtures of tyre types, or binding brakes.*

Vehicle pulls to one side

- [ ] Defective tyre (see *"Weekly checks"*)
- [ ] Excessive wear in suspension or steering components (Chapters 1 and 10)
- [ ] Incorrect front wheel alignment (Chapter 10)
- [ ] Accident damage to steering or suspension components (Chapter 1)

Wheel wobble and vibration

- [ ] Front roadwheels out of balance (vibration felt mainly through the steering wheel) (Chapters 1 and 10)
- [ ] Rear roadwheels out of balance (vibration felt throughout the vehicle) (Chapters 1 and 10)
- [ ] Roadwheels damaged or distorted (Chapters 1 and 10)
- [ ] Faulty or damaged tyre (see *"Weekly checks"*)
- [ ] Worn steering or suspension joints, bushes or components (Chapters 1 and 10)
- [ ] Wheel bolts loose (Chapters 1 and 10)

Excessive pitching and/or rolling around corners, or during braking

- [ ] Defective shock absorbers (Chapters 1 and 10)
- [ ] Broken or weak spring and/or suspension component (Chapters 1 and 10)
- [ ] Worn or damaged anti-roll bar or mountings (Chapter 10)

Wandering or general instability

- [ ] Incorrect front wheel alignment (Chapter 10)
- [ ] Worn steering or suspension joints, bushes or components (Chapters 1 and 10)
- [ ] Roadwheels out of balance (Chapters 1 and 10)
- [ ] Faulty or damaged tyre (see *"Weekly checks"*)
- [ ] Wheel bolts loose (Chapters 1 and 10)
- [ ] Defective shock absorbers (Chapters 1 and 10)

Excessively-stiff steering

- [ ] Seized steering linkage balljoint or suspension balljoint (Chapters 1 and 10)
- [ ] Broken or incorrectly-adjusted auxiliary drivebelt (Chapter 1)
- [ ] Incorrect front wheel alignment (Chapter 10)
- [ ] Steering gear damaged (Chapter 10)

Excessive play in steering

- [ ] Worn steering column/intermediate shaft joints (Chapter 10)
- [ ] Worn track rod balljoints (Chapters 1 and 10)
- [ ] Worn steering gear (Chapter 10)
- [ ] Worn steering or suspension joints, bushes or components (Chapters 1 and 10)

Lack of power assistance

- [ ] Broken or incorrectly-adjusted auxiliary drivebelt (Chapter 1)
- [ ] Incorrect power steering fluid level (see *"Weekly checks"*)
- [ ] Restriction in power steering fluid hoses (Chapter 1)
- [ ] Faulty power steering pump (Chapter 10)
- [ ] Faulty steering gear (Chapter 10)

Tyre wear excessive

Tyres worn on inside or outside edges

- [ ] Tyres under-inflated (wear on both edges) (see *"Weekly checks"*)
- [ ] Incorrect camber or castor angles (wear on one edge only) (Chapter 10)
- [ ] Worn steering or suspension joints, bushes or components (Chapters 1 and 10)
- [ ] Excessively-hard cornering
- [ ] Accident damage

Tyre treads exhibit feathered edges

- [ ] Incorrect toe setting (Chapter 10)

Tyres worn in centre of tread

- [ ] Tyres over-inflated (see *"Weekly checks"*)

Tyres worn on inside and outside edges

- [ ] Tyres under-inflated (see *"Weekly checks"*)

Tyres worn unevenly

- [ ] Tyres/wheels out of balance (Chapter 1)
- [ ] Excessive wheel or tyre run-out (Chapter 1)
- [ ] Worn shock absorbers (Chapters 1 and 10)
- [ ] Faulty tyre (see *"Weekly checks"*)

Electrical system

Note: *For problems associated with the starting system, refer to the faults listed under "Engine" earlier in this Section.*

Battery will not hold a charge for more than a few days

- [ ] Battery defective internally (Chapter 5)
- [ ] Battery terminal connections loose or corroded (see *"Weekly checks"*)
- [ ] Auxiliary drivebelt worn or incorrectly adjusted (Chapter 1)
- [ ] Alternator not charging at correct output (Chapter 5)
- [ ] Alternator or voltage regulator faulty (Chapter 5)
- [ ] Short-circuit causing continual battery drain (Chapters 5 and 12)

Electrical system (continued)

Ignition/no-charge warning light remains illuminated with engine running

- [ ] Auxiliary drivebelt broken, worn, or incorrectly adjusted (Chapter 1)
- [ ] Alternator brushes worn, sticking, or dirty (Chapter 5)
- [ ] Alternator brush springs weak or broken (Chapter 5)
- [ ] Internal fault in alternator or voltage regulator (Chapter 5)
- [ ] Broken, disconnected, or loose wiring in charging circuit (Chapter 5)

Ignition/no-charge warning light fails to come on

- [ ] Warning light bulb blown (Chapter 12)
- [ ] Broken, disconnected, or loose wiring in warning light circuit (Chapter 12)
- [ ] Alternator faulty (Chapter 5)

Lights inoperative

- [ ] Bulb blown (Chapter 12)
- [ ] Corrosion of bulb or bulbholder contacts (Chapter 12)
- [ ] Blown fuse (Chapter 12)
- [ ] Faulty relay (Chapter 12)
- [ ] Broken, loose, or disconnected wiring (Chapter 12)
- [ ] Faulty switch (Chapter 12)

Instrument readings inaccurate or erratic

Instrument readings increase with engine speed

- [ ] Faulty voltage regulator (Chapter 12)

Fuel or temperature gauges give no reading

- [ ] Faulty gauge sender unit (Chapters 3 and 4)
- [ ] Wiring open-circuit (Chapter 12)
- [ ] Faulty gauge (Chapter 12)

Fuel or temperature gauges give continuous maximum reading

- [ ] Faulty gauge sender unit (Chapters 3 and 4)
- [ ] Wiring short-circuit (Chapter 12)
- [ ] Faulty gauge (Chapter 12)

Horn inoperative, or unsatisfactory in operation

Horn operates all the time

- [ ] Horn push either earthed or stuck down (Chapter 12)
- [ ] Horn cable-to-horn push earthed (Chapter 12)

Horn fails to operate

- [ ] Blown fuse (Chapter 12)
- [ ] Cable or cable connections loose, broken or disconnected (Chapter 12)
- [ ] Faulty horn (Chapter 12)

Horn emits intermittent or unsatisfactory sound

- [ ] Cable connections loose (Chapter 12)
- [ ] Horn mountings loose (Chapter 12)
- [ ] Faulty horn (Chapter 12)

Windscreen wipers inoperative, or unsatisfactory in operation

Wipers fail to operate, or operate very slowly

- [ ] Wiper blades stuck to screen, or linkage seized or binding (Chapters 1 and 12)
- [ ] Blown fuse (Chapter 12)
- [ ] Cable or cable connections loose, broken or disconnected (Chapter 12)
- [ ] Faulty relay (Chapter 12)
- [ ] Faulty wiper motor (Chapter 12)

Wiper blades sweep over too large or too small an area of the glass

- [ ] Wiper arms incorrectly positioned on spindles (Chapter 1)
- [ ] Excessive wear of wiper linkage (Chapter 12)
- [ ] Wiper motor or linkage mountings loose or insecure (Chapter 12)

Wiper blades fail to clean the glass effectively

- [ ] Wiper blade rubbers worn or perished (see "Weekly checks")
- [ ] Wiper arm tension springs broken, or arm pivots seized (Chapter 12)
- [ ] Insufficient windscreen washer additive to adequately remove road film (see "Weekly checks")

Windscreen washers inoperative, or unsatisfactory in operation

One or more washer jets inoperative

- [ ] Blocked washer jet (Chapter 1)
- [ ] Disconnected, kinked or restricted fluid hose (Chapter 12)
- [ ] Insufficient fluid in washer reservoir (see "Weekly checks")

Washer pump fails to operate

- [ ] Broken or disconnected wiring or connections (Chapter 12)
- [ ] Blown fuse (Chapter 12)
- [ ] Faulty washer switch (Chapter 12)
- [ ] Faulty washer pump (Chapter 12)

Washer pump runs for some time before fluid is emitted from jets

- [ ] Faulty one-way valve in fluid supply hose (Chapter 12)

Electric windows inoperative, or unsatisfactory in operation

Window glass will only move in one direction

- [ ] Faulty switch (Chapter 12)

Window glass slow to move

- [ ] Regulator seized or damaged, or in need of lubrication (Chapter 11)
- [ ] Door internal components or trim fouling regulator (Chapter 11)
- [ ] Faulty motor (Chapter 11)

Window glass fails to move

- [ ] Blown fuse (Chapter 12)
- [ ] Faulty relay (Chapter 12)
- [ ] Broken or disconnected wiring or connections (Chapter 12)
- [ ] Faulty motor (Chapter 11)

Central locking system inoperative, or unsatisfactory in operation

Complete system failure

- [ ] Blown fuse (Chapter 12)
- [ ] Faulty relay (Chapter 12)
- [ ] Broken or disconnected wiring or connections (Chapter 12)
- [ ] Faulty motor (Chapter 11)

Latch locks but will not unlock, or unlocks but will not lock

- [ ] Faulty master switch (Chapter 12)
- [ ] Broken or disconnected latch operating rods or levers (Chapter 11)
- [ ] Faulty relay (Chapter 12)
- [ ] Faulty motor (Chapter 11)

One solenoid/motor fails to operate

- [ ] Broken or disconnected wiring or connections (Chapter 12)
- [ ] Faulty operating assembly (Chapter 11)
- [ ] Broken, binding or disconnected latch operating rods or levers (Chapter 11)
- [ ] Fault in door latch (Chapter 11)

A

ABS (Anti-lock brake system) A system, usually electronically controlled, that senses incipient wheel lockup during braking and relieves hydraulic pressure at wheels that are about to skid.

Air bag An inflatable bag hidden in the steering wheel (driver's side) or the dash or glovebox (passenger side). In a head-on collision, the bags inflate, preventing the driver and front passenger from being thrown forward into the steering wheel or windscreen.

Air cleaner A metal or plastic housing, containing a filter element, which removes dust and dirt from the air being drawn into the engine.

Air filter element The actual filter in an air cleaner system, usually manufactured from pleated paper and requiring renewal at regular intervals.

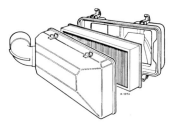

Air filter

Allen key A hexagonal wrench which fits into a recessed hexagonal hole.

Alligator clip A long-nosed spring-loaded metal clip with meshing teeth. Used to make temporary electrical connections.

Alternator A component in the electrical system which converts mechanical energy from a drivebelt into electrical energy to charge the battery and to operate the starting system, ignition system and electrical accessories.

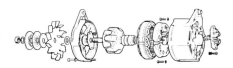

Alternator (exploded view)

Ampere (amp) A unit of measurement for the flow of electric current. One amp is the amount of current produced by one volt acting through a resistance of one ohm.

Anaerobic sealer A substance used to prevent bolts and screws from loosening. Anaerobic means that it does not require oxygen for activation. The Loctite brand is widely used.

Antifreeze A substance (usually ethylene glycol) mixed with water, and added to a vehicle's cooling system, to prevent freezing of the coolant in winter. Antifreeze also contains chemicals to inhibit corrosion and the formation of rust and other deposits that would tend to clog the radiator and coolant passages and reduce cooling efficiency.

Anti-seize compound A coating that reduces the risk of seizing on fasteners that are subjected to high temperatures, such as exhaust manifold bolts and nuts.

Anti-seize compound

Asbestos A natural fibrous mineral with great heat resistance, commonly used in the composition of brake friction materials. Asbestos is a health hazard and the dust created by brake systems should never be inhaled or ingested.

Axle A shaft on which a wheel revolves, or which revolves with a wheel. Also, a solid beam that connects the two wheels at one end of the vehicle. An axle which also transmits power to the wheels is known as a live axle.

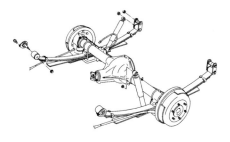

Axle assembly

Axleshaft A single rotating shaft, on either side of the differential, which delivers power from the final drive assembly to the drive wheels. Also called a driveshaft or a halfshaft.

B

Ball bearing An anti-friction bearing consisting of a hardened inner and outer race with hardened steel balls between two races.

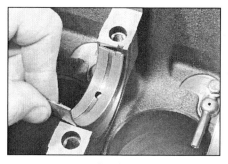

Bearing

Bearing The curved surface on a shaft or in a bore, or the part assembled into either, that permits relative motion between them with minimum wear and friction.

Big-end bearing The bearing in the end of the connecting rod that's attached to the crankshaft.

Bleed nipple A valve on a brake wheel cylinder, caliper or other hydraulic component that is opened to purge the hydraulic system of air. Also called a bleed screw.

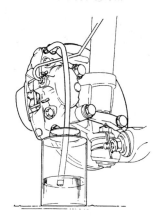

Brake bleeding

Brake bleeding Procedure for removing air from lines of a hydraulic brake system.

Brake disc The component of a disc brake that rotates with the wheels.

Brake drum The component of a drum brake that rotates with the wheels.

Brake linings The friction material which contacts the brake disc or drum to retard the vehicle's speed. The linings are bonded or riveted to the brake pads or shoes.

Brake pads The replaceable friction pads that pinch the brake disc when the brakes are applied. Brake pads consist of a friction material bonded or riveted to a rigid backing plate.

Brake shoe The crescent-shaped carrier to which the brake linings are mounted and which forces the lining against the rotating drum during braking.

Braking systems For more information on braking systems, consult the *Haynes Automotive Brake Manual*.

Breaker bar A long socket wrench handle providing greater leverage.

Bulkhead The insulated partition between the engine and the passenger compartment.

C

Caliper The non-rotating part of a disc-brake assembly that straddles the disc and carries the brake pads. The caliper also contains the hydraulic components that cause the pads to pinch the disc when the brakes are applied. A caliper is also a measuring tool that can be set to measure inside or outside dimensions of an object.

Camshaft A rotating shaft on which a series of cam lobes operate the valve mechanisms. The camshaft may be driven by gears, by sprockets and chain or by sprockets and a belt.

Canister A container in an evaporative emission control system; contains activated charcoal granules to trap vapours from the fuel system.

Canister

Carburettor A device which mixes fuel with air in the proper proportions to provide a desired power output from a spark ignition internal combustion engine.

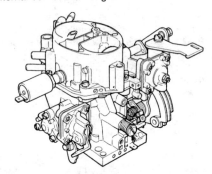

Carburettor

Castellated Resembling the parapets along the top of a castle wall. For example, a castellated balljoint stud nut.

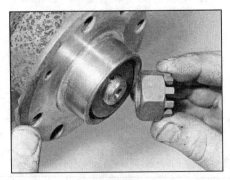

Castellated nut

Castor In wheel alignment, the backward or forward tilt of the steering axis. Castor is positive when the steering axis is inclined rearward at the top.

Catalytic converter A silencer-like device in the exhaust system which converts certain pollutants in the exhaust gases into less harmful substances.

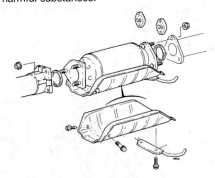

Catalytic converter

Circlip A ring-shaped clip used to prevent endwise movement of cylindrical parts and shafts. An internal circlip is installed in a groove in a housing; an external circlip fits into a groove on the outside of a cylindrical piece such as a shaft.

Clearance The amount of space between two parts. For example, between a piston and a cylinder, between a bearing and a journal, etc.

Coil spring A spiral of elastic steel found in various sizes throughout a vehicle, for example as a springing medium in the suspension and in the valve train.

Compression Reduction in volume, and increase in pressure and temperature, of a gas, caused by squeezing it into a smaller space.

Compression ratio The relationship between cylinder volume when the piston is at top dead centre and cylinder volume when the piston is at bottom dead centre.

Constant velocity (CV) joint A type of universal joint that cancels out vibrations caused by driving power being transmitted through an angle.

Core plug A disc or cup-shaped metal device inserted in a hole in a casting through which core was removed when the casting was formed. Also known as a freeze plug or expansion plug.

Crankcase The lower part of the engine block in which the crankshaft rotates.

Crankshaft The main rotating member, or shaft, running the length of the crankcase, with offset "throws" to which the connecting rods are attached.

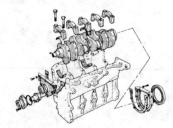

Crankshaft assembly

Crocodile clip See Alligator clip

D

Diagnostic code Code numbers obtained by accessing the diagnostic mode of an engine management computer. This code can be used to determine the area in the system where a malfunction may be located.

Disc brake A brake design incorporating a rotating disc onto which brake pads are squeezed. The resulting friction converts the energy of a moving vehicle into heat.

Double-overhead cam (DOHC) An engine that uses two overhead camshafts, usually one for the intake valves and one for the exhaust valves.

Drivebelt(s) The belt(s) used to drive accessories such as the alternator, water pump, power steering pump, air conditioning compressor, etc. off the crankshaft pulley.

Accessory drivebelts

Driveshaft Any shaft used to transmit motion. Commonly used when referring to the axleshafts on a front wheel drive vehicle.

Driveshaft

Drum brake A type of brake using a drum-shaped metal cylinder attached to the inner surface of the wheel. When the brake pedal is pressed, curved brake shoes with friction linings press against the inside of the drum to slow or stop the vehicle.

Drum brake assembly

E

EGR valve A valve used to introduce exhaust gases into the intake air stream.

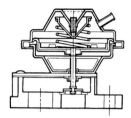

EGR valve

Electronic control unit (ECU) A computer which controls (for instance) ignition and fuel injection systems, or an anti-lock braking system. For more information refer to the *Haynes Automotive Electrical and Electronic Systems Manual.*

Electronic Fuel Injection (EFI) A computer controlled fuel system that distributes fuel through an injector located in each intake port of the engine.

Emergency brake A braking system, independent of the main hydraulic system, that can be used to slow or stop the vehicle if the primary brakes fail, or to hold the vehicle stationary even though the brake pedal isn't depressed. It usually consists of a hand lever that actuates either front or rear brakes mechanically through a series of cables and linkages. Also known as a handbrake or parking brake.

Endfloat The amount of lengthwise movement between two parts. As applied to a crankshaft, the distance that the crankshaft can move forward and back in the cylinder block.

Engine management system (EMS) A computer controlled system which manages the fuel injection and the ignition systems in an integrated fashion.

Exhaust manifold A part with several passages through which exhaust gases leave the engine combustion chambers and enter the exhaust pipe.

Exhaust manifold

F

Fan clutch A viscous (fluid) drive coupling device which permits variable engine fan speeds in relation to engine speeds.

Feeler blade A thin strip or blade of hardened steel, ground to an exact thickness, used to check or measure clearances between parts.

Feeler blade

Firing order The order in which the engine cylinders fire, or deliver their power strokes, beginning with the number one cylinder.

Flywheel A heavy spinning wheel in which energy is absorbed and stored by means of momentum. On cars, the flywheel is attached to the crankshaft to smooth out firing impulses.

Free play The amount of travel before any action takes place. The "looseness" in a linkage, or an assembly of parts, between the initial application of force and actual movement. For example, the distance the brake pedal moves before the pistons in the master cylinder are actuated.

Fuse An electrical device which protects a circuit against accidental overload. The typical fuse contains a soft piece of metal which is calibrated to melt at a predetermined current flow (expressed as amps) and break the circuit.

Fusible link A circuit protection device consisting of a conductor surrounded by heat-resistant insulation. The conductor is smaller than the wire it protects, so it acts as the weakest link in the circuit. Unlike a blown fuse, a failed fusible link must frequently be cut from the wire for replacement.

G

Gap The distance the spark must travel in jumping from the centre electrode to the side

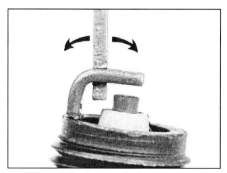

Adjusting spark plug gap

electrode in a spark plug. Also refers to the spacing between the points in a contact breaker assembly in a conventional points-type ignition, or to the distance between the reluctor or rotor and the pickup coil in an electronic ignition.

Gasket Any thin, soft material - usually cork, cardboard, asbestos or soft metal - installed between two metal surfaces to ensure a good seal. For instance, the cylinder head gasket seals the joint between the block and the cylinder head.

Gasket

Gauge An instrument panel display used to monitor engine conditions. A gauge with a movable pointer on a dial or a fixed scale is an analogue gauge. A gauge with a numerical readout is called a digital gauge.

H

Halfshaft A rotating shaft that transmits power from the final drive unit to a drive wheel, usually when referring to a live rear axle.

Harmonic balancer A device designed to reduce torsion or twisting vibration in the crankshaft. May be incorporated in the crankshaft pulley. Also known as a vibration damper.

Hone An abrasive tool for correcting small irregularities or differences in diameter in an engine cylinder, brake cylinder, etc.

Hydraulic tappet A tappet that utilises hydraulic pressure from the engine's lubrication system to maintain zero clearance (constant contact with both camshaft and valve stem). Automatically adjusts to variation in valve stem length. Hydraulic tappets also reduce valve noise.

I

Ignition timing The moment at which the spark plug fires, usually expressed in the number of crankshaft degrees before the piston reaches the top of its stroke.

Inlet manifold A tube or housing with passages through which flows the air-fuel mixture (carburettor vehicles and vehicles with throttle body injection) or air only (port fuel-injected vehicles) to the port openings in the cylinder head.

J

Jump start Starting the engine of a vehicle with a discharged or weak battery by attaching jump leads from the weak battery to a charged or helper battery.

L

Load Sensing Proportioning Valve (LSPV) A brake hydraulic system control valve that works like a proportioning valve, but also takes into consideration the amount of weight carried by the rear axle.

Locknut A nut used to lock an adjustment nut, or other threaded component, in place. For example, a locknut is employed to keep the adjusting nut on the rocker arm in position.

Lockwasher A form of washer designed to prevent an attaching nut from working loose.

M

MacPherson strut A type of front suspension system devised by Earle MacPherson at Ford of England. In its original form, a simple lateral link with the anti-roll bar creates the lower control arm. A long strut - an integral coil spring and shock absorber - is mounted between the body and the steering knuckle. Many modern so-called MacPherson strut systems use a conventional lower A-arm and don't rely on the anti-roll bar for location.

Multimeter An electrical test instrument with the capability to measure voltage, current and resistance.

N

NOx Oxides of Nitrogen. A common toxic pollutant emitted by petrol and diesel engines at higher temperatures.

O

Ohm The unit of electrical resistance. One volt applied to a resistance of one ohm will produce a current of one amp.

Ohmmeter An instrument for measuring electrical resistance.

O-ring A type of sealing ring made of a special rubber-like material; in use, the O-ring is compressed into a groove to provide the sealing action.

O-ring

Overhead cam (ohc) engine
An engine with the camshaft(s) located on top of the cylinder head(s).

Overhead valve (ohv) engine An engine with the valves located in the cylinder head, but with the camshaft located in the engine block.

Oxygen sensor A device installed in the engine exhaust manifold, which senses the oxygen content in the exhaust and converts this information into an electric current. Also called a Lambda sensor.

P

Phillips screw A type of screw head having a cross instead of a slot for a corresponding type of screwdriver.

Plastigage A thin strip of plastic thread, available in different sizes, used for measuring clearances. For example, a strip of Plastigage is laid across a bearing journal. The parts are assembled and dismantled; the width of the crushed strip indicates the clearance between journal and bearing.

Plastigage

Propeller shaft The long hollow tube with universal joints at both ends that carries power from the transmission to the differential on front-engined rear wheel drive vehicles.

Proportioning valve A hydraulic control valve which limits the amount of pressure to the rear brakes during panic stops to prevent wheel lock-up.

R

Rack-and-pinion steering A steering system with a pinion gear on the end of the steering shaft that mates with a rack (think of a geared wheel opened up and laid flat). When the steering wheel is turned, the pinion turns, moving the rack to the left or right. This movement is transmitted through the track rods to the steering arms at the wheels.

Radiator A liquid-to-air heat transfer device designed to reduce the temperature of the coolant in an internal combustion engine cooling system.

Refrigerant Any substance used as a heat transfer agent in an air-conditioning system. R-12 has been the principle refrigerant for many years; recently, however, manufacturers have begun using R-134a, a non-CFC substance that is considered less harmful to the ozone in the upper atmosphere.

Rocker arm A lever arm that rocks on a shaft or pivots on a stud. In an overhead valve engine, the rocker arm converts the upward movement of the pushrod into a downward movement to open a valve.

Rotor In a distributor, the rotating device inside the cap that connects the centre electrode and the outer terminals as it turns, distributing the high voltage from the coil secondary winding to the proper spark plug. Also, that part of an alternator which rotates inside the stator. Also, the rotating assembly of a turbocharger, including the compressor wheel, shaft and turbine wheel.

Runout The amount of wobble (in-and-out movement) of a gear or wheel as it's rotated. The amount a shaft rotates "out-of-true." The out-of-round condition of a rotating part.

S

Sealant A liquid or paste used to prevent leakage at a joint. Sometimes used in conjunction with a gasket.

Sealed beam lamp An older headlight design which integrates the reflector, lens and filaments into a hermetically-sealed one-piece unit. When a filament burns out or the lens cracks, the entire unit is simply replaced.

Serpentine drivebelt A single, long, wide accessory drivebelt that's used on some newer vehicles to drive all the accessories, instead of a series of smaller, shorter belts. Serpentine drivebelts are usually tensioned by an automatic tensioner.

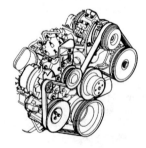

Serpentine drivebelt

Shim Thin spacer, commonly used to adjust the clearance or relative positions between two parts. For example, shims inserted into or under bucket tappets control valve clearances. Clearance is adjusted by changing the thickness of the shim.

Slide hammer A special puller that screws into or hooks onto a component such as a shaft or bearing; a heavy sliding handle on the shaft bottoms against the end of the shaft to knock the component free.

Sprocket A tooth or projection on the periphery of a wheel, shaped to engage with a chain or drivebelt. Commonly used to refer to the sprocket wheel itself.

Starter inhibitor switch On vehicles with an

automatic transmission, a switch that prevents starting if the vehicle is not in Neutral or Park.

Strut See MacPherson strut.

T

Tappet A cylindrical component which transmits motion from the cam to the valve stem, either directly or via a pushrod and rocker arm. Also called a cam follower.

Thermostat A heat-controlled valve that regulates the flow of coolant between the cylinder block and the radiator, so maintaining optimum engine operating temperature. A thermostat is also used in some air cleaners in which the temperature is regulated.

Thrust bearing The bearing in the clutch assembly that is moved in to the release levers by clutch pedal action to disengage the clutch. Also referred to as a release bearing.

Timing belt A toothed belt which drives the camshaft. Serious engine damage may result if it breaks in service.

Timing chain A chain which drives the camshaft.

Toe-in The amount the front wheels are closer together at the front than at the rear. On rear wheel drive vehicles, a slight amount of toe-in is usually specified to keep the front wheels running parallel on the road by offsetting other forces that tend to spread the wheels apart.

Toe-out The amount the front wheels are closer together at the rear than at the front. On front wheel drive vehicles, a slight amount of toe-out is usually specified.

Tools For full information on choosing and using tools, refer to the *Haynes Automotive Tools Manual.*

Tracer A stripe of a second colour applied to a wire insulator to distinguish that wire from another one with the same colour insulator.

Tune-up A process of accurate and careful adjustments and parts replacement to obtain the best possible engine performance.

Turbocharger A centrifugal device, driven by exhaust gases, that pressurises the intake air. Normally used to increase the power output from a given engine displacement, but can also be used primarily to reduce exhaust emissions (as on VW's "Umwelt" Diesel engine).

U

Universal joint or U-joint A double-pivoted connection for transmitting power from a driving to a driven shaft through an angle. A U-joint consists of two Y-shaped yokes and a cross-shaped member called the spider.

V

Valve A device through which the flow of liquid, gas, vacuum, or loose material in bulk may be started, stopped, or regulated by a movable part that opens, shuts, or partially obstructs one or more ports or passageways. A valve is also the movable part of such a device.

Valve clearance The clearance between the valve tip (the end of the valve stem) and the rocker arm or tappet. The valve clearance is measured when the valve is closed.

Vernier caliper A precision measuring instrument that measures inside and outside dimensions. Not quite as accurate as a micrometer, but more convenient.

Viscosity The thickness of a liquid or its resistance to flow.

Volt A unit for expressing electrical "pressure" in a circuit. One volt that will produce a current of one ampere through a resistance of one ohm.

W

Welding Various processes used to join metal items by heating the areas to be joined to a molten state and fusing them together. For more information refer to the *Haynes Automotive Welding Manual.*

Wiring diagram A drawing portraying the components and wires in a vehicle's electrical system, using standardised symbols. For more information refer to the *Haynes Automotive Electrical and Electronic Systems Manual.*

Note: References throughout this index are in the form - "Chapter number"•"Page number"

A

Accelerator cable
  carburettor models - 4A•5
  fuel injection models - 4B•3
Accelerator pedal
  carburettor models - 4A•6
  fuel injection models - 4B•3
Aerial - 12•12
Air cleaner air temperature control system - 4A•3
Air cleaner assembly
  carburettor models - 4A•3
  fuel injection models - 4B•2
Air cleaner element (filter)
  check and clean - 1•8
  renewal - 1•15
Air conditioning system
  component removal and refitting - 3•8
  compressor drivebelt - 1•8
  general information and precautions - 3•7
  refrigerant level check - 1•10
Airflow sensor - 4B•8
Alternator
  drivebelt - 1•7, 1•17
  removal and refitting - 5•6
  testing and overhaul - 5•7
Antifreeze
  capacity - 1•2
  identifying leaks - 0•9
  level check - 0•11
  renewal - 1•17
  type - 0•16
Automatic transmission - 7B•1 et seq
Automatic transmission
  fluid level check - 1•12
  fluid renewal - 1•16
  overhaul, general information - 7B•6
  removal and refitting - 7B•5
Auxiliary cooling fan - 3•3
Auxiliary drivebelts - 1•7, 1•17

B

Battery
  check - 0•15
  removal and refitting - 5•3
  Safety first! - 0•5
  testing and charging - 5•2
Bleeding
  brake hydraulic system - 9•2
  clutch hydraulic system - 6•5
  power steering system - 10•14
Body electrical systems - 12•1 et seq
Bodywork and fittings - 11•1 et seq
Bonnet
  lock - 11•5
  removal, refitting and adjustment - 11•4
  release cable - 11•5
Boot lid (Saloon models)
  lock components - 11•12
  removal, refitting and adjustment - 11•11
Brake fluid
  level check - 0•12
  renewal - 1•18
Brake light switch - 9•20
Brake pedal - 9•17
  free play check - 1•14
Braking system - 9•1 et seq

Bulbs
  check - 0•15
  ratings - 12•1
  removal and refitting - 12•6, 12•8
Bumpers - 11•4
Buying spare parts - REF•3

C

Cables
  accelerator - 4A•5, 4B•3
  bonnet release - 11•5
  choke - 4A•6
  clutch - 6•3
  gearchange - 7A•3
  handbrake - 9•19
  kickdown - 7B•4
  selector - 7B•2
  speedometer drive - 12•11
Camshaft - 2A•9
Capacities - 1•2
Carburettor
  air cleaner element - 1•8, 1•15
  fault diagnosis, overhaul and adjustments - 4A•7
  general information - 4A•6
  idle speed and mixture check - 1•11
  removal and refitting - 4A•7
Cassette player - 12•12
Catalytic converter
  general information and precautions - 4C•2, 4C•3
  removal and refitting:
    carburettor models - 4A•10
    fuel injection models - 4B•10
Central locking system components - 11•13
Centre console - 11•15
Charging system - 5•6
Choke cable - 4A•6
Cigar lighter - 12•4
Clock - 12•4
Clutch - 6•1 et seq
Clutch
  bleeding - 6•5
  cable - 6•3
  check and adjustment - 6•2
  fluid level - 0•12
  master cylinder - 6•3
  pedal - 6•6
  pedal free play check - 1•14
  release mechanism - 6•7
  removal, inspection and refitting - 6•6
Compression test - 2A•3
Conversion factors - REF•2
Coolant
  capacity - 1•2
  identifying leaks - 0•9
  level check - 0•11
  pump - 3•4
  renewal - 1•17
  temperature sensor - 4B•8
  type - 0•16
Cooling fan switch - 3•4
Cooling system hoses - 3•2
Cooling, heating and ventilation systems - 3•1 et seq
Courtesy light switch - 12•5
Crank angle sensor - 4B•8
Crankcase ventilation hose check - 1•17
Crankshaft
  inspection - 2B•10

refitting - 2B•12
removal - 2B•9
oil seals - 2A•13
Cylinder block/crankcase - 2B•9
Cylinder head
cleaning and inspection - 2B•7
dismantling - 2B•6
reassembly - 2B•8
removal and refitting - 2A•10
Cylinder head cover - 2A•4

D

Dashpot/idle-up actuator - 4C•2, 4C•3
Diagnostic test - 1•9
Dim-dip lighting system (UK models only) - 12•13
Dimensions - REF•1
Distributor - 5•4
Door - 11•6
inner trim panel - 11•7
latch, lock cylinder and handle components - 11•8
Door mounted switch - 12•5
Door window glass and regulator - 11•10
Drivebelts
air conditioning compressor - 1•7, 1•17
alternator - 1•7, 1•17
engine timing belt - 1•17, 2A•6
power steering pump - 1•7, 1•17
Driveshaft and gaiter check - 1•14
Driveshafts - 8•1 et seq
Driveshafts
overhaul - 8•4
rubber gaiters - 8•2

E

EGR system check - 1•17
Electric window switch - 12•5
Electrical fault-finding
body electrical systems - 12•2
engine electrical systems - 5•2
Electronic control unit - 4B•7
Emissions control systems - 4C•1 et seq
Engine electrical systems - 5•1 et seq
Engine in-car repair procedures - 2A•1 et seq
Engine
coolant renewal - 1•17
initial start-up after overhaul - 2B•16
oil and filter renewal - 1•7
oil level check - 0•11
overhaul:
dismantling sequence - 2B•6
general information - 2B•3
reassembly sequence - 2B•11
removal methods and precautions - 2B•4
removal, separation and refitting - 2B•4
Engine removal and overhaul procedures - 2B•1 et seq
Engine/transmission mountings - 2A•15
Evaporative emissions control system - 4C•1, 4C•2
check - 1•11
Exhaust gas recirculation (EGR) system - 4C•1, 4C•2
Exhaust manifold
carburettor models - 4A•9
fuel injection models - 4B•9
Exhaust system
carburettor models - 4A•9
check - 1•14
fuel injection models - 4B•9
Exterior light units - 12•9
Exterior mirror - 11•14

F

Facia and glovebox - 11•16
Facia mounted switches - 12•5
Fault finding - REF•12 et seq
automatic transmission - REF•12, REF•16
braking system - REF•12, REF•16
carburettor - 4A•7
clutch - REF•12, REF•15
cooling system - REF•12, REF•14
driveshafts - REF•12, REF•16
electrical system - REF•12, REF•17
engine - REF•12, REF•13
engine electrical systems - 5•2
fuel and exhaust systems - REF•12, REF•15
manual transmission - REF•12, REF•15
suspension and steering - REF•12, REF•17
Filters
air - 1•2, 1•8, 1•15
fuel - 1•2, 1•11, 1•15
oil - 1•2, 1•7
Fluid cooler - 7B•5
Fluid types - 0•16
Flywheel/driveplate - 2A•14
Fog light bulb - 12•8
Front brake
caliper - 9•12
check - 1•13
disc - 9•10
pads - 9•4
Front bumper - 11•4
Front hub bearings - 10•4
Front indicator - 12•9
bulb - 12•7
Front suspension
anti-roll bar - 10•7
lower arm - 10•6
lower arm balljoint - 10•7
radius arm (early models) - 10•7
strut: - 10•5
Front swivel hub assembly - 10•3
Fuel and evaporative emission hose check - 1•17
Fuel and exhaust systems:
carburettor engines - 4A•1 et seq
multi-point fuel injection models - 4B•1 et seq
Fuel filter
check - 1•11
renewal - 1•15
Fuel gauge sender unit
carburettor models - 4A•4
fuel injection models - 4B•5
Fuel injection system
air cleaner element - 1•8, 1•15
component removal and refitting - 4B•6
depressurisation - 4B•4
filter renewal - 1•15
general information - 4B•4
idle speed and mixture check - 1•11, 4B•5
testing and adjustment - 4B•5
Fuel injectors - 4B•6
Fuel pressure regulator - 4B•6
Fuel pump
carburettor models - 4A•4
fuel injection models - 4B•8
Fuel rail - 4B•6
Fuel rating - 4A•2, 4B•2
Fuel tank
carburettor models - 4A•5
fuel injection models - 4B•5
Fuses - 0•15, 12•3

G

Gearchange
  cables - 7A•3
  lever assembly - 7A•3
  mechanism - 7A•2
  rod assembly - 7A•2
General information
  air cleaner air temperature control system - 4A•3
  air conditioning system - 3•7
  automatic transmission - 7B•2
  body electrical systems - 12•2
  bodywork and fittings - 11•1
  braking 1system - 9•2
  carburettor - 4A•6
  catalytic converter - 4C•3
  clutch - 6•2
  cooling, heating and ventilation systems - 3•2
  dim-dip lighting system (UK models only) - 12•13
  driveshafts - 8•1
  driveshaft overhaul - 8•4
  electrical fault-finding:
    body electrical systems - 12•2
    engine electrical systems - 5•2
  emission control systems - 4C•1
  engine electrical systems - 5•2
  engine in-car repair procedures - 2A•3
  engine removal and overhaul procedures - 2B•3
  exhaust system - 4A•9
  fuel and exhaust systems:
    carburettor models - 4A•3
    fuel injection models - 4B•2
  fuses and relays - 12•3
  headlight beam alignment - 12•10
  ignition system - 5•3
  manual transmission - 7A•2
  routine maintenance - 1•6
  sunroof - 11•14
  suspension and steering - 10•3
  unleaded petrol - 4A•6
  wheel alignment and steering angles - 10•16
General repair procedures - REF•4
Glossary of technical terms - REF•19

H

Handbrake
  adjustment - 9•18
  cables - 9•19
  lever - 9•19
  operation check - 1•13
Headlight
  beam alignment - 12•10
  bulb - 12•6
  removal and refitting - 12•9
Heater/ventilation components - 3•5
High level stop light bulb - 12•7, 12•8
Horn - 12•11
Hose and fluid leak check - 1•9
Hydraulic pipes and hoses - 9•3
Hydraulic system bleeding
  brake - 9•2
  clutch - 6•5

I

Identifying leaks - 0•9
Idle mixture CO content - 1•2
Idle speed and mixture check - 1•2, 1•11

Idle speed control motor - 4B•7
If your car won't start - 0•6
Ignition HT coil - 5•4
Ignition switch - 5•7
Ignition system
  general information - 5•3
  testing - 5•3
Ignition timing - 1•10, 5•6
Inlet air temperature sensor - 4B•8
Inlet manifold
  carburettor models - 4A•9
  fuel injection models - 4B•8
Instrument panel - 12•10
Intensive maintenance - 1•6
Introduction to
  roadside repairs - 0•6
  the Hyundai Pony - 0•4
  Weekly checks - 0•10

J

Jacking and vehicle support - REF•5
Jet air system - 4C•1, 4C•2
Jump starting - 0•7

K

Kickdown cable - 7B•4

L

Loudspeakers - 12•13
Locks
  bonnet - 11•5
  boot - 11•12
  door - 11•8
  tailgate - 11•13
Lubricants - 0•16

M

Main and big-end bearings - 2B•11
Maintenance
  bodywork and underframe - 11•1
  procedures - 1•6
  schedule - 1•1
  upholstery and carpets - 11•2
  weekly checks - 0•10
Major body damage - 11•4
Manifold absolute pressure sensor - 4B•8
Manual transmission - 7A•1 et seq
Manual transmission oil
  level check - 1•12
  renewal - 1•16
Master cylinder - 9•15
Minor body damage - 11•2
Mixture check - 1•2, 1•11
MOT test checks - REF•8

N

Number plate light bulb - 12•7

O

Oil - 1•2, 0•16
Oil and filter renewal - 1•7
Oil level check - 0•11
Oil pressure warning light switch - 5•8
Oil pump and pick-up strainer - 2A•11
Oxygen sensor - 4C•2, 4C•3

P

PCV valve check - 1•16
Pedals
    accelerator - 4A•6
    brake - 9•17
    clutch - 6•6
Piston rings- 2B•14
Piston/connecting rod assembly
    inspection - 2B•10
    refitting and big-end bearing running clearance check - 2B•14
    removal - 2B•8
Positive crankcase ventilation system - 4C•1, 4C•2
Power steering
    bleeding - 10•14
    fluid level check - 0•13
    pump drivebelt - 1•8
    pump removal and refitting - 10•15

R

Radiator - 3•2
    grille - 11•6
Radio - 12•12
Rear axle assembly - 10•10
Rear brake
    drum - 9•10
    shoes - 1•13, 9•6
    pressure-regulating valve - 9•19
Rear bumper - 11•4
Rear hub
    removal and refitting - 10•8
    bearings - 1•14, 10•9
Rear light
    bulbs - 12•7
    cluster - 12•9
Rear suspension
    coil spring - 10•9
    shock absorber - 10•9
Rear wheel cylinder - 9•15
Reference - REF•1 et seq
Reversing light switch
    automatic transmission - 7B•5
    manual transmission - 7A•4
Roadside repairs - 0•6
Rocker arm assembly - 2A•4
Routine Maintenance and Servicing - 1•1 et seq

S

Safety First! - 0•5
Screen washer fluid level - 0•12
Seats and seat belts - 11•14
Secondary air supply system - 4C•2, 4C•3
Selector cable - 7B•2
Selector lever assembly - 7B•4
Sidelight bulb - 12•6
Spark plug
    check and clean - 1•11
    renewal - 1•15
    type - 1•2
Speedometer drive
    automatic transmission - 7B•5
    manual transmission - 7A•4
Speedometer drive cable - 12•11
Starter inhibitor switch - 7B•5
Starter motor - 5•7
Starting system - 5•7
Steering and suspension check - 1•13

Steering column
    combination switch - 12•4
    intermediate shaft - 10•12
    lock - 10•13
    removal, inspection and refitting - 10•12
Steering gear assembly - 10•13
    rubber gaiters - 10•14
Steering wheel - 10•11
Stop-light switch - 9•20
Sump - 2A•11
Sunroof - 11•14
Suspension and steering - 10•1 et seq
Switches - 9•20, 12•4

T

Tailgate and support strut (Hatchback models) - 11•12
    lock and handle components - 11•13
    wiper motor - 12•12
Temperature gauge coolant sensor - 3•5
Thermostat - 3•3
Throttle housing - 4B•5
Throttle position sensor - 4B•7
Timing belt
    removal, inspection and refitting - 1•17, 2A•6
    check - 1•17
    sprockets and tensioner pulley - 2A•7
Tools and working facilities - REF•6
Top dead centre (TDC) for No 1 piston
    locating - 2A•3
    sensor - 4B•8
Towing - 0•9
Track rod - 10•15
    balljoint - 10•15
Transmission - *see* Manual or Automatic transmission
Tyres
    condition and pressure check- 0•14
    pressures - 0•16
    sizes - 10•1

U

Underbonnet check points - 0•10
Unleaded petrol
    carburettor models - 4A•2, 4A•6
    fuel injection models - 4B•2, 4B•3

V

Vacuum servo unit - 9•18
    check valve - 9•18
Valve clearances - 1•2, 1•10
Vehicle identification - REF•3
Vehicle speed sensor - 4B•8

W

Weekly checks - 0•10
Weights - REF•1
Wheel alignment and steering angles - 10•16
Wheel bearings
    front - 10•4
    rear - 10•9
Wheel changing - 0•8
Wiper arm - 12•11
Wiper blades - 0•13
Wiper motor
    tailgate - 12•12
    windscreen - 12•11
Wiring diagrams - 12•14

Haynes Manuals – The Complete UK Car List

Title	Book No.
ALFA ROMEO Alfasud/Sprint (74 - 88) up to F *	0292
Alfa Romeo Alfetta (73 - 87) up to E *	0531
AUDI 80, 90 & Coupe Petrol (79 - Nov 88) up to F	0605
Audi 80, 90 & Coupe Petrol (Oct 86 - 90) D to H	1491
Audi 100 & 200 Petrol (Oct 82 - 90) up to H	0907
Audi 100 & A6 Petrol & Diesel (May 91 - May 97) H to P	3504
Audi A3 Petrol & Diesel (96 - May 03) P to 03	4253
Audi A4 Petrol & Diesel (95 - Feb 00) M to V	3575
Audi A4 Petrol & Diesel (Mar 00 - Aug 04) W to 04	4609
AUSTIN A35 & A40 (56 - 67) up to F *	0118
Austin/MG/Rover Maestro 1.3 & 1.6 Petrol (83 - 95) up to M	0922
Austin/MG Metro (80 - May 90) up to G	0718
Austin/Rover Montego 1.3 & 1.6 Petrol (84 - 94) A to L	1066
Austin/MG/Rover Montego 2.0 Petrol (84 - 95) A to M	1067
Mini (59 - 69) up to H *	0527
Mini (69 - 01) up to X	0646
Austin/Rover 2.0 litre Diesel Engine (86 - 93) C to L	1857
Austin Healey 100/6 & 3000 (56 - 68) up to G *	0049
BEDFORD CF Petrol (69 - 87) up to E	0163
Bedford/Vauxhall Rascal & Suzuki Supercarry (86 - Oct 94) C to M	3015
BMW 316, 320 & 320i (4-cyl) (75 - Feb 83) up to Y *	0276
BMW 320, 320i, 323i & 325i (6-cyl) (Oct 77 - Sept 87) up to E	0815
BMW 3- & 5-Series Petrol (81 - 91) up to J	1948
BMW 3-Series Petrol (Apr 91 - 99) H to V	3210
BMW 3-Series Petrol (Sept 98 - 03) S to 53	4067
BMW 520i & 525e (Oct 81 - June 88) up to E	1560
BMW 525, 528 & 528i (73 - Sept 81) up to X *	0632
BMW 5-Series 6-cyl Petrol (April 96 - Aug 03) N to 03	4151
BMW 1500, 1502, 1600, 1602, 2000 & 2002 (59 - 77) up to S *	0240
CHRYSLER PT Cruiser Petrol (00 - 03) W to 53	4058
CITROËN 2CV, Ami & Dyane (67 - 90) up to H	0196
Citroën AX Petrol & Diesel (87 - 97) D to P	3014
Citroën Berlingo & Peugeot Partner Petrol & Diesel (96 - 05) P to 55	4281
Citroën BX Petrol (83 - 94) A to L	0908
Citroën C15 Van Petrol & Diesel (89 - Oct 98) F to S	3509
Citroën C3 Petrol & Diesel (02 - 05) 51 to 05	4197
Citroën CX Petrol (75 - 88) up to F	0528
Citroën Saxo Petrol & Diesel (96 - 04) N to 54	3506
Citroën Visa Petrol (79 - 88) up to F	0620
Citroën Xantia Petrol & Diesel (93 - 01) K to Y	3082
Citroën XM Petrol & Diesel (89 - 00) G to X	3451
Citroën Xsara Petrol & Diesel (97 - Sept 00) R to W	3751
Citroën Xsara Picasso Petrol & Diesel (00 - 02) W to 52	3944
Citroën ZX Diesel (91 - 98) J to S	1922
Citroën ZX Petrol (91 - 98) H to S	1881
Citroën 1.7 & 1.9 litre Diesel Engine (84 - 96) A to N	1379
FIAT 126 (73 - 87) up to E *	0305
Fiat 500 (57 - 73) up to M *	0090
Fiat Bravo & Brava Petrol (95 - 00) N to W	3572
Fiat Cinquecento (93 - 98) K to R	3501
Fiat Panda (81 - 95) up to M	0793
Fiat Punto Petrol & Diesel (94 - Oct 99) L to V	3251
Fiat Punto Petrol (Oct 99 - July 03) V to 03	4066
Fiat Regata Petrol (84 - 88) A to F	1167
Fiat Tipo Petrol (88 - 91) E to J	1625
Fiat Uno Petrol (83 - 95) up to M	0923

Title	Book No.
Fiat X1/9 (74 - 89) up to G *	0273
FORD Anglia (59 - 68) up to G *	0001
Ford Capri II (& III) 1.6 & 2.0 (74 - 87) up to E *	0283
Ford Capri II (& III) 2.8 & 3.0 V6 (74 - 87) up to E	1309
Ford Cortina Mk III 1300 & 1600 (70 - 76) up to P *	0070
Ford Escort Mk I 1100 & 1300 (68 - 74) up to N *	0171
Ford Escort Mk I Mexico, RS 1600 & RS 2000 (70 - 74) up to N *	0139
Ford Escort Mk II Mexico, RS 1800 & RS 2000 (75 - 80) up to W *	0735
Ford Escort (75 - Aug 80) up to V *	0280
Ford Escort Petrol (Sept 80 - Sept 90) up to H	0686
Ford Escort & Orion Petrol (Sept 90 - 00) H to X	1737
Ford Escort & Orion Diesel (Sept 90 - 00) H to X	4081
Ford Fiesta (76 - Aug 83) up to Y	0334
Ford Fiesta Petrol (Aug 83 - Feb 89) A to F	1030
Ford Fiesta Petrol (Feb 89 - Oct 95) F to N	1595
Ford Fiesta Petrol & Diesel (Oct 95 - Mar 02) N to 02	3397
Ford Fiesta Petrol & Diesel (Apr 02 - 05) 02 to 54	4170
Ford Focus Petrol & Diesel (98 - 01) S to Y	3759
Ford Focus Petrol & Diesel (Oct 01 - 04) 51 to 54	4167
Ford Galaxy Petrol & Diesel (95 - Aug 00) M to W	3984
Ford Granada Petrol (Sept 77 - Feb 85) up to B *	0481
Ford Granada & Scorpio Petrol (Mar 85 - 94) B to M	1245
Ford Ka (96 - 02) P to 52	3570
Ford Mondeo Petrol (93 - Sept 00) K to X	1923
Ford Mondeo Petrol & Diesel (Oct 00 - Jul 03) X to 03	3990
Ford Mondeo Petrol & Diesel (July 03 - 07) 03 to 56	4619
Ford Mondeo Diesel (93 - 96) L to N	3465
Ford Orion Petrol (83 - Sept 90) up to H	1009
Ford Sierra 4-cyl Petrol (82 - 93) up to K	0903
Ford Sierra V6 Petrol (82 - 91) up to J	0904
Ford Transit Petrol (Mk 2) (78 - Jan 86) up to C	0719
Ford Transit Petrol (Mk 3) (Feb 86 - 89) C to G	1468
Ford Transit Diesel (Feb 86 - 99) C to T	3019
Ford 1.6 & 1.8 litre Diesel Engine (84 - 96) A to N	1172
Ford 2.1, 2.3 & 2.5 litre Diesel Engine (77 - 90) up to H	1606
FREIGHT ROVER Sherpa Petrol (74 - 87) up to E	0463
HILLMAN Avenger (70 - 82) up to Y	0037
Hillman Imp (63 - 76) up to R *	0022
HONDA Civic (Feb 84 - Oct 87) A to E	1226
Honda Civic (Nov 91 - 96) J to N	3199
Honda Civic Petrol (Mar 95 - 00) M to X	4050
HYUNDAI Pony (85 - 94) C to M	3398
JAGUAR E Type (61 - 72) up to L *	0140
Jaguar MkI & II, 240 & 340 (55 - 69) up to H *	0098
Jaguar XJ6, XJ & Sovereign; Daimler Sovereign (68 - Oct 86) up to D	0242
Jaguar XJ6 & Sovereign (Oct 86 - Sept 94) D to M	3261
Jaguar XJ12, XJS & Sovereign; Daimler Double Six (72 - 88) up to F	0478
Jeep Cherokee Petrol (93 - 96) K to N	1943
LADA 1200, 1300, 1500 & 1600 (74 - 91) up to J	0413
Lada Samara (87 - 91) D to J	1610
LAND ROVER 90, 110 & Defender Diesel (83 - 07) up to 56	3017
Land Rover Discovery Petrol & Diesel (89 - 98) G to S	3016
Land Rover Discovery Diesel (Nov 98 - Jul 04) S to 04	4606
Land Rover Freelander Petrol & Diesel (97 - Sept 03) R to 53	3929
Land Rover Freelander Petrol & Diesel (Oct 03 - 06) 53 to 56	4623
Land Rover Series IIA & III Diesel (58 - 85) up to C	0529

Title	Book No.
Land Rover Series II, IIA & III 4-cyl Petrol (58 - 85) up to C	0314
MAZDA 323 (Mar 81 - Oct 89) up to G	1608
Mazda 323 (Oct 89 - 98) G to R	3455
Mazda 626 (May 83 - Sept 87) up to E	0929
Mazda B1600, B1800 & B2000 Pick-up Petrol (72 - 88) up to F	0267
Mazda RX-7 (79 - 85) up to C *	0460
MERCEDES-BENZ 190, 190E & 190D Petrol & Diesel (83 - 93) A to L	3450
Mercedes-Benz 200D, 240D, 240TD, 300D & 300TD 123 Series Diesel (Oct 76 - 85) up to C	1114
Mercedes-Benz 250 & 280 (68 - 72) up to L *	0346
Mercedes-Benz 250 & 280 123 Series Petrol (Oct 76 - 84) up to B *	0677
Mercedes-Benz 124 Series Petrol & Diesel (85 - Aug 93) C to K	3253
Mercedes-Benz C-Class Petrol & Diesel (93 - Aug 00) L to W	3511
MGA (55 - 62) *	0475
MGB (62 - 80) up to W	0111
MG Midget & Austin-Healey Sprite (58 - 80) up to W *	0265
MINI Petrol (July 01 - 05) Y to 05	4273
MITSUBISHI Shogun & L200 Pick-Ups Petrol (83 - 94) up to M	1944
MORRIS Ital 1.3 (80 - 84) up to B	0705
Morris Minor 1000 (56 - 71) up to K	0024
NISSAN Almera Petrol (95 - Feb 00) N to V	4053
Nissan Bluebird (May 84 - Mar 86) A to C	1223
Nissan Bluebird Petrol (Mar 86 - 90) C to H	1473
Nissan Cherry (Sept 82 - 86) up to D	1031
Nissan Micra (83 - Jan 93) up to K	0931
Nissan Micra (93 - 02) K to 52	3254
Nissan Primera Petrol (90 - Aug 99) H to T	1851
Nissan Stanza (82 - 86) up to D	0824
Nissan Sunny Petrol (May 82 - Oct 86) up to D	0895
Nissan Sunny Petrol (Oct 86 - Mar 91) D to H	1378
Nissan Sunny Petrol (Apr 91 - 95) H to N	3219
OPEL Ascona & Manta (B Series) (Sept 75 - 88) up to F *	0316
Opel Ascona Petrol (81 - 88)	3215
Opel Astra Petrol (Oct 91 - Feb 98)	3156
Opel Corsa Petrol (83 - Mar 93)	3160
Opel Corsa Petrol (Mar 93 - 97)	3159
Opel Kadett Petrol (Nov 79 - Oct 84) up to B	0634
Opel Kadett Petrol (Oct 84 - Oct 91)	3196
Opel Omega & Senator Petrol (Nov 86 - 94)	3157
Opel Rekord Petrol (Feb 78 - Oct 86) up to D	0543
Opel Vectra Petrol (Oct 88 - Oct 95)	3158
PEUGEOT 106 Petrol & Diesel (91 - 04) J to 53	1882
Peugeot 205 Petrol (83 - 97) A to P	0932
Peugeot 206 Petrol & Diesel (98 - 01) S to X	3757
Peugeot 206 Petrol & Diesel (02 - 06) 51 to 06	4613
Peugeot 306 Petrol & Diesel (93 - 02) K to 02	3073
Peugeot 307 Petrol & Diesel (01 - 04) Y to 54	4147
Peugeot 309 Petrol (86 - 93) C to K	1266
Peugeot 405 Petrol (88 - 97) E to P	1559
Peugeot 405 Diesel (88 - 97) E to P	3198
Peugeot 406 Petrol & Diesel (96 - Mar 99) N to T	3394
Peugeot 406 Petrol & Diesel (Mar 99 - 02) T to 52	3982
Peugeot 505 Petrol (79 - 89) up to G	0762
Peugeot 1.7/1.8 & 1.9 litre Diesel Engine (82 - 96) up to N	0950
Peugeot 2.0, 2.1, 2.3 & 2.5 litre Diesel Engines (74 - 90) up to H	1607

* Classic reprint

Title	Book No.
PORSCHE 911 (65 - 85) up to C	0264
Porsche 924 & 924 Turbo (76 - 85) up to C	0397
PROTON (89 - 97) F to P	3255
RANGE ROVER V8 Petrol (70 - Oct 92) up to K	0606
RELIANT Robin & Kitten (73 - 83) up to A *	0436
RENAULT 4 (61 - 86) up to D *	0072
Renault 5 Petrol (Feb 85 - 96) B to N	1219
Renault 9 & 11 Petrol (82 - 89) up to F	0822
Renault 18 Petrol (79 - 86) up to D	0598
Renault 19 Petrol (89 - 96) F to N	1646
Renault 19 Diesel (89 - 96) F to N	1946
Renault 21 Petrol (86 - 94) C to M	1397
Renault 25 Petrol & Diesel (84 - 92) B to K	1228
Renault Clio Petrol (91 - May 98) H to R	1853
Renault Clio Diesel (91 - June 96) H to N	3031
Renault Clio Petrol & Diesel (May 98 - May 01) R to Y	3906
Renault Clio Petrol & Diesel (June 01 - 04) Y to 54	4168
Renault Espace Petrol & Diesel (85 - 96) C to N	3197
Renault Laguna Petrol & Diesel (94 - 00) L to W	3252
Renault Laguna Petrol & Diesel (Feb 01 - Feb 05) X to 54	4283
Renault Mégane & Scénic Petrol & Diesel (96 - 99) N to T	3395
Renault Mégane & Scénic Petrol & Diesel (Apr 99 - 02) T to 52	3916
Renault Megane Petrol & Diesel (Oct 02 - 05) 52 to 55	4284
Renault Scenic Petrol & Diesel (Sept 03 - 06) 53 to 06	4297
ROVER 213 & 216 (84 - 89) A to G	1116
Rover 214 & 414 Petrol (89 - 96) G to N	1689
Rover 216 & 416 Petrol (89 - 96) G to N	1830
Rover 211, 214, 216, 218 & 220 Petrol & Diesel (Dec 95 - 99) N to V	3399
Rover 25 & MG ZR Petrol & Diesel (Oct 99 - 04) V to 54	4145
Rover 414, 416 & 420 Petrol & Diesel (May 95 - 98) M to R	3453
Rover 45/MG ZS Petrol & Diesel (99 - 05) V to 55	4384
Rover 618, 620 & 623 Petrol (93 - 97) K to P	3257
Rover 75/MG ZT Petrol & Diesel (99 - 06) S to 06	4292
Rover 820, 825 & 827 Petrol (86 - 95) D to N	1380
Rover 3500 (76 - 87) up to E *	0365
Rover Metro, 111 & 114 Petrol (May 90 - 98) G to S	1711
SAAB 95 & 96 (66 - 76) up to R *	0198
Saab 90, 99 & 900 (79 - Oct 93) up to L	0765
Saab 900 (Oct 93 - 98) L to R	3512
Saab 9000 (4-cyl) (85 - 98) C to S	1686
Saab 9-3 Petrol & Diesel (98 - Aug 02) R to 02	4614
Saab 9-5 4-cyl Petrol (97 - 04) R to 54	4156
SEAT Ibiza & Cordoba Petrol & Diesel (Oct 93 - Oct 99) L to V	3571
Seat Ibiza & Malaga Petrol (85 - 92) B to K	1609
SKODA Estelle (77 - 89) up to G	0604
Skoda Fabia Petrol & Diesel (00 - 06) W to 06	4376
Skoda Favorit (89 - 96) F to N	1801
Skoda Felicia Petrol & Diesel (95 - 01) M to X	3505
Skoda Octavia Petrol & Diesel (98 - Apr 04) R to 04	4285
SUBARU 1600 & 1800 (Nov 79 - 90) up to H *	0995
SUNBEAM Alpine, Rapier & H120 (67 - 74) up to N *	0051
SUZUKI Supercarry & Bedford/Vauxhall Rascal (86 - Oct 94) C to M	3015
Suzuki SJ Series, Samurai & Vitara (4-cyl) Petrol (82 - 97) up to P	1942
TALBOT Alpine, Solara, Minx & Rapier (75 - 86) up to D	0337

Title	Book No.
Talbot Horizon Petrol (78 - 86) up to D	0473
Talbot Samba (82 - 86) up to D	0823
TOYOTA Avensis Petrol (98 - Jan 03) R to 52	4264
Toyota Carina E Petrol (May 92 - 97) J to P	3256
Toyota Corolla (80 - 85) up to C	0683
Toyota Corolla (Sept 83 - Sept 87) A to E	1024
Toyota Corolla (Sept 87 - Aug 92) E to K	1683
Toyota Corolla Petrol (Aug 92 - 97) K to P	3259
Toyota Corolla Petrol (July 97 - Feb 02) P to 51	4286
Toyota Hi-Ace & Hi-Lux Petrol (69 - Oct 83) up to A	0304
Toyota Yaris Petrol (99 - 05) T to 05	4265
TRIUMPH GT6 & Vitesse (62 - 74) up to N *	0112
Triumph Herald (59 - 71) up to K *	0010
Triumph Spitfire (62 - 81) up to X	0113
Triumph Stag (70 - 78) up to T *	0441
Triumph TR2, TR3, TR3A, TR4 & TR4A (52 - 67) up to F *	0028
Triumph TR5 & 6 (67 - 75) up to P *	0031
Triumph TR7 (75 - 82) up to Y *	0322
VAUXHALL Astra Petrol (80 - Oct 84) up to B	0635
Vauxhall Astra & Belmont Petrol (Oct 84 - Oct 91) B to J	1136
Vauxhall Astra Petrol (Oct 91 - Feb 98) J to R	1832
Vauxhall/Opel Astra & Zafira Petrol (Feb 98 - Apr 04) R to 04	3758
Vauxhall/Opel Astra & Zafira Diesel (Feb 98 - Apr 04) R to 04	3797
Vauxhall/Opel Calibra (90 - 98) G to S	3502
Vauxhall Carlton Petrol (Oct 78 - Oct 86) up to D	0480
Vauxhall Carlton & Senator Petrol (Nov 86 - 94) D to L	1469
Vauxhall Cavalier Petrol (81 - Oct 88) up to F	0812
Vauxhall Cavalier Petrol (Oct 88 - 95) F to N	1570
Vauxhall Chevette (75 - 84) up to B	0285
Vauxhall/Opel Corsa Diesel (Mar 93 - Oct 00) K to X	4087
Vauxhall Corsa Petrol (Mar 93 - 97) K to R	1985
Vauxhall/Opel Corsa Petrol (Apr 97 - Oct 00) P to X	3921
Vauxhall/Opel Corsa Petrol & Diesel (Oct 00 - Sept 03) X to 53	4079
Vauxhall/Opel Corsa Petrol & Diesel (Oct 03 - Aug 06) 53 to 06	4617
Vauxhall/Opel Frontera Petrol & Diesel (91 - Sept 98) J to S	3454
Vauxhall Nova Petrol (83 - 93) up to K	0909
Vauxhall/Opel Omega Petrol (94 - 99) L to T	3510
Vauxhall/Opel Vectra Petrol & Diesel (95 - Feb 99) N to S	3396
Vauxhall/Opel Vectra Petrol & Diesel (Mar 99 - May 02) T to 02	3930
Vauxhall/Opel Vectra Petrol & Diesel (June 02 - 06) 02 to 56	4618
Vauxhall/Opel 1.5, 1.6 & 1.7 litre Diesel Engine (82 - 96) up to N	1222
VW 411 & 412 (68 - 75) up to P *	0091
VW Beetle 1200 (54 - 77) up to S	0036
VW Beetle 1300 & 1500 (65 - 75) up to P	0039
VW 1302 & 1302S (70 - 72) up to L *	0110
VW Beetle 1303, 1303S & GT (72 - 75) up to P	0159
VW Beetle Petrol & Diesel (Apr 99 - 01) T to 51	3798
VW Golf & Jetta Mk 1 Petrol 1.1 & 1.3 (74 - 84) up to A	0716
VW Golf, Jetta & Scirocco Mk 1 Petrol 1.5, 1.6 & 1.8 (74 - 84) up to A	0726
VW Golf & Jetta Mk 1 Diesel (78 - 84) up to A	0451
VW Golf & Jetta Mk 2 Petrol (Mar 84 - Feb 92) A to J	1081
VW Golf & Vento Petrol & Diesel (Feb 92 - Mar 98) J to R	3097

Title	Book No.
VW Golf & Bora Petrol & Diesel (April 98 - 00) R to X	3727
VW Golf & Bora 4-cyl Petrol & Diesel (01 - 03) X to 53	4169
VW Golf & Bora Petrol & Diesel (04 - 07) 53 to 07	4610
VW LT Petrol Vans & Light Trucks (76 - 87) up to E	0637
VW Passat & Santana Petrol (Sept 81 - May 88) up to E	0814
VW Passat 4-cyl Petrol & Diesel (May 88 - 96) E to P	3498
VW Passat 4-cyl Petrol & Diesel (Dec 96 - Nov 00) P to X	3917
VW Passat Petrol & Diesel (Dec 00 - May 05) X to 05	4279
VW Polo & Derby (76 - Jan 82) up to X	0335
VW Polo (82 - Oct 90) up to H	0813
VW Polo Petrol (Nov 90 - Aug 94) H to L	3245
VW Polo Hatchback Petrol & Diesel (94 - 99) M to S	3500
VW Polo Hatchback Petrol (00 - Jan 02) V to 51	4150
VW Polo Petrol & Diesel (02 - May 05) 51 to 05	4608
VW Scirocco (82 - 90) up to H *	1224
VW Transporter 1600 (68 - 79) up to V	0082
VW Transporter 1700, 1800 & 2000 (72 - 79) up to V *	0226
VW Transporter (air-cooled) Petrol (79 - 82) up to Y *	0638
VW Transporter (water-cooled) Petrol (82 - 90) up to H	3452
VW Type 3 (63 - 73) up to M *	0084
VOLVO 120 & 130 Series (& P1800) (61 - 73) up to M *	0203
Volvo 142, 144 & 145 (66 - 74) up to N *	0129
Volvo 240 Series Petrol (74 - 93) up to K	0270
Volvo 262, 264 & 260/265 (75 - 85) up to C *	0400
Volvo 340, 343, 345 & 360 (76 - 91) up to J	0715
Volvo 440, 460 & 480 Petrol (87 - 97) D to P	1691
Volvo 740 & 760 Petrol (82 - 91) up to J	1258
Volvo 850 Petrol (92 - 96) J to P	3260
Volvo 940 Petrol (90 - 96) H to N	3249
Volvo S40 & V40 Petrol (96 - Mar 04) N to 04	3569
Volvo S70, V70 & C70 Petrol (96 - 99) P to V	3573
Volvo V70 / S80 Petrol & Diesel (98 - 05) S to 55	4263

AUTOMOTIVE TECHBOOKS

Title	Book No.
Automotive Electrical and Electronic Systems Manual	3049
Automotive Gearbox Overhaul Manual	3473
Automotive Service Summaries Manual	3475
Automotive Timing Belts Manual – Austin/Rover	3549
Automotive Timing Belts Manual – Ford	3474
Automotive Timing Belts Manual – Peugeot/Citroën	3568
Automotive Timing Belts Manual – Vauxhall/Opel	3577

DIY MANUAL SERIES

Title	Book No.
The Haynes Air Conditioning Manual	4192
The Haynes Manual on Bodywork	4198
The Haynes Manual on Brakes	4178
The Haynes Manual on Carburettors	4177
The Haynes Car Electrical Systems Manual	4251
The Haynes Manual on Diesel Engines	4174
The Haynes Manual on Engine Management	4199
The Haynes Manual on Fault Codes	4175
The Haynes Manual on Practical Electrical Systems	4267
The Haynes Manual on Small Engines	4250
The Haynes Manual on Welding	4176

* Classic reprint

CL22.4/07

Preserving Our Motoring Heritage

<
The Model J Duesenberg Derham Tourster. Only eight of these magnificent cars were ever built – this is the only example to be found outside the United States of America

Almost every car you've ever loved, loathed or desired is gathered under one roof at the Haynes Motor Museum. Over 300 immaculately presented cars and motorbikes represent every aspect of our motoring heritage, from elegant reminders of bygone days, such as the superb Model J Duesenberg to curiosities like the bug-eyed BMW Isetta. There are also many old friends and flames. Perhaps you remember the 1959 Ford Popular that you did your courting in? The magnificent 'Red Collection' is a spectacle of classic sports cars including AC, Alfa Romeo, Austin Healey, Ferrari, Lamborghini, Maserati, MG, Riley, Porsche and Triumph.

A Perfect Day Out

Each and every vehicle at the Haynes Motor Museum has played its part in the history and culture of Motoring. Today, they make a wonderful spectacle and a great day out for all the family. Bring the kids, bring Mum and Dad, but above all bring your camera to capture those golden memories for ever. You will also find an impressive array of motoring memorabilia, a comfortable 70 seat video cinema and one of the most extensive transport book shops in Britain. The Pit Stop Cafe serves everything from a cup of tea to wholesome, home-made meals or, if you prefer, you can enjoy the large picnic area nestled in the beautiful rural surroundings of Somerset.

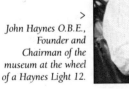

>
John Haynes O.B.E., Founder and Chairman of the museum at the wheel of a Haynes Light 12.

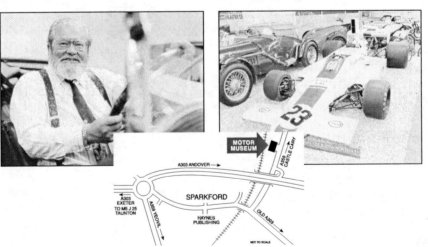

<
Graham Hill's Lola Cosworth Formula 1 car next to a 1934 Riley Sports.

The Museum is situated on the A359 Yeovil to Frome road at Sparkford, just off the A303 in Somerset. It is about 40 miles south of Bristol, and 25 minutes drive from the M5 intersection at Taunton.
Open 9.30am - 5.30pm (10.00am - 4.00pm Winter) 7 days a week, *except Christmas Day, Boxing Day and New Years Day*
Special rates available for schools, coach parties and outings Charitable Trust No. 292048